THE
ADVENTUROUS
GARDENER

Where to Buy the Best Plants in New York and New Jersey

THE
ADVENTUROUS
GARDENER

Where to Buy
the Best Plants in
NEW YORK AND NEW JERSEY

By Ruah Donnelly

THE HORTICULTURAL PRESS

Copyright © 2005 The Horticultural Press

ISBN 0-9677303-2-5
Library of Congress Control Number: 2004109080

Dedication: To Steve Dinkelaker

Photograms: Ann Parker
                 "Crown Imperial" and "Jack-in-the-Pulpit"
                 From *Botanical Metamorphics,* copyright © Ann Parker

Woodcuts: Jacques Hnizdovsky
                 Copyright © 1985 S. Hnizdovsky. All rights reserved.
                 Web site: *www.hnizdovsky.com*

Book Design: Dede Cummings and Carolyn Kasper
                 DC Design, Brattleboro, Vermont
                 Web site: *www.dedecummingsdesigns.com*

Publicity: Justine Johnson, Johnson-Lorenz Communications
                 Phone (413) 527-1920; fax (413) 527-7003
                 E-mail: *johnsonlorenz@charter.net*

Book Orders: Nancy Quick, The Horticultural Press
                 c/o Publishers Storage & Shipping Corp.
                 46 Development Road, Fitchburg, MA 01420
                 Phone (877) 427-3362; fax (978) 348-1233
                 E-mail: *orders@pssc.com*
                 Web site: *www.adventurousgardener.com*

Text for *International Bonsai* and *The Violet Barn*
          Used by permission of *Horticulture* magazine

Printed in Canada

CONTENTS

ACKNOWLEDGMENTS

WE WISH to thank Massachusetts artist Ann Parker for continued permission to use her photograms on *The Adventurous Gardener* book covers. Her luminous front-cover image of the red Crown Imperial *(Fritillaria imperialis)* provides an irresistible icon for the passions that motivate gardeners. Fine woodcuts by the late Jacques Hnizdovsky are used for illustration by the kind permission of Stephanie Hnizdovsky and David R. Godine, Publisher.

Special thanks are due to the many gardeners, writers, club members, and nursery professionals who provided information and help during the research and writing of this book. Naming names would be a gargantuan task, but we cannot resist thanking Fred Spicer, Jane Milliman, Jeanne Will, Lisa Miller, Ellen Zachos, Steve Scanniello, and Dick Cook. Of the generous nursery folk to whom this book pays tribute, we're grateful to Rick Hedrick, Hitch Lyman, Ellen Hornig, Steve Kristoph, Heidi and Rick Hesselein, Ken Selody, Paige St. John, and Gretchen Niedermayer. For private hospitality we're thankful to Marcia Chapman and Marty Luther, Deirdre Donnelly and Ed Lomas, Jim Williamson, Penny Miller, Dan Rosenblatt, and John and Christina Donnelly.

Nancy Quick of Publishers Storage & Shipping Corp. has been a wise and indispensable companion throughout the book-making process. Dede Cummings and Carolyn Kasper of DC Design deserve praise for their fine book design. Text was polished with valuable critiques from Mary V. Dearborn, Jane Roy Brown, Dick and Tommy Dearborn, and Duncan Brine. Line editing was accomplished gracefully by Candace Akins. We're grateful for the public relations guidance of Justine Johnson of Johnson-Lorenz Communications. Parts of this book were first published in *Horticulture* magazine, thanks to Trish Wesley Umbrel and Sarah Begg.

Finally, we wish to thank Steve Dinkelaker, to whom this book is dedicated, for his love and support during those periods of intense absorption without which no book that is any good can be written.

—RUAH DONNELLY

INTRODUCTION

The most valuable information a garden book has to offer is the names of the plantsmen who supply the material described, for that is all the reader really needs to know. Once he has the plants, he can discover the rest for himself.

—ELIZABETH LAWRENCE

G ARDENING —getting out there with your shovel and gloves—offers immediate satisfactions in the form of rewarding work, fresh air, healthful exertion, and the enjoyment of plants flourishing under care.

Hunting out great nurseries and acquiring distinctive garden plants engages a more complex set of desires—the wish to discover and experiment; to collect, savor, and preserve; to wow the neighbors, stump the experts, and (for ecological gardeners, anyway) maybe even save the planet.

Gardeners in New York and New Jersey live in a rich cultural region with countless resources readily at hand—some well-known, some hidden in obscurity. From Buffalo to New York City and east to Montauk, from Rochester to Trenton and south to Cape May, horticulture of every description has flourished in this region for more than 200 years. Illustrious parks and private gardens are only part of the story. Behind the scenes, a vibrant community of growers, hybridizers, specialists, and plant explorers is busily engaged in the art and science of horticulture.

Because of climatic and ecological differences, New York and New Jersey support remarkable horticultural diversity. Universities such as Rutgers and Cornell provide strong academic leadership, linking cutting-edge research with living archives of heritage plants. Breeders in both states produce improved, disease-resistant plants unheard-of 20 years ago—from daylilies and dogwoods to dwarf conifers, hardy nut trees, apple rootstocks, and improved vegetable seeds. Stylish nurseries grow choice ornamentals and show them off in virtuoso display gardens. Expert growers introduce exciting newcomers and revive time-tested classics. Naturalists mine the region's fine storehouse of native flora. Small or large, well-known or obscure, all have the one ingredient common to great nurseries—really good plants.

This is a practical book, intended to help gardeners find good plants. Information about regional nurseries is surprisingly hard to come by. When it comes to sourcing good plants in a particular locale, most garden manuals—whether for dream gardens or dirt gardens—leave gardeners adrift. We hope to fill the gap by publishing what amounts to field notes on the nurseries we found while scouting around New York and New Jersey for good plants.

Specialty Nurseries of New York and New Jersey

American horticulture was practically invented in New York and New Jersey, and a close look at today's nurseries suggests that much is still being invented. Plant specialists are horticulture's advance men. With their energy and curiosity, they do gardeners an immense service: they find, test, sort, and grow great garden plants—some new, some just new to us. As we discovered in researching plant sources, this region is home to some of the smartest plantsmen and finest nurseries in America.

Long Island's horticulture is as old as any in the country. William Prince, America's first nurseryman, started growing fine plants 250 years ago on the flat sandy grounds of Long Island—an area that still supports a vibrant green industry. Exotic collectors' shrubs are the specialty of one eminent Long Island nursery; another, run by a venerable farm family, sells container stock through the local Agway. East End herb and flower farms grow colorful deer-resistant plants in gardenesque settings. Big-tree specialists handle huge specimens. A landscape architect pioneers the use of Long Island's native plants. Growers offer sumptuous tropicals and bedding plants to wholesale customers (and allow savvy home gardeners to sneak in the back door).

In central and western New York, from the Mohawk Valley to the Finger Lakes, cold wet meadows that once supported Iroquois agriculture still offer valuable breeding grounds for vegetable hybrids, as well as new, disease-resistant fruit trees and cold-hardy nut specimens. Many upstate nurserymen retain the spirit of discovery that stirred 19th-century settlement. Some experiment with plants from Asia, South America, and South Africa or test the hardiness of plants seldom considered for cold-climate gardens—cyclamen, arum, and fuchsia. Others assemble collections of rare heirloom iris, snowdrops, roses, peonies, fancy-leaf pelargoniums, and Victorian-era bedding plants. Hybridizers breed northern-adapted Siberian iris and daylilies. Propagators quarry rare trees from a once-renowned arboretum. Naturalists grow native trees and shrubs for affordable landscaping. An internationally known bonsai master practices his art in an oriental courtyard.

In eastern New York, rich fine-art and farming traditions converge to influence Hudson Valley horticulture. Two gifted plantsmen vet fine plants for high-fashion gardens. Nearby, an organic farm preserves a legacy of open-pollinated vegetable seed. A world-famous rock garden offers cuttings from its alpine collection. A poetic Westchester nurseryman chooses garden plants just to please his bees. In the Catskills, a retired couple grows the area's freshest perennials, while a Huguenot old-timer grafts rare maples and conifers. A licensed wildcrafter grows native ginseng for woodland plantations. Even New York City has a presence, for its urban green markets draw plants from the entire region.

New Jersey is known as the Garden State for good reason, however the license plate may amuse outsiders. Any gardener who ventures off the super-highways discovers nurseries of exceptional merit, tucked away in the rolling North Jersey landscape (now edged by suburbia). Rare magnolias, exotic Japanese maples, rescued Franklin trees, and a world-class rhododendron collection are the prizes of specialist growers. The region's finest topiary artist operates on ground cut from the family sod farm. In South Jersey, where sandy lowlands sweep down to the Delaware Bay shore, practical truck farms produce native dune grass and Rutgers-bred asparagus crowns. The region's largest orchid supplier offers discounts on blooming orchids. A grower of dwarf conifer opens his greenhouses once a year, along with a famous daylily breeder and a celebrated collectors' nursery—attracting an annual pilgrimage of sophisticated gardeners.

A Word about Nursery Selection

We believe that a good nursery is one that engages the mind and heart of the gardener—and in cases of obsession, let us concede the soul as well. We cannot pretend to have found every good nursery in New York and New Jersey. Because nursery hunting is an art rather than a science, it is almost impossible to assemble an authoritative list. We have, however, performed arduous research and tried hard to be comprehensive. Each of the nurseries profiled here has special merit—something unusual that distinguishes its work. With few exceptions, each one knows and grows its own plants— good plants, the kind gardeners yearn for in their gardens.

We caution that some of these nurseries are small potatoes compared to the busy commercial outlets patronized by most gardeners. We have nothing against the business of horticulture; indeed, some of our best friends are garden centers. This book does profile independent garden centers that share many qualities we look for in a great nursery. Mostly, though, we think it's better to focus on propagators, plantsmen, hybridizers, and horticulturists—

even the skilled little guys whose importance exceeds the sum of their inventory.

Our main concern is plant quality, even when it means praising a nursery that is small by commercial standards. We assume that people can find their way to a commercial garden center. But without guidance, how will gardeners ever discover the small-scale specialist, buried in the country, too preoccupied with plants to run an ad? Or the world-class grower offering limited retail access, without fanfare? Or the noted hybridizer selling plant divisions quietly, to support his or her work?

Most specialty nurseries are run by skilled professionals who grow exceptional plants, offer depth of inventory, and don't focus all that much on sales. Often these aren't so much business enterprises as plant lovers who need to earn a living. Expert plantsmen propagate and grow, breed and study, collect and categorize, discover and display, save and rescue. It's all about good plants—plants that challenge and excite and stretch us out into subjects we didn't know; plants that make us see things anew.

The best way to get to know a plant is to buy one and try it in your garden. Learning a plant's origins and history is a great beginning. But like people, good plants surprise us with their hidden merits, their adaptability, their finesse. As we seek the new and unusual, we find ourselves appreciating the great traditions of horticulture. As we seek less burdensome, more naturalistic ways to garden, native plants gain importance, as do plants that are suited to our region and to the style and conditions of our gardens. All gardeners need is good plants. With them in hand, we have faith that gardeners will learn all that plants have to teach them.

Reflections on Gardening

Gardening is an ancient activity, among the most important achievements of human culture. Even the most ordinary garden plants connect a gardener to thousands of years of human effort—to the canny toil of a long chain of gardening forebears in choosing and cultivating beneficial plants. Garden plants are an inheritance, a legacy derived from the wild order of nature and from centuries of human effort in cottage gardens, physic gardens, palaces, monasteries, and farms. Even the newest hybrids rely on ancient chains of DNA. Garden plants are at once a rich inheritance and the ultimate in affordable antiques.

A garden is the dynamic result of the gardener's choices—a series of choices about time, placement, structure, color, style, ecology, and ornament—about making the kind of living room that nature provides. Gardens invite creatures into our lives, both flora and fauna, and open doors to the natural world. Through the medium of the garden, each of us develops a fluency with the news of wind and water; an ear for the language of birds; a friendship with bats, worms, and ladybugs; an appreciation for the needs and habits of insects, fungi, voles, deer, and "the creatures that crawl upon the earth." If we are the guests of plant life on earth—if mortal life depends on plants—then gardening is a way of honoring our hosts.

Gardens help us see time, not through the measure of our lives, but through nature and the earth. A garden provides engaging physical work, food for thought, a connection with living things and their seasons, spiritual refuge, and a reminder of death and the possibilities of renewal. Making a garden is a fugitive act of human hope, organization, and genius. Considered in the right way, a garden contains all the ingredients of happiness.

EASTERN
NEW YORK

EASTERN NEW YORK

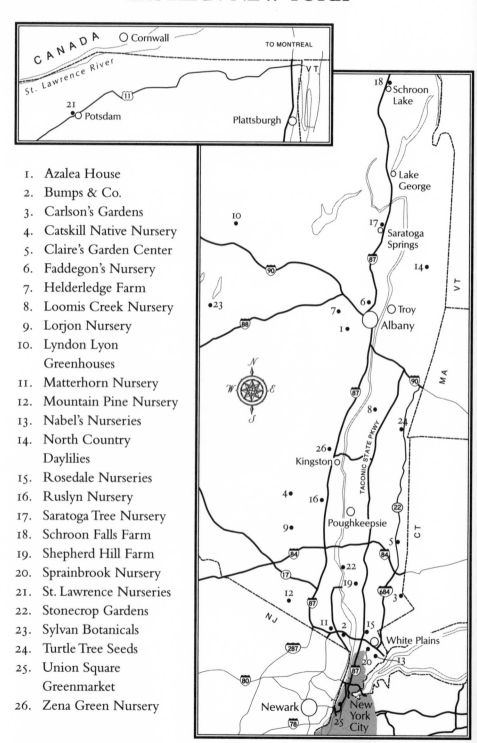

1. Azalea House
2. Bumps & Co.
3. Carlson's Gardens
4. Catskill Native Nursery
5. Claire's Garden Center
6. Faddegon's Nursery
7. Helderledge Farm
8. Loomis Creek Nursery
9. Lorjon Nursery
10. Lyndon Lyon Greenhouses
11. Matterhorn Nursery
12. Mountain Pine Nursery
13. Nabel's Nurseries
14. North Country Daylilies
15. Rosedale Nurseries
16. Ruslyn Nursery
17. Saratoga Tree Nursery
18. Schroon Falls Farm
19. Shepherd Hill Farm
20. Sprainbrook Nursery
21. St. Lawrence Nurseries
22. Stonecrop Gardens
23. Sylvan Botanicals
24. Turtle Tree Seeds
25. Union Square Greenmarket
26. Zena Green Nursery

Eastern New York

AZALEA HOUSE FLOWERING SHRUB FARM

P.O. Box 49, 40 Voorheesville Avenue, Voorheesville, NY 12186
(518) 765-2917; (518) 765-2574; fax (518) 765-7259
www.capital.net/com/azaleahs/plantbuy.htm; e-mail *azaleahs@capital.net*
Andrew Van Cleve

Classic own-root roses and grafted lilacs. Small specialty grower. Catalog on Web site. No mail order. Limited retail sales in June; check for details. Stock sold through area retailers; inquire for specifics. Plant photos and articles on Web site. Garden design consultations.

Azalea House Flowering Shrub Farm is a specialty grower of classic roses and lilacs in greater Albany. Its plants are sold through local retailers; it is open to gardeners sporadically, in May and June, when enough stock is available. This micro-nursery specializes in "locally successful cultivars" of classic roses and lilacs—plants that should appeal to collectors of romantic old-garden shrubs that are difficult to find in commerce.

Sole proprietor Andrew Van Cleve is a passionate plant propagator and researcher with a solid understanding of garden history and design. He has talked to Fr. John Fiala about lilacs and to David Austin and Graham Stuart Thomas about roses. He builds his own cold frames and compost heaps. He trained in agronomy at SUNY Cobleskill before quitting in rebellion. "I rebel by growing things," he says. "I worked for the post office for 30 years to support my gardening habit."

Classic and historic roses are his specialty. When Van Cleve finds a great rose, he traces its family tree in search of further treasures. Particular interests are *Rosa wichuriana* progeny (such as 'White Cockade' and 'American Pillar') and *Rosa multiflora* hybrids (such as 'Seven Sisters' and 'Veilchenblau'). He also values Canadian Explorer roses, the Kordes roses bred for German public parks, and the dressier *Rosa rugosa* hybrids, such as 'Blanc Double de Coubert' and 'Fru Dagmar Hastrup'. Famous antiques include the Apothecary rose (*Rosa gallica* 'Officinalis'), the Jacobite rose *(Rosa alba maxima),* velvet-red 'Tuscany Superb', and the incomparable white 'Madame Hardy'.

All roses are grown on their own roots, a process thought to improve longevity and resilience. "A lot of places are now grafting virused roses, which suffer from lack of vigor and sudden death," Van Cleve says. "I grow all my plants organically, without fungicides, so anything virused is weeded out. They have to be healthy to survive."

Lilacs are Azalea House's other specialty. Van Cleve grows 40 classic lilacs, including near-yellow 'Primrose', gold-variegated 'Aecubifolia', white-and-purple 'Sensation', and a variety called 'Dark Purple' discovered in Albany. Wild lilacs include Chinese littleleaf lilac *(Syringa microphylla superba)* and cutleaf lilac *(S. laciniata).*

Azalea House propagates its stock in two organic Zone 5 growing areas. Van Cleve roots cuttings in sand, pots them up, and mulches them with compost. Drip lines are rigged on overhead wires. Worms ascend and mix in the compost. Eventually, mature plants are sold in 2-, 5- and 7-gallon pots. "My nurseries are small and look grungy, but the roses and lilacs will take off," says Van Cleve. "The biggest arboreta in the world use the same methods."

For a small operation, Azalea House's Web site is baroque. Site visitors can access flower photographs, plant lists, cultivation reports, a brief history of lilac culture, cross-listings by hybridizer, a garden calendar (crammed with chores), reflections on sustainable garden design, articles on edible gardening, and a local garden index for sites around Albany.

Gardeners interested in the nursery's plants must take some trouble to acquire them. "I plan to hold retail sales each year at my house the last two weeks in June," Van Cleve says. "The roses and lilacs on my Web site are the ones I am trying to propagate regularly and grow to a saleable size. People can contact me and I can tell them where to buy them."

Van Cleve is justly proud of the influence he exerts on Capitol District gardening. Over the years, his plants have brought a wild loveliness to places that might never have known such glamour. "When I'm in a neighborhood and see an Apothecary's rose, I know it's one of mine. People see 'Harrison's Double Yellow' rose, and they think it is a century old, but it was planted by me," he says. "I'm going to die one day, and they're going to plant me under some rose bush."

Nearby attractions: Yonder Farms, 4301 Albany Street, Albany, NY, 12205 (518-456-6823), sells some Azalea House roses and lilacs. Van Cleve designed its flowering hedgerows, using a formula he attributes to England's Hidcote: "formal lines with informal contents, planted with abandon." He'll give garden tours there by arrangement on weekends, May through July. Another local outlet for Azalea House plants is Black Creek Nursery, Route 146, Altamont, NY 12009 (518-861-5274).

BUMPS & CO.

323 Strawtown Road, West Nyack, NY 10994
(914) 353-0513
E-mail *breland@optonline.net*
Ron and Otti Breland

Antique flowering plants. Ornamental salvia, campanula, penstemon, larkspur, delphinium, poppy. Annual vines. Heirloom vegetables. *Small specialty nursery. Open Mother's Day through mid-July, daily, 9 to 5, and by appointment. Free catalog. No mail order. Organic. Display garden. Beehives. Visitors welcome.*

It seems almost impossible that Bumps & Co., a delightfully quirky nursery on a leafy byway in West Nyack, should be located only 25 miles from downtown Manhattan. This small, home-based nursery exudes country air. At the driveway of an old homestead, near a gnarled apple tree, a "Honey for Sale" sign implies the presence of honeybees. Enigmatic bees form the soul of this garden. Indeed, the nursery is in some respects deliberately planted just to please the bees.

Ron Breland and his wife, Otti, who settled here 30 years ago, are the founders, owners, and work crew of Bumps & Co. "Bumps" was a nickname of Gertrude Jekyll, the renowned English gardener whose garden philosophy the couple share. "At Bumps & Co., we grow everything with one eye toward Gertrude Jekyll and the other toward sound, sustainable ecological practices," the Brelands write in their small catalog. "We grow plants because we love them, Bumps and all."

Since 1996, Ron Breland, a former commercial photographer, has dedicated his attention to the entwined arts of gardening and beekeeping. Otti Breland, an Austrian native, is a professional nurse whose groundedness and sweet temper seem essential here. In 2001, *New York Times* writer Ann Raver, a Bumps & Co. admirer, devoted two articles to the nursery and its bees. "We're famous for three things," says Breland. "The first two are Ann Raver's articles. The third is that you can't find us. Oh, and the fourth is that we keep all the good stuff for ourselves, unless I go off somewhere and Otti sells it and I have to call to get it back. This happened with Thomas Jefferson's 'Marseilles' fig tree. We're the only nursery that will pay people not to take stuff."

For bees, Bumps & Co. is haven and heaven. For gardeners, it is a rich source of bee-loved cottage-garden plants—vivid salvias, campanulas, penstemons, larkspurs, delphiniums, and poppies. Sunny garden rows house a tangle of bright flowering plants, mostly pollen-rich, old-fashioned sun-worshippers equipped with fetching hues, sweet fragrances, convenient landing pads, petal markers (or "bee guides") and other lures and accommo-dations designed especially for honeybees. Ornamental vegetables and festooning annual vines have potency to evoke thermal delight, in the gardener as in the bees.

Sage is in unusual supply. Lovers of purple sage will appreciate *Salvia purpurea* as well as a dozen red salvias, some wild blues, and two rare yellows. As Gertrude Jekyll remarked, "None of these salvias is reliably hardy but their vivid flowers and attractive habits make them worth growing." Ron Breland touts salvias as deer-proof, varmint-proof, and drought-proof. "They're witching-hour wonders that bloom when everything else has its tongue hanging out. The woodchuck has tremendous respect for this plant," he says.

The Bumps & Co. campanula collection is similarly affluent in rich blues. The 20-odd choices include Canterbury-bells, milky bellflower, peach-bells, chimney bellflower, and the little tussock bellflower of rock gardens. Several species *(Campanula ochroleuca, C. primulifolia, C. takesimana)* are quite rare in commerce, in one case because the plant *(C. rapunculoides)* is too exuberant for gardens. Harmonizing well with the sages and campanulas is a diverse supply of pretty flowering spikes (larkspurs and delphiniums).

Many nursery plants have a romantic toughness that keeps them looking good when the garden goes semi-wild. The penstemons, which are mostly American wildflowers, come in a dozen forms. The silken poppies self-sow freely and are elegant even in dishevelment. Graceful pliant shrubs occasionally make their way into the collection, such as butterfly bush buddleia and cutleaf chaste plant *(Vitex negundo* var. *heterophylla).*

Vegetable gardeners may approach the nursery for gourmet and heirloom varieties of tomatoes, peppers, and the rest. The 25 named tomatoes include yellow, pink, and red forms of the heirloom 'Brandywine'; red grape and yellow pear tomatoes; 'Pompeii' sauce tomato; 'San Marzano', reputedly the world's best cooking tomato; and 'Radiator Charlie', a "mortgage lifter" made famous during the Great Depression. Sweet, hot, and ornamental peppers include something infamous called 'Rat Turd'. Other heirlooms include prehistoric kale, lemon cucumber, and 'Cherokee Trail of Tears' pole bean.

Bumps & Co. is well worth a visit, and as it does not offer mail order, a visit is pretty much required. The small catalog lists the annual plant supply, with the stated caveat that "the slings and arrows of outrageous fortune will undoubtedly modify this list." Prices are reasonable and quantities vary, especially after the nursery has had its early going-over by salvia *aficionados*. The more time is spent here, the more desirable things seem. Spring visitors may be granted a tour of seed-tray production (in the Brelands' kitchen). Overwintered cuttings are kept in the nursery's four-by-eight-foot "hotbeds," a series of inexpensive plant shelters crafted and built by the ingenious Ron Breland.

Nursery visitors should not leave without paying their respects at the bee sanctuary. Behind nursery ground, under a canopy of tulip poplars, honeybees are housed in five-sided hives, crafted according to a sacred architecture. The hives look like Buddhist stupas. According to Breland, "Bees are an umbrella species. If you take care of them, other things will take care of themselves. It has to do with human consciousness. Bees ask you to be wakeful."

Breland approaches the bees reverentially, announcing his presence with a ceremonial drift of smoke from smoldering white sage *(Salvia apiana)*. "Bees are like a cloud, passing over the landscape," he says. "Successful beekeepers go with the shadows." When asked how to create a bee-friendly meadow, he quotes Emily Dickinson: "To make a prairie it takes a clover and one bee, / One clover, and a bee, / And revery. / The revery alone will do, / If bees are few."

Bumps & Co. is one of those rare nurseries that seem to sustain people in unknowable ways. "We have a loyal following of people who just like to be here," says Breland. "No one imagined something like this in Rockland County. It's what I hope a business to be. A living art."

Directions: From New York City, take the Henry Hudson Parkway north and merge onto the Saw Mill River Parkway north. Exit onto New York State Thruway (Route 87) north, cross the Tappan Zee Bridge, and at exit 12/West Nyack, turn left off the ramp and stay in the right lane. Turn immediately right onto Snake Hill Road. At the T-junction, turn left onto Old Mill Road. In 0.2 mile, at 4-way intersection, turn right onto Strawtown Road/Route 23 north. The nursery is about a mile on the left.

Nearby attractions: The Hudson River towns of Nyack and Piermont have good food, antiques, and boutiques. Hook Mountain, Route 9W, Upper Nyack, with a panoramic view of the Hudson's mountainous ridges, is an exceptional vantage for watching migrating hawks and soaring raptors which, like bees, are considered indicator species of ecological health. The Hudson Valley Raptor Center, Stanfordville (845-758-6957; www.hvraptors.com), and the Hawk Migration Association of North America (www.hmana.org) have information on hawk watches along this major flyway; September and October are the busiest months.

CARLSON'S GARDENS

P.O. Box 305, 26 Salem Hill Road, South Salem, NY 10590

(914) 763-5958

www.carlsonsgardens.com; e-mail *bob@carlsonsgardens.com*

Bob Carlson

Hardy azaleas and rhododendrons. Boxwood and mountain laurel. *Small specialty nursery. Open early April until the ground freezes. Open by appointment. Mail order. Catalog on Web site. Large plants available at nursery. Planting and selection advice. Plant photos, bloom calendar, and selection criteria on Web site. Display garden. Visitors welcome. Call ahead.*

Once in a while a plant will take hold of a man and not let go. Thirty years ago, Bob Carlson was a data processing executive living on Long Island, where he started growing azaleas from seed for the fun of it. Everything grows on Long Island, so of course his seedlings flourished. When they bloomed, he immediately fell for sweet azaleas. "It was the perfume that got me," he recalls. "Then I got into it, like dancing."

Today, Carlson is well into his second career as a breeder and propagator of fine azalea and rhododendron hybrids. Carlson's Gardens is the nursery he founded in Westchester, 50 miles north of New York City. It occupies wooded acreage surrounding his home, where his collection grows liberally, in filigreed layers, under an oaken canopy. The gardens produce a breathtaking floral display that goes on for months in spring and summer, followed by an intricate blaze of fall foliage in yellow, red, wine, and orange. Because many Carlson azaleas are evergreen, they look picturesque in winter as well.

Of all the garden plants introduced to us from Asia, the rhododendron genus (which includes azaleas) stands out for its imposing garden presence. As Maggie Campbell-Culver observes in *The Origin of Plants*, "The glut of new Rhododendron species which was released into numerous parks and woodlands in the first half of the twentieth century enabled enthusiastic gardeners to set about breeding, crossing and hybridizing with an abandonment which echoes the tulipomania of the mid-seventeenth century." Hybridizing zeal has long vibrated in America, where by now a rhododendron must exist for every conceivable garden site.

Bob Carlson has developed his own azalea hybrids. The 'Carlson's Face 'em Down' series (*Rhododendron mucronatum* selections) cover up "the bare bottoms of leggier plants." His 'Carlson's Brave' evergreen azaleas have multi-season color in cold Zone 6. Dwarf evergreen 'Jeepers Creepers' azaleas make good fillers and ground covers. For shrubby season-extenders, 'Carlson's Postscripts' deciduous azaleas bloom in summer in mixed colors. Carlson names hybrids after song titles of the swing era, such as Bennie Goodman's 'Angels Sing' and Jelly Roll Morton's 'Choptank River'.

Carlson also sells other people's hybrids. The 'Gable' azaleas came from Joseph Gable, a pioneer of American rhododendron breeding whose evergreen azaleas have an informal beauty well suited to woodlands. The evergreen 'Glenn Dale' azaleas were bred by B. Y. Morrison, a National Arboretum director and American Horticultural Society founder. They have proven hardy at Carlson's Gardens, though of hardiness Morrison himself wrote, "Nothing in the world would induce me to make a zone map! . . . And as for the usual zone maps . . . pfui!" New Yorkers might like 'Manhattan', a bold tough rose-pink bloomer.

Some of Carlson's stock seems decidedly Japanese. Polly Hill's famous 'North Tisbury' azaleas, named for the site of her Martha's Vineyard arboretum, offer what Carlson calls "ground-breaking and ground-covering hybrids" of a prostrate Japanese evergreen azalea. Carlson offers a dozen of Hill's ground-cover shrubs, including tomato-red 'Joseph Hill' and deep rose 'Wintergreen'. From New Jersey breeder Robert Gartrell come 'Robin Hill' and 'Gartrell' evergreen azaleas, a baker's dozen of large-flowered Japanese satsuki hybrids.

For deciduous azaleas, Carlson grows the 'Knaphill-Exbury' hybrids from England, admired for their "unequalled range of colors in big showy trusses"—Day-Glo scarlet, emergency orange, butter yellow, and deep rose. Miscellaneous finery (the Mezitt azaleas, the 'Northern Lights' series) are grown here, along with some rare and valuable small-leaf rhododendrons bred by Gable and Nearing. Various hardy evergreen, small-leaf, large-leaf, and "yak" *(R. yakusimanum)* rhododendron hybrids round out Carlson's frilly inventory.

The nursery grows "our natives" and "their natives." "Our" natives include the American rosebay, flame, pink-shell, pinxterbloom, Cumberland, coast, and swamp azaleas, plus some color-changing hybrids that embellish the plants' delightful wildness. "Their" natives feature, among other Asians, the royal azalea of Korea *(Rhododendron schlippenbachii)*, a collector's item whose round bluish leaves and soft pink flowers are among the prettiest of the genus. Carlson himself labors to breed new showy hybrids of the native sweet azalea *(R. arborescens),* coast azalea *(R. atlanticum),* and flame azalea *(R. calendulaceum).* Hardy boxwood and mountain laurel cultivars (particularly the Richard Jaynes kalmia hybrids) are a new addition to the broadleaf evergreen repertoire. Expect hostas next!

Carlson's Gardens sells plants according to plant size, not pot size—a welcome innovation given the vagaries of the plant trade. Stock of some 2000 varieties is pot-grown and acclimated to this Zone 6 setting. Plants up to 36 inches are shipped; larger stock must be picked up at the nursery. The nursery is equipped with a sophisticated high-tech Web site about which customers rave, just as they do about Carlson's careful packing arrangements and overall plant quality.

In the unblinking manner of Web sites, the nursery operates 24/7 online. (In real time, the nursery is open by appointment.) A digital photo gallery displays stunning color pictures of each plant. Browse-and-buy features allow the inventory to be searched by name, type, color, breeder, hardiness, and fragrance—there goes Saturday afternoon. Planting and growing guides offer expert advice. The bloom calendar is based on Carlson's 30 years of observation. To date, this is surely the most complex and sophisticated Web site in horticulture.

An amusing sidelight of both catalog and Web site is Carlson's verse, part humorous doggerel, part sly limerick. Their theme is horticulture, salted with sex and politics. "Smart Bushes," for example, goes as follows: *No one-term bushes here who lack / the genes to get invited back. / No duct tape needed for in fact / Ours won't mind if they're bushwhacked.* Viagra and Polly Hill's prostrate azaleas are coupled in other verse.

Directions: From Route 84, take exit 3 in Connecticut, turn onto Route 7 south, and turn right onto Route 35 south (going west), passing into New York State. Take the first right after Route 123 onto Spring Street; in South Salem, turn right at the fork onto Main Street, and in one block turn left onto Salem Hill Road. The nursery is the last drive on the left; enter at the second gate. From New York City, take the Henry Hudson Parkway north to the Saw Mill River Parkway north. At the end, turn right on Route 35 east, and in 7.3 miles, turn right onto Spring Street; follow directions above. From the Merritt Parkway, take Connecticut exit 38, turn onto Route 123 north, and in 11 miles, turn left onto Route 35 east; follow directions above. Call ahead.

Nearby attractions: Salem Country Deli, 112 Spring Street, South Salem, NY 10590 (914-763-8902), makes fresh sandwiches. Horse & Hound Inn, 94 Spring Street, South Salem, NY 10590 (914-763-3108; www.thehorseandhoundinn.com), is a chef-owned historic inn (dinner daily; lunch Friday through Sunday). Barbara Israel Garden Antiques, 296 Mt. Holly Road, Katonah, NY 10536 (212-744-6281; www.barbaraisrael.com), is a prominent source for vintage terra-cotta and fine garden antiques. The Hammond Museum Japanese Stroll Garden, Deveau Road, North Salem (914-669-5033; www.hammondmuseum.org), serves lunch on the terrace.

CATSKILL NATIVE NURSERY

607 Samsonville Road (County Route 3), Kerhonkson, NY 12446
(845) 626-2758
www.catskillnativenursery.com; e-mail *info@catskillnativenursery.com*
Francis Groeters and Diane Greenberg

Native perennials, fruits, shrubs, and trees. Herbs. Small specialty nursery. Open from mid-April to first hard frost, Thursday through Monday, 9:30 to 6, Friday, 9:30 to 7. Closed Tuesday and Wednesday. Call for exact dates. Mailing list. Catalog on Web site. No mail order (occasional small orders accepted). Ecological gardening advice. July 4th butterfly count. Festivals, workshops, talks, teas, yoga. Pottery and garden art. Botanical prints. Garden club tours. Gift certificates. Display gardens. Visitors welcome.

Sometimes the hardest plants to appreciate are those under foot. North America is home to a diverse and sophisticated flora whose beauty has only begun to be admired by gardeners. Communities of plants, evolved in living response to place, form a unique regional heritage belonging to no one, and to everyone. Their rightness in our landscape is inherent in their being. Gardeners who fall in love with them say there is no going back.

Catskill Native Nursery is a native plant nursery devoted to growing regional flora and encouraging its use in gardens. The nursery is located on an old farm in a pleasantly rural town in the foothills of the Catskill Mountains. Francis Groeters and Diane Greenberg started the nursery in 1987 as a "green business" to meet the region's growing demand for ecological garden plants.

The couple is well suited to the important work they have undertaken in support of regional flora. Groeters is an evolutionary ecologist with a PhD in biology who spent his post-doctorate years studying insects. He met Greenberg, a professional horticulturist with a 150-year-old farmhouse and a dream of making a nursery. "The old fields had become a monoculture of goldenrod," Groeters says. "We decided to grow ornamental native plants for home gardeners, also for hard-core native plant people who want Hudson Valley and Catskills plants. The area lacked a native plant nursery and we wanted to fill the niche."

Despite the seriousness of its mission, the nursery has an almost whimsical air. In a gentle hollow behind the old farmhouse, potted plants and herbs surround a potting shed, rustic arbor, and cedar shade houses

Groeters built to Greenberg's design. Tea parties are held in the garden. Birds and birdhouses abound. The truck's hand-painted slogan is "Gardening for a Better Environment." The nursery's culinary and healing herbs—which Greenberg calls "Green Witch" herbs—support classes in soap-making, aromatherapy, and even garden yoga.

Catskill Native's inventory is rich in ornamental native perennials for woodland, meadow, pond, and bog garden. Its 600-odd native varieties comprise an exceptional selection, especially for a small nursery. Plants are propagated and grown on-site in 2-quart and gallon pots. All are healthy, well tended, and reasonably priced—qualities of excellence that account for customer affection and quickening demand. "I'm not sure how we do it," says Groeters. "We don't have that much space."

Irresistible examples of nursery-propagated wild perennials are pink coreopsis, purple trillium, blue cohosh, wild columbine, tall meadow rue, marsh marigold, and speckled wood lily. Curious gardeners might try the hyssop-leaved thoroughwort, narrow-leaved mountain mint, or round-leaved bluebell. The nursery also grows a good supply of native grasses, ferns, and wood sedges, not omitting the popular little bluestem *(Schizachyrium scoparium)*, which turns golden-brown in autumn.

A subspecialty is indigenous flora of the Catskills and Hudson Valley, grown from wild seed collected locally. The nursery propagates local genotypes of New York aster, sweet white violet, and green-headed coneflower *(Rudbeckia laciniata)*. Catskills ornamentals include bloodroot *(Sanguinaria canadensis)*, cardinal flower *(Lobelia cardinalis)* and hairy beard-tongue *(Penstemon hirsutus)*. As the owners state on their Web site, "Gardening with native plants should not be thought of as an intrusion of political correctness into the horticultural world, but as an attempt to develop gardens that possess a regional identity."

Besides perennials, Catskill Native Plants sells intriguing fruits, shrubs, and trees native to the eastern United States. Among these are excellent garden and landscape plants that are uncommon in commerce, such as hardy persimmon, northern pecan, sassafras, cucumber tree *(Magnolia acuminata),* rosebay rhododendron, highbush blueberry, spicebush *(Lindera benzoin),* and hobblebush *(Viburnum lantanoides).*

Seed flats near the wildlife pond presage future nursery offerings of mapleleaf viburnum, wild ginger, purple angelica, and white baneberry with red berries. *Tiarella cordifolia* 'Lulu Leaf'" is a beautiful form of native foamflower that Groeters found growing locally.

"Nobody's growing these plants," says Groeters. "I'm also trying to propagate *Trillium undulatum* and a native scutillaria, as well as northern monkshood *[Aconitum noveboracense]*, the only federally endangered species here in the Catskills."

Catskill Native Nursery is a delightful destination where visitors are given a warm welcome. Gardeners interested in learning more about using native plants in their gardens will enjoy the nursery's workshops and display gardens, including a native orchard and bog gardens shimmering with dragonflies. As they state on their Web site, "With the use of beautiful, low-maintenance native plants you can provide food and habitat for both yourself and the small creatures we share the world with. Many natives are becoming scarce in the wild. Help restore biodiversity, starting in your own gardens, by incorporating native plants into your landscape."

Directions: The nursery is south of the Catskill Mountains, 24 miles from New Paltz and 20 miles from Kingston. From the south on Route 87, take exit 16/New Paltz; turn onto Route 299 west; and at the end, turn right onto Route 44/55 west. In Kerhonkson, turn right onto Route 209 north. In 1 mile turn left onto Route 3/Samsonville Road; the nursery is 5 miles on the left. From the north on Route 87, take exit 19/Kingston, turn onto Route 209 south, and pass through Stone Ridge (great antique shops). In Kerhonkson, turn right onto Route 3/Samsonville Road; the nursery is 5 miles on the left. From New Jersey, take Route 17 north to the Wurtsboro/Ellenville exit, turn onto Route 209 north to Kerhonkson, and follow directions above.

Nearby attractions: Kelder's Farm, 5755 Route 209, Kerhonkson, NY (845-626-7137; www.kelderfarm.com), is an 1836 family farm with fresh flowers and vegetable seedlings, plus corn maze and petting zoo. Rainbow Diner, Route 209, Kerhonkson (845-626-4635), is open daily, 7 to 9. Herbalist Susun Weed (www.susunweed.com) offers day-long plant workshops in her garden in Woodstock, complete with talking stick ceremony, wild-food lunch, and weed walk.

Related sources: The New York Flora Atlas shows the distribution of native plants in New York State (www.nyflora.org). The Mountain Top Arboretum, Route 23C, Tannersville, NY 12485 (518-589-3903; www.mtarbor.org), has indigenous plants of the Catskill Mountain forest.

CLAIRE'S GARDEN CENTER
Haviland Hollow Road, Patterson, NY 12563
(914) 878-6632 phone and fax
Glen Waruch

Perennials. Annuals, herbs, vegetables, and roses. *Small specialty nursery. Open year-round, daily 9 to 5. Extended hours Friday through Sunday in May. Closed major holidays. Catalog $3, with discount coupons. No mail order. Garden gift shop. Information booth. Gift certificates. Visitors welcome.*

Claire's Garden Center is a pleasant, well-loved grower of flowering plants and their companions in Patterson, just north of Danbury, Connecticut. Owner Glen Waruch, often seen in trim gray beard and baseball cap, bought Claire's some 30 years ago from its founder, the original Claire. The nursery's low-key charm and good plant values resonate with gardeners seeking fresh-grown stock within reasonable distance of New York City. Asked to define its long-standing allure, customers tend to smile and say, "Oh, Claire's is Claire's."

Claire's produces most of its own annuals and perennials in cold frames and greenhouses located at the garden center and on the hill above and keeps track of perennial plants that are "hardy" as opposed to "marginal." Potted plants are arranged beneath arbors and in a painted wooden barn topped by a cockerel weathervane. Along a fence, container displays spill their fountains of color. A pond garden shows off aquatic plants. A garden shed houses terracotta pots and lightweight plastic counterparts, which work well in places where they have to be lugged around. Garden supplies anticipate all needs with gloves, stakes, wind chimes, books, bulk wildflower seed, organic fertilizer, and bales of straw.

The nursery is pet-friendly. Dogs roam the premises, cats curl on coconut mats, geese honk on the hill. Fluttering and pecking underfoot are the owner's chickens and guinea hens. Waruch defends their presence. "My children!" he crows. "They're good weeders." When he says things like, "the rabbit is getting a new wife," staff members roll their eyes.

Claire's catalog lists more than 1000 varieties of perennial plants, ranging from *Acanthus mollis* (bear's-breech) to *Zauschneria* 'Orange Carpet' (an unusual drought-tolerant ground cover). New introductions are added every year. To get a sense of Claire's exceptional depth, we counted 24 kinds of iris; 36 phlox; 41 large- and small-flowered clematis; 28 astilbes; 27 delphiniums;

20 double and single peonies; 9 Oriental tree peonies; and 5 kinds of lady's-mantle, including 3 dwarf forms. Collections of 50 hostas and 30 daylilies are populated with good performance plants. Stylish news-getters include peach verbascum, pink monarda, 'Patty's Plum' Oriental poppy, giant rose mallows, and the coveted white martagon lily.

Shade gardeners can enrich their gardens with native woodlanders—such as Canadian ginger, Virginia bluebells, and *Galax urceolata*—and Asian woodlanders, such as ladybells and the stunning Japanese jack-in-the-pulpit *(Arisaema sikokianum)*. Diversity reigns among handsome ferns and epimediums. Tiarella and heuchera hybrids are ornate, with fluted or incised edges and plum or chartreuse foliage. Fall-blooming perennials include a terrific array of meadow plants and grasses.

Purists might wish that a few plants be eliminated as noxious invasives, such as porcelain vine and bishop's weed, but for the most part, Claire's list represents the cream of current perennial-garden fare. Especially welcome are valuable plants that are hard to source, such as prostrate veronica, white Japanese primrose, and cyclamen-leaved Korean violet. A rosy purple ornamental onion (*Allium thunbergii* 'Ozawa') reportedly blooms until January here. There is always something no one has ever heard of, such as *Leptinella squalida* (a two-inch ferny ground cover) or *Scrophularia auriculata* (variegated figwort).

The nursery's catalog exhorts, "Although Claire's specializes in perennials, we don't want you to overlook our choice varieties of annuals, vegetables, herbs, hybrid roses, antique and specialty roses, flowering shrubs, garden mums, flowering cabbage and kale, and ground covers." Herbs for medicinal, culinary, and cosmetic uses are supplemented by ornamental creeping thyme (20 kinds), verbena (20 kinds), and annual salvia (30 kinds). Herbs such as double white feverfew and 'Kent Beauty' oregano double as decorative fillers in flower beds.

Colorful annuals come in all shapes and shades—cannas, coleus, snapdragons, stock, pansies, petunias, and pelargoniums. Vegetable seeds and seedlings are delicious staples that are worth the trouble to grow, such as heirloom tomatoes, white eggplant, Scotch leek, self-blanching celery, cardoon, sweet white onions, and hot peppers. A few perennial-friendly shrubs, such as ferny lime-green elderberry, round out the inventory.

The roses are in a class by themselves: highly rated modern hybrid climbers, floribundas, grandifloras, teas, shrub roses, antique climbers and ramblers, heirloom shrubs, landscape roses, patio roses, and David Austin

English hybrids. Besides classics such as white 'Iceberg' and pink climbing 'New Dawn', gardeners find such gorgeous long bloomers as 'Topaz Jewel', the best yellow rugosa; Griffith Buck's rosy 'Country Dancer'; and 'William Baffin', an exceptionally tough strawberry-pink Canadian climber. Beloved by collectors are apricot-cream 'Buff Beauty' (1939) and some antique Bourbon roses, none of which can be trusted in Zone 4 or 5. The David Austin roses feature his best efforts—yellow 'Graham Stuart Thomas' and apricot 'Abraham Darby'. *Rosa glauca*, a wild rose with bluish foliage, makes a superb landscape presence. In all, some 150 varieties of roses, many AARS winners, offer vigorous, hardy, disease-tolerant flowering of a glory achieved by few other garden shrubs.

Claire's has the grace to be open year-round. Visiting is a must, for there's no mail order and no Web site. Spring is high season, when the nursery overflows and plant selection is at its peak. Sales are first-come-first-served, except for roses, which can be reserved from January to May. Being small and independent, Claire's doesn't promise to have all plants in stock at all times. An excellent printed catalog, running nearly 100 pages, contains the plant lists and a yearly calendar of events. At Christmas, poinsettias make a red and pink explosion. Ice-bound gardeners are encouraged to visit in winter, Claire's busiest growing season.

In fall, the growing season winds down and perennial plants are discounted. We once bought an obscure pot crammed with Labrador violets, aggressive little spreaders decked in purple foliage, useful for carpeting under a tree. The pot was originally something else, but the self-seeding violets had taken over; so instead of protest a new tag was popped into the pot and we got a good price. At Claire's, even the accidents seem to be happy ones.

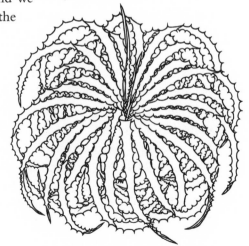

Directions: From Route 287 in White Plains, take exit 9A onto Route 684 north. From Route I-84 in Brewster, take exit 20 onto Route 684 north. When Route 684 becomes Route 22 north, continue straight on Route 22 for 8 miles. At the Putnam Diner (845-878-8000), turn right onto Haviland Hollow Road. The nursery is on the left.

Nearby attractions: Horticultural Design, 21 Bluebird Inn Road, Pawling, NY 12564 (845-855-9023), is a naturalistic display garden of remarkable artistry and diversity, created by landscape designer Duncan Brine; open for scheduled tours and by appointment. Heinchon's Dairy Farm, 110 East Main Street (Route 22), Pawling, NY 12564 (845-855-5440), is a century-old family dairy with delicious homemade ice cream. Exceptional food and baked goods can be sampled at McKinney & Doyle Corner Bakery and Fine Foods Café, 10 Charles Colman Boulevard, Pawling, NY 12564 (845-855-3875; www.mckinneyanddoyle.com).

FADDEGON'S NURSERY

1140 Troy-Schenectady Road (Route 7), Latham, NY 12110
(518) 785-6726; fax (518) 785-0650
www.faddegons.com; e-mail *info@faddegons.com*
The Faddegon family

Annuals, perennials, nursery stock, houseplants. *Independent garden center. Open year-round, Monday through Saturday, 9 to 6, Sunday, 10 to 4. Longer spring hours. No catalog or mail order. Online garden shop. Seminars. Supply catalogs posted on Web site. Gift shop. Seasonal items. Visitors welcome.*

Every urban region has a full-service garden center that outperforms the competition and warrants inclusion in any good-plant-source recommendation. Near Albany, it's Faddegon's. Cornelius Faddegon founded Faddegon's Nursery 85 years ago to grow blue spruce trees on land he worked himself. Today, Faddegon's is a 40-acre commercial garden center and landscaping operation that boasts of being "the largest interior plantscape company" in the Capital region, mainly supplying office and condo facilities.

Faddegon's is known for its vast variety of garden plants. The garden center staff is knowledgeable, the stock excellent, and even tricky plants, like evergreens, are well cared for. The staff is proud of keeping abreast of the latest horticultural trends, each year introducing hot new varieties of annuals, and perennials alongside last year's best sellers. A "National Parks" rose collection and "Twice as Nice" daylily collection offer popular branded hybrids. A full line of ornamental trees and shrubs comes from Iseli Nurseries, a specialty grower in Oregon, for which Faddegon's is an outlet. Japanese maples, dwarf conifers, topiary, and trough gardens figure among the high-value imports.

Home gardeners say they're rarely disappointed, for Faddegon's usually has what they want and will order anything that's not on hand. All nursery stock is bought in, except for some in-ground specimens used by the landscaping department. Plants aren't cheap, but quality is good and prices appropriate, considering the high level of retail service. Bargain hunters can always haunt the fall sales, when selected containers, perennials, and roses are half price. Orchid-of-the-month discounts and like promotions take place in the exotic houseplant section. Faddegon's is a local Agway, with supplies ranging from topiary frames to squirrel food and garden clogs—and lamps, and jewelry. Sure, it's a grocery store for gardeners, but it's a good one.

Directions: From Route 87 (Adirondack Northway), take exit 6 onto Route 7 west. Faddegon's is 2.5 miles on the left, just past the intersection of Albany-Shaker Road.

Nearby attractions: Story's Nursery, 4265 Route 67, Freehold, NY 12431 (518-634-7754; www.storysnursery.com) is a large, superbly stocked garden center on 35 acres in the foothills of the Catskills south of Albany, known for its A to Z holdings of garden plants (perennials, annuals, grasses, aquatics, herbs, roses), fine woody ornamentals, and award-winning landscape design.

HELDERLEDGE FARM
435 Picard Road (Route 307), Altamont, NY 12009
(518) 765-4702; fax (518) 765-4578
www.helderledge.com; e-mail *helderledge@capital.net*
Paul and Mardell Steinkamp

Hardy perennials, hostas, and aquatics. Unusual woody plants. *Small landscape designers' nursery. Open Mid-April through October, daily, 9 to 5. Call for exact dates and fall hours. No catalog or mail order. Sunny Border "Gold Pot" perennials. Coupon rewards for purchases. Landscape design and installation services. Free lecture walks on Saturdays in May, Sundays in June, at 10. Display gardens. Visitors welcome.*

Helderledge Nursery is a creative dream garden surrounding a small nursery that specializes in the kind of plants landscape architects like to use in water and shade gardens. That's because the owners, Paul and Mardell Steinkamp, are landscape architects, and their dream garden consists of what they call a "visually significant complex of pools" embraced by shade and wetland plants.

Thirty years ago, the Steinkamps worked as landscape architects for the state and lived in an Albany townhouse with 12 tomato plants. (As urban frontiersmen, they were instrumental in helping to preserve Albany's Center Square from road improvements.) They bought a 38-acre farm in the Helderberg Mountain valley, west of Albany, as a second home and place to garden. By 1982, having fallen in love with country life, they decided to leave Albany and start a nursery and landscape design business in an old cider house. In 1997, the couple won *Garden Design* magazine's Golden Trowel Award in the professional category for the "little oasis" of modernistic ponds, bridges, and bogs at the heart of their garden.

The Steinkamps collect plants from all over the world. With the help of staff and the occasional daughter, the couple grows many of their own perennials, both to stock the retail nursery and to feed their landscaping business. Mardell Steinkamp is New York's representative for Sunny Border Nurseries, a high-quality perennial supplier in Connecticut, and gets the cream of that crop (including their coveted "Gold Pot" plants). Helderledge plants come in good-size containers and are well priced. All are hardy to Zone 5, as proven by their vibrant presence in display gardens.

The Steinkamps grow brand-new perennial cultivars and time-tested standbys. Enticements are of the soft-sell variety, in the form of instructive talks, good labels, and unrestrained display gardens that ribbon around the nursery and adjacent Steinkamp home. Unlike the manicured, almost prissy gardens that many landscapers now install even in country places, the Steinkamps' garden uses good structure to support wildish displays of self-seeders, late-bloomers, and other rambunctious performers that accord well with the rural landscape.

The stock is interesting and varied: flowering perennials, ground covers, fine hostas, and many self-sustainers such as Carolina lupine, persicaria, blue dune grass, and diamond grass. A refined group of daylilies survives from the days when Paul Steinkamp was an active collector and breeder. The Sunny Border repertoire includes exciting new introductions, colored and textured perennials, a new line of "bodacious temperennials," and "hot new sempervivums" for dry gardens.

The nursery ground is picturesquely shaded by aged 'Northern Spy' apple trees that drop edible fruit in autumn. A sense of abandon is enhanced by big, striking pre-planted containers that develop a kind of feral beauty late in the season. Good roses and locally grown shrubs and trees (including pretty birches, witch hazels, and kousa dogwoods) add depth to the perennial stock. Seed from double-salmon cabbage poppies is sold in small packets in autumn.

The Steinkamps have a special interest in low-maintenance grasses and self-sowers for difficult sites—what horticulturist Luther Burbank once called "educated weeds." In 2004, the Bethlehem Garden Club persuaded the Steinkamps to design a section of median strip with drought- and salt-tolerant prairie plants—what some call a hellstrip. (The plant list included *Rudbeckia* 'Goldsturm', *Sedum* 'Autumn Joy', *Persicaria polymorpha*, *Silphium perfoliatum*, Russian sage, and some very big grasses.) Club ladies planted their highway garden wearing yellow hard hats and orange safety vests, which made the local news.

The garden was such a hit with area residents that another median-strip planting was promptly commissioned. "It's been a real introduction to great big perennials and grasses, the ones that look like they've always been there," says Paul Steinkamp. "It's like something German garden designers would do—self-sustaining meadow plants with interest in all seasons, even winter."

For all their achievements, the Steinkamps insist that running a nursery— growing what they call "the finest plants in the fittest form"—is not what inspires them. What they love is the process of creation—the imaginative interchange between people and landscape by which great gardens are made. Their writings describe the garden as a frame, a sanctuary, a gathering of sound and light; as a place of heightened self-awareness; as a medium for holding nature close. As the Steinkamps say, "We never lose interest in the subject of the garden, as a space for people, as a sculpture of light and shadow, of patterns on the ground, and as a foil for the sky. Gardens, after all, are the artifacts of culture and time."

Directions: Helderledge is 13 miles west of Albany. From Route 787 in Albany, take Western Avenue (Route 20) west to Guilderland, turn left onto Route 155, and in Voorheesville, turn right onto Route 85A west. In 0.7 mile, turn right onto Route 156 toward Altamont. In 1.7 miles, turn left onto Tygert Road and, at the end, turn right onto Picard Road. The nursery is 0.5 mile on the left. From Route 90 west of Albany, take exit 4 onto New Scotland Avenue/Route 85 west, turn right on Route 85A east, and turn left on Route 307. The nursery is 2 miles on the left.

Nearby attractions: A Steinkamp-designed "median strip" garden is located at the corner of Kenwood and Cherry Avenue in Delmar. Four Corners Luncheonette, 2 Grove Street, Delmar (518-439-0172), is a great little café on a side street opposite the U.S. Post Office. Near the nursery, Indian Ladder Farms, 342 Altamont Road, Altamont (518-765-2956; www.indianladderfarms.com), is an ecological family-run apple orchard with a fresh-food café in season. Thatcher State Park, Route 157, Altamont, protects the Helderberg Escarpment and affords shivery cliff-edge views to Vermont. Wellington Herbs and Spices, 649 Rickard Hill Road, Schoharie (518-295-7366; www.wellingtonsherbsandspices.com), runs an herbal tearoom surrounded by herb gardens and pretty views.

LOOMIS CREEK NURSERY

29 Van Deusen Road, Hudson, NY 12534
(518) 851-9801
www.loomiscreek.com; e-mail info@loomiscreek.com
Bob Hyland and Andrew Beckman

Perennials for Zones 4-6. Tender perennials, annuals, tropicals, vines, and shrubs. Small specialty nursery. Open April through July 4th, daily, 9 to 5; July 5 through mid-October, Thursday through Sunday, 9 to 5. Call for precise dates. Catalog on Web site. Free plant list at nursery. No mail order. Custom plant orders. Integrated Pest Management. Seasonal containers. Expert advice. Landscape design. Display gardens. Visitors welcome.

Once in a while, a brand-new retail nursery excites everyone with its prospects for enlivening horticulture in an entire region. In 2003, Loomis Creek Nursery opened its doors: rolling metal gates, deer-proofed with 6-inch mesh, beside an 1820 farmhouse near Hudson.

Almost instantly, luxuriant borders and displays made Loomis Creek seem like a nursery veteran. A handsome wooden outbuilding rapidly emerged from a lumber pile. Stylish perennials gathered in a graveled sales yard in the company of tall ornamental grasses. Decorative tropicals made floral explosions beside a Gothic-style greenhouse. A red cypress vine twirled fetchingly around a granite post, just in time for a camera flash.

The proprietors of Loomis Creek Nursery are two of New York's best-known horticultural insiders: Bob Hyland, former vice president of Horticulture and Operations at Brooklyn Botanic Garden, past president of Manhattan's Metro Hort Group, and one-time associate of Pennsylvania's Longwood Gardens and San Francisco's Strybing Arboretum; and Andrew Beckman, a Longwood Gardens graduate, head gardener to Martha Stewart, Deputy Garden Editor at *Martha Stewart Living Omnimedia,* and past gardener to Peter Wooster and Stephen Sondheim.

With such lustrous credentials, the only mystery is why two delightful, knowledgeable men are working their hands to the bone running a nursery. "Most of us have a pipe dream of starting a little nursery," Hyland says. "The original passion is all about plants."

Loomis Creek's dazzling inventory focuses on garden-worthy perennials for Zones 4 to 6 and showy annuals and tender perennials for containers and borders. The nursery's goal is to offer what it calls "underused, out-of-the-ordinary species and cultivars," both native and exotic, for mixed borders, meadows, and containers. Choice flowering shrubs for mixed borders are being added to the inventory, along with more flowering vines and even more ornamental grasses.

Plant choices are designed to get the most out of every inch of leaf or flower. Applying their combined knowledge and experience, Hyland and Beckman almost invariably select the best-performing plants, with the nicest form, in the most gorgeous floral and foliage tones. Reviewing the plant list, one is impressed by their surety of judgment, tempting the ordinary gardener to bypass self-doubt and turn the whole matter over to experts. Garden design services are available on a limited basis. "We tend to be generalists," says Hyland, as if this were easy. "It's about growing good plants and combining textures and colors in innovative ways."

The nursery's main absorption is with what are described as "bold archi-tectural perennials and ornamental grasses"—plants that add drama, color, and structure to the garden. A good example can be seen in a Gertrude Jekyll-inspired border combining burgundy fountain grass, bronze-leaved tobacco, variegated pink dianthus, and striped yucca. To realize similarly rich effects in other gardens, Loomis Creek offers giant angelicas, big-flowered hibiscuses, perennial red-hot pokers, and striped grasses with exotic plumage. Essential to making the party work are attractive fillers such as small-flowered clematis vines, white baptisia, and *Kalimeris integrifolia*, a frothy little Mongolian daisy that stands up well to drought and heat.

Loomis Creek also likes to pair colorful textured foliage with jungle plants. This lush style is readily identified in a tropical border inspired by Brazilian designer Roberto Burle Marx, where red castor beans and incandescent cannas pose against a cool backdrop of sky-blue *Salvia uliginosa*. Such theatrical statements are not just displays—Loomis Creek has the inventory to back them up: velvet amaranths, creamy angel's-trumpets, paint-splashed coleus, caladiums smeared silver and rose, and fancy-leaf pelargoniums in irrepressible hues. Felts, filigrees, and watered silk effects give such foliage the glamour of *haute couture*.

With an almost civic consciousness, Loomis Creek promotes plants deserving greater attention from gardeners. Fine shade plants, for example, include maple-leaved *Kirengeshoma palmata*, silver-leaved Korean violet, golden ligularia, and one or two glorious Japanese iris. Biennials of the cottage garden, such as foxgloves and hollyhocks, are another interest. Late summer and fall-blooming plants extend the season—improved coneflowers, huge joe-pye weeds, wildish asters, a goldenrod called 'Fireworks', and a tall, somewhat unruly group of verbascums.

The proprietors are "avid plantsmen" committed to making their nursery a plant-lover's destination and inspiring source of horticultural knowledge. Plant list and gardens are likely to change each year, reflecting unusual finds, improved selections, and the irrepressible creative energy of the owners. Plant photos on the Web site provide a welcome preview of their intentions.

All nursery stock is beautifully grown and reasonably priced, especially considering its provenance. Perennials generally come in deep quart and gallon containers, grasses and tropicals in 2-gallon pots, and annuals in 8-cell packs and 3¼-inch pots. Plants are grown from cutting and plugs, with more on-site propagation likely as the nursery matures. Because each cultivar is grown in smaller quantities, some things sell out and selection shifts during the season. Larger quantities or unlisted plants can readily be custom ordered.

Starting a nursery is challenging and exhilarating. Rain and drought bedevil the sophisticated horticulturist just as sorely as his hay-baling forebears. But Hyland and Beckman are game, their nursery is already amazing, and they appear to be having fun. "We have great plans and vision," Hyland says. "Hopefully, the economy and Mother Nature will cooperate."

Directions: Loomis Creek is near Hudson, 2 hours north of Manhattan; 35 miles from Albany; 25 miles from Great Barrington, Massachusetts; and 40–45 miles from Falls Village, Connecticut. From I-87, take exit 21 and turn left onto Route 23 east. Cross the Hudson River on the toll bridge. In 5.6 miles, at the 2nd traffic light, turn left onto Route 23/9H north. In 3.9 miles, at a traffic light, turn left onto Route 23B west. In 0.5 mile, turn left onto Stone Mill Road. In 1 mile, turn right on Van Deusen Road; the nursery is on the left. From the Taconic State Parkway, exit onto Route 23 (Hillsdale/Claverack) and turn west on Route 23. In 5.5 miles, pass through the first traffic light in Claverack where Route 23 changes to 23B. In 0.5 mile, turn left onto Stone Mill Road. In 1 mile, turn right on Van Deusen Road; the nursery is on the left.

Nearby attractions: The area is full of amusements justifying a prolonged visit. Loomis Creek's Web site lists area accommodations; see also www.agmkt.state.ny.us (fresh local produce stands) and www.hudsonvalley.org (regional information). Customers can rent Loomis Creek's cute 1-bedroom guest cottage (518-851-9731) for short periods; it comes with an in-ground swimming pool and charming garden. Hudson is a hip town with good antiques stores and cafés, including Swoon Kitchenbar, 340 Warren Street (518-822-8938; www.swoonkitchenbar.com), a Manhattan-quality bistro with Hudson prices. The Secret Gardener, 250 Warren Street, Hudson (518-822-0992), sells containers and cut flowers. Dia:Beacon, 3 Beekman Street, Beacon (845-440-0100; www.diaart.org), is a major contemporary art museum in a renovated Nabisco plant; note the crabapple and hawthorn orchard in the parking lot, designed by Robert Irwin. Down a mile-long avenue of black locust trees, Montgomery Place, Route 9G, Annandale on Hudson (914-758-5461), is an unspoiled 434-acre estate on a bluff overlooking the Hudson River; a horticultural showplace since the 1930s, its lovely gardens are meticulously maintained (open daily except Tuesdays, April through October; picnicking allowed).

LORJON NURSERY
918 Hill Avenue, Pine Bush, NY 12566-6408
(845) 744-5847; fax (845) 744-6628
Loraine and John Lewis

Perennials, grasses, and companion shrubs. Small specialty nursery. Open April through Thanksgiving, Monday through Saturday, 9 to 5, Sunday, 9 to 1. Call for exact dates. Catalog $2. Retail/wholesale. No mail order. Design consultation. Garden supplies. Display garden. Visitors welcome.

"Gardening is largely a question of mixing one sort of plant with another sort of plant, and of seeing how they marry happily together; and if you see they don't marry happily, then you must hoick one of them out and be quite ruthless about it," wrote British designer Vita Sackville-West in 1950. "The true gardener must be brutal, and imaginative for the future."

For today's gardener, the brutality of matchmaking is greatly eased by a ready source of garden plants that have already worked out their differences. Lorjon Nursery in Pine Bush, west of Poughkeepsie, is just the place to find good prospects or replace plants that fail marriage counseling.

Lorjon was founded by Loraine Lewis and her husband, John—hence "Lorjon"—in the lovely old horse country south of the Catskills. The Lewises live and garden on rolling acreage that's part of a gentleman's farm once belonging to Loraine's father. Loraine Lewis is a retired schoolteacher who began experimenting with Christmas trees in 1981, bought an old greenhouse to graft rhododendron cuttings, and eventually found her *métier* in growing perennials. "They're way more fun," she says. "It's a hobby that got out of hand." John Lewis is a semiretired lawyer, which means that he still practices law but wears shorts to work in summer and helps out in the garden.

Lorjon is one of those sporting, all-around great nurseries that's good at everything it does. The Lewises love plants without being too eccentric about it. Their main focus is cultivating fine named varieties of hardy perennials and such mannerly companions as grasses, vines, herbs, roses, and flowering shrubs. Each species is represented by a menu of cultivars that are healthy, happy, fit, smart, colorful, and good-looking.

The plant list begins with 160 species of perennials, each one multiplied by many cultivated varieties. Stalwarts of the sunny border include anise hyssops, bee balms, sedums, anemones, good campanulas and yarrows, and numerous daylilies. Lorjon grows all the yellow sunflowers beginning with the letter H—helenium, helianthus, helianthemum, and heliopsis. Collections of iris, peony, phlox, and hosta demonstrate good taste and good variety.

The shade flora includes hellebores, toad lilies, gingers, Chinese corydalis, variegated Solomon's-seal, and a wide variety of ferns. For fairy gardens, there are columbines, ladybells, and tiny alpines. Intriguing natives include celandine poppy (*Stylophorum diphyllum*), poppy mallow (*Callirhoe involucrata*), and Indian pink (*Spigelia marilandica*). It's always heartening to find the lesser treasures, such as blackberry lily, crocosmia, and crambe (sea kale).

Supplementing Lorjon's perennial list are companion plants whose main function is to weave and swish. The swishers include many rustling grasses, which bring structure, movement, and noise to the sunny garden and look surprisingly well with the stationary roses, of which there is also a nice collection. The weavers include vines, particularly clematis, and an excellent flowering shrub collection (hydrangea, dogwood, clethra, buddleia, lilac, and viburnum) supplemented by garden-worthy evergreens. As with the perennials, these have been selected by confident hands culling for performance and decorative merit.

As a retail and wholesale nursery, Lorjon is a favorite haunt of the region's top landscapers. Perennials come in 1- and 2-gallon pots and most shrubs in 3- and 5-gallon sizes. Prices for plants are uniformly reasonable—often half what they might go for further south—and the plantsmanship superb. Loraine Lewis can often be seen at dawn among the hoophouses, Felco pruners in hand, assiduously grooming the nursery stock. Healthy plants fairly burst from their pots.

Retail customers are warmly welcomed but are expected to read labels and exercise a degree of self-help without making large demands on a hard-working staff. It helps to know what you want in advance. A plant list is available by mail and at the nursery, but there is no mail order and plants must be picked up on-site. Regional gardeners attracted by plant values find this nursery a destination worth traveling for. The garden shop in the old barn carries good garden supplies.

Beautiful display gardens decorate Lorjon's driveway and greenhouses, meriting special notice for their flair in combining perennials, grasses, and shrubs. Credit is due to the owners' daughter, Kerry Lewis, a landscape architect who's designed many distinguished Boston-area gardens and is known for her skill with residential landscapes.

These gardens are vibrant and imaginative. One special, long-blooming arrangement, called "Kerry's Combo," interweaves a miniature pink rose ('The Fairy') with ornamental purple oregano ('Herrenhausen') and rosy-purple cranesbills ('Alpen Glow' and 'Giuseppii'). Another happy marriage employs a neat edge of magenta cranesbills against a backdrop of grapey spires (*Salvia nemorosa* 'Caradonna') and deep violet spikes (*Veronica spicata* 'Royal Candles').

Directions: Pine Bush is west of Poughkeepsie. From Route 84, take exit 8 and follow Route 52 west. In Pine Bush, take a sharp left (south) onto Hill Avenue, just after Larry's Service Center; the nursery is 0.2 mile on the left. From Route 87, take exit 17 onto Route 17K west. In 10 miles, turn right onto Route 208 north. In 3 miles, turn left onto Route 52 west; follow directions above.

Nearby attractions: The Oriental House, 78 Main Street, Pine Bush (845-744-8663), is a Zagat-rated Korean restaurant in town. On a nearby mountain ridge, Mohonk Mountain House, 1000 Mountain Rest Road, New Paltz, NY 12561 (845-255-1000; www.mohonk.com), is a grand Victorian castle-resort on 7800 acres, overlooking Lake Mohonk. This National Historic Landmark has 85 miles of hiking trails and superb, award-winning Victorian gardens. The grounds feature a garden gift shop, greenhouse, museum, picnic areas, stables, and an observation tower; garden-related events take place through the year.

LYNDON LYON GREENHOUSES
P.O. Box 249, 14 Mutchler Street, Dolgeville, NY 13329
(315) 429-8291; (315) 429-3820
www.lyndonlyon.com; e-mail *info@lyndonlyon.com*
Paul Sorano

African violets. Cape primroses, gesneriads, begonias. Orchids. Family-run specialty greenhouses. Office open Monday through Friday, 8 to 4. Greenhouses open Monday through Friday, 8 to 5, Saturday, 10 to 4, Sunday, noon to 4; closed Sundays from October through March. Call ahead during winter months. Mail order. Catalog $3. Catalog on Web site. Minimum order 3 plants or 10 leaf packages. Cancellation fee $5. Orders shipped May 1 to October 31, weather permitting. Winter orders shipped beginning May 1 in order received. Visitors welcome.

Lyndon Lyon Greenhouses is a distinguished mail-order nursery in the Adirondacks famed for African violets since the 1950s. Owner Paul Sorano, grandson of the founder, took over the greenhouses in 1982. Sorano now runs them with the help of his daughter, Kristi, and Debbie Herringshaw, a skilled manager and hybridizer.

The nursery features more than 400 varieties of African violets, as well as numerous Cape primrose hybrids (*Streptocarpus* spp.) and exotic houseplants. New hybrids are introduced each season. According to Sorano, in the fast-paced world of African violets, "things are new for only a few years." Demand for Lyndon Lyon's African violets comes "from all over the planet," including Russia and Japan, where the greenhouse is considered one of the top sources in the world.

Lyndon Lyon, the nursery's founder, was a factory foreman whose niece gave him a single African violet leaf in 1949. Lyon became so interested that he joined the African Violet Society of America (AVSA), then two years old, and studied plant genetics by reading his son's college texts. He began hybridizing on the second floor of his home, eventually tearing down the walls to accommodate a rapidly increasing collection. In 1953, Lyon stunned the African violet world by breeding the first double pink African violet. His double pink hybrids swept the top AVSA awards in 1954 and caused a traffic jam at the annual convention.

Surging demand led Lyon to build a greenhouse, quit his factory job, and go into the African violet business. Catalog sales began in 1955 and have not abated since. Lyon designed three-tiered wooden benches lit by fluorescent lights that since became an industry standard. His redwood-and-glass Lord & Burnham greenhouses are still in use today. Late in life, Lyon acquired and demolished an empty factory building where he had once labored, turning it into a parking lot for his customers.

Besides the famous double pinks, Lyon pioneered the development of miniature, variegated, and trailing African violets. He bred distinctive star-shaped blooms that remain a nursery specialty, from green-edged pink stars to blue-edged white stars. As Sorano recalls, "Grandpa was responsible for introducing most of the modern colors, styles, and sizes. He got started early, when there was not much around except blue violets." The AVSA Honor Roll of African Violets, venerating named hybrids that appeared on the Best Varieties List for five consecutive years, lists 66 Lyndon Lyon hybrids—far more than any other hybridizer in history. Lyon was inducted into the AVSA Hall of Fame in 1999.

Today, Lyndon Lyon Greenhouses continues to sell classic, cutting-edge African violets of remarkable diversity, mostly its own hybrids. Fancy flowers are decorated with ruffles, bicolors, pinwheel stripes, glitter edges, thumbprints, and splashed "fantasy" markings. Some new varieties, such as pink 'Super Duper', have giant 3-inch blooms; the micro-minis are so tiny that they fit in 1-inch pots. Flower colors range from white, pink, blue, and purple to unusual corals, reds, and a rare green. 'Banana Split', a warm cream, is as near as the nursery gets to break-through yellow. Recent AVSA award winners include 'Plumberry Glow', a variegated white with fruit-colored thumbprints, and 'Neon Fantasy', deep purple with frilled edges and pink fantasy puffs. Ruffled green 'Irish Flirt', bred by Sorano's former wife, has won more show awards than any semi-mini in history.

Besides African violets, Lyndon Lyon Green-houses grows 53 varieties of Cape primrose *(Streptocarpus × hybridus)*, a refined African violet relative producing delicate blue and white trumpet-like flowers. Beginning in the mid-1970s, new generations of hardier, prettier, and better behaved Cape primrose hybrids increased the plant's popularity with home gardeners. Today, the nursery grows original hybrids such as 'Vampire's Kiss', the blackest-red to date; 'Black Magic', the darkest purple; and 'Poochie', an unusual maroon-streaked coral. A newcomer, 'Lollipop Dream', has plum-red blossoms with yellow stripes, purple veining, a white throat, and black spots.

When African violets and Cape primroses cease to charm, gardeners can turn to their cousins, a group of unpronounceable gesneriads offered by Lyndon Lyon Greenhouses for home conditions. Like African violets, easy-care chiritas have variegated foliage and showy flowers. Nematanthus, or "goldfish plant," has pouch-shaped flowers in acidic orange. Aeschynanthus is called "lipstick plant" for the blazing flowers that seem to emerge from a tube of lipstick. Gesneriads include free-flowering columneas and flame violets (*Episcia* spp.) with silver, raspberry, and chocolate foliage. Unrelated to gesneriads but easily as ornate, the rex or "painted leaf" begonias produce pebbled foliage tinted with plum, black, silver, and rose.

Lyndon Lyon Greenhouses publishes a mail-order catalog in print and on its Web site. Web photos are helpful in deciphering African violet descriptions, which are lingo-laden throughout the industry. Customers are welcome to stop in and see the nursery, buy plants, and view Sorano's private collection of some 200 orchids. Orchids are sold only at the greenhouses. "I was bitten by the orchid bug in 1987, on a trip to Florida," Sorano recalls. "Now I understand what I couldn't figure out before—just what makes people go crazy for plants!"

Directions: Take I-90 to exit 29A. Continue straight for 2 miles. After crossing the canal bridge, turn right onto Route 5 east. In about 0.2 mile, at a flashing yellow light, turn left onto Route 167 north. In 6 miles, in Dolgeville, Route 167 becomes Main Street. Just before a large stone factory building, turn right onto Van Buren Street. In two blocks, turn right onto Mutchler Street and go up a small hill directly into the nursery parking lot.

Nearby attractions: The African Violet Society of America (www.avsa.org) posts a large photo library on its Web site. The town of Herkimer is famous for "Herkimer diamonds," quartz crystals used for meditation and healing. Casual prospectors and serial diggers rent goggles and crack hammers to work the Herkimer Diamond Mine or Ace of Diamonds Mine (open April to October daily; from Route I-90 exit 30, go 9 miles north on Route 28).

MATTERHORN NURSERY

227 Summit Park Road, Spring Valley, NY 10977

(845) 354-5986; fax (845) 354-4749

www.matterhornnursery.com; e-mail *matterhorn@ucs.net*

Matt and Ronnie Horn

Perennials, aquatics, annuals, roses, woody plants, evergreens. Open year-round, Monday through Saturday, 8 to 5, Sunday, 10 to 5. No catalog. No mail order. Large display gardens. Admission to David Austin rose garden $5. Garden ornaments. Books and supplies. Expert gardening advice. Guided tours by arrangement. Holiday events. Visitors welcome.

Matterhorn Nursery is a stylish, well-stocked, high-end garden center complex in Westchester County, 20 miles north of New York City. Owner Matt Horn, a Cornell graduate, founded the nursery in 1981 as a wholesaler to landscapers (which he still is). In 1996, Horn and his wife, Ronnie, opened their retail business to meet the demand from educated gardeners for superior plants. Matterhorn is, of course, a clever play on Horn's own name. The nursery logo is Matterhorn peak in the Swiss Alps, reflecting the nursery's aspiration to excellence.

Over the years, Matterhorn's 35 acres have been converted into a stunning destination-garden showcase. Called the "Disneyland of garden centers," this seemingly vast site is embellished with ponds, bridges, fountains, perennial borders, grass garden, a quarter-mile wooded wetland path, and a conservatory. Even the parking lot is landscaped. Matterhorn's Gardener's Village houses specialty shops devoted to gifts, pottery, books, garden supplies, country florist, bird pavilion, furniture, and back-yard golf. In 2004, David Austin (the son) cut the ribbon on a 3-acre David Austin (the father) rose garden, which almost immediately won the Perennial Plant Association's coveted Landscape Design Honor Award. With its 30 retail buildings and 10 acres of groomed grounds, Matterhorn seems more like a small village than a garden center. A warren of little shops offers lifestyle items—candles and cabanas, gargoyles and gas grills. Actor Mel Gibson is rumored to shop here.

Buildings and gardens aside, Matterhorn is a comprehensive source for high-quality landscape plants. The encyclopedic range includes ornamental perennials, showy annuals, culinary herbs, alpines, woody shrubs and trees, evergreens, and dwarf conifers. Although fall mums and seasonal items are grown here, most stock is bought in from Etera, Blooms of Bressingham, Log House Plants, Heritage Perennials, Proven Winners, Monrovia, and other upscale suppliers.

Matterhorn's perennial plant aesthetic takes its cue from the Anglophilic flower border common to wealthy suburbs. The nursery is known for its selections of peony, hosta, ornamental grass, long-blooming perennials, and Steppable ground covers. During a local water shortage, Matterhorn assembled an abundant collection of drought-tolerant perennials—annual grasses, succulents, meadow perennials, and silver-leaved herbs such as lamb's-ears, sage, and artemisia. Rock-garden gems are offered in small pots and in rustic troughs beautifully landscaped with tiny conifers. Bonsai, orchids, and tropical foliage plants are sold in the conservatory.

Water gardening is a specialty. Matterhorn's new Aquatic House, full of gurgling holding tanks, offers the area's best selection of aquatic plants, fish, and pond supplies. The tanks support some 50 varieties of lotus, hardy water lilies, and tropical water lilies, both day- and night-blooming. Water lilies come in pink, red, white, yellow, "changeable" (peachy-gold), and (in tropical lilies only) elegant blues and purples. Floaters, marginals, bog plants, and submerged aquatics are in stock, including several water-loving iris. Also useful for wetland edges are many sedges, ferns, and clump-forming bamboos found in the perennial and shrub departments.

The tree and shrub stock is similarly diverse, with special assemblages of azalea, rhodo-dendron, dwarf conifer, false cypress, and Japanese maple. The nursery carries wonderful specimens such as weeping bald cypress, weeping katsura, varie-gated aralia, and camperdown elm. Also present are drought-tolerant natives such as Eastern red cedar, fringe tree *(Chionanthus virginicus),* sourwood *(Oxydendrum arboreum),* Kentucky coffee tree, and ornamental forms of honey locust. Ground-cover shrubs include heaths, heathers, and a dwarf sweet box *(Sarcococca hookerana* var. *humilis)* recommended by the Pennsylvania Horticultural Society. The new David Austin rose garden signals an energetic commitment to English shrub roses, supplemented with hybrid teas, climbers, carpet roses, and patio and tree roses.

Matterhorn's prices are expensive, some say outrageous. Others shrug. Price tags are generally three times higher than at Wal-Mart, making this a bad place to buy petunias. According to a profile in the *Wall Street Journal's Startup Journal,* though, prices don't matter much to Matterhorn's suburban customer base. The plants are terrific and the ambience pleasant. "I think of the higher prices as an entry fee, because coming here is like coming to a park," said one New Jersey gardener. "It's all so beautiful."

As a card-carrying member of many professional societies, Matterhorn prides itself on its gardening advice. More than 100 gardening guides address common questions, like how to plant a hedge, prune clematis, or survive drought. Short talks and tours are given regularly. The nursery has a snap-to-it air that makes the act of shopping more efficient than in most garden centers. This is fortunate, for there's no catalog or plant list to help with planned purchasing, and the distractions of so many lifestyle displays make it hard to concentrate on horticulture. The snack bar gives sustenance to weary customers. The ornamental grass garden is a nice place to sit and consider buying more plants. A Children's Shop and petting zoo offer relief to mothers with small children.

Nursery credentials are unrivaled. Matterhorn is recognized for its accomplished landscape design, earning the Outstanding Landscape Award from the New York State Nurserymen Association and Best of Show from the New York Flower Show, among other honors. Matterhorn is master designer for Macy's Flower Show, held in April at Macy's in Manhattan, and plays a leading role in other area shows. A 10,000-square-foot greenhouse was purpose-built to force plants for spring displays. (The Macy's show alone absorbs 30,000 plants.) Matterhorn has won industry awards for creative merchandising and customer service, such as an innovative kids' nature walk devised to animate October sales. Its $3 million or more in annual sales makes it one of the nation's most successful garden centers.

Matt Horn himself is a certified nurseryman, certified Master Pond Keeper, and past regional president of the Perennial Plant Association. He's also a dedicated environmentalist working hard to help state and local governments deal with water usage and development. In his childhood, Rockland County had 17,360 acres of farmland; now it has 250. Though not exactly a farmer, Horn lives upon and uses the garden center grounds as a vibrant horticultural preserve, with interpreted display gardens rivaling many botanical gardens.

Directions: From the Palisades Parkway, take exit 12 /Pomona and turn onto Route 45 south. Take the first right onto Pomona Road and the second left onto Summit Park Road. The nursery is 0.2 mile on the right. From Route 17 south, pass the New York/New Jersey border, take the Suffern exit, and follow Route 202 east. In 6 miles, in Mt. Ivy, turn right onto Route 45 south and follow directions above.

MOUNTAIN PINE NURSERY
117 Warwick Turnpike, Warwick, NY 10990
(845) 986-7079
www.mtnpinenursery.com; e-mail *mtnpine@warwick.net*
Bill and Debbie Korwan

Perennials, ornamental herbs, vines, and companion shrubs. *Family-run nursery and garden center. Open mid-April through October, Monday through Saturday, 9 to 6, Sunday, 10 to 4. Closed major holidays. Catalog $4.95. No mail order. Seminars. Design and landscaping services. Display gardens. Visitors welcome.*

Mountain Pine Nursery is a perennial plant specialist on 35 acres in lower New York, west of the Hudson. This pleasant semi-rural area, with its horse barns and vintage towns, is not very far from the New Jersey border and shuddering big-truck traffic on Route 17. Proprietors Bill and Debbie Korwan began the nursery in 1989 with 75 kinds of perennials; today they offer 2300. This burgeoning inventory, along with good horticultural amenities, make Mountain Pine a natural destination for the area's plant lovers.

The focus here is on mainstream ornamental perennials. Most are grown at the nursery, except for certain trademarked plants such as Sunny Border Gold perennials, a designer label from one of the region's best wholesalers. New-plant introductions are assembled in special collections such as 'New Millennium' delphiniums, strong-stemmed lilies, unusual hellebores, and agastaches in novelty colors. A "featured plant" display shows off the Perennial Plant Association's Plant of the Year (Japanese painted fern in 2004, for example) and other promotional plants the nursery is proud of.

A descriptive catalog lists Mountain Pine's full inventory of perennials, ornamentals, grasses, and herbs. Selection is clearly biased toward bright-colored, long-flowering plants that perform well without serious coddling—11 yarrows, for example, and summer phlox in all imaginable colors (32 varieties). Big fleshy waterside plants include Japanese petasites and several orange and gold ligularias. Self-supporting monkshood hybrids come in desirable colors, such as pink 'Rubellum' and metallic 'Stainless Steel'.

Some of Mountain Pine's more unusual plants are easier to find in garden magazines than in nurseries. These range from pink lily-of-the-valley and the fragrant double-flowered white hosta ('Aphrodite') to such archaic presences as giant scabious (*Cephalaria gigantea*) and prairie coneflower (*Ratibida columnifera*). An evergreen alpine sub-shrub, *Paxistima canbyi,* is great at mending holes in the border. Tree peonies and Japanese kirengeshoma are perfect foils for dramatic natives such as dark purple bugbane (*Cimicifuga racemosa* 'Hillside Black Beauty') and extra-large rodgersia (*R. pinnata* 'Big Mama').

Perennials are also grouped for specific uses—the 30 species used to draw birds and butterflies, for example, or the ornamental herbs grouped for their unpalatability to deer. The native perennials group deserves mention for its trillium, wild ginger, bloodroot, pink and white varieties of turtlehead, and native germander known as wood sage (*Teucrium canadense*). There's also creeping phlox (1990 Perennial Plant of the Year) and a pleasantly invasive golden wood poppy (*Stylophorum diphyllum*). Purists, though, might hope the nursery will drop loosestrife, even if the cultivar (*Lysimachia ciliata* 'Autopurpureum') is reportedly "not as invasive as some."

As Mountain Pine's ground has expanded to 35 acres, its growing areas and display gardens have kept pace. The sales area is gardenesque, with plants in containers juxtaposed as they might be in a garden. Most plants come in well priced 1- or 2-gallon pots. Besides formal landscaping services, the owners will sketch garden designs for a nominal charge applied toward plant purchases.

Display gardens were enlarged in 2004. Each garden is named for the employee who has to weed it—a remarkable example of positive ego reinforcement, given the dog-labor normally required for perennial bed maintenance. Ed is therefore not only a staff member but also a parking-lot island; Karin, a knot garden; Bobbi, a cottage garden; and the pond and waterfall that ousted the family swimming pool, Bill.

Directions: From Route 17, take exit 124 (Goshen), turn left off the ramp, and follow Route 17A/94 south through Warwick, and at the Warwick Shop Rite, turn left onto Warwick Turnpike/Route 21. Pass the Warwick Drive-In and in 1 mile, the nursery is on the left. From Route 287 in New Jersey, take exit 55, turn right onto Ringwood Turnpike, follow along the Wanaque Reservoir, and bear right onto Upper Greenwood Lake Turnpike. Bear right where the road becomes Warwick Turnpike; the nursery is on the right, just over the New York State line.

Nearby attractions: Warwick Valley Winery & Distillery, 114 Little York Road, Warwick, NY 10990 (845-258-4858; www.wvwinery.com), makes wine, premium hard apple cider, and framboise from its own orchards and vineyards (open daily, 11 to 6, chef-made lunch on weekends). The vineyard's Web site lists local B & Bs. Applewood Winery (845-988-9292; www.applewoodorchardsandwinery.com) is another Warwick-based vineyard. The Warwick Valley Farmers Market, South Street parking lot, Warwick (845-986-2720) offers perennials and local goat cheese, mushrooms, and organic produce (open spring through fall, Sundays, 9 to 2). Philip Pine Indy Tree Farm, 172 Route 94 south, Warwick, NY 10990 (845-988-1511), stocks ornamental trees and shrubs of all sizes; owner Frank Chokilo, a former produce farmer of hippie appearance, has no plant list and gives no guarantees, but has great wholesale and retail prices. (He once asked, "Do I look like the kind of guy with a plant list?")

NABEL'S NURSERIES
1485 Mamaroneck Avenue, White Plains, NY 10605
(914) 949-3963; fax (914) 949-3766
Paul Nabel

Annuals, perennials, herbs, vines. Shrubs, trees, roses, houseplants. *Family-run garden center. Open year-round, daily, 8 to 5. Closed major holidays. No catalog. No mail order. Plant list available to industry professionals. Small display beds. Seasonal plants. Visitors welcome.*

The closer you get to a city, the harder it is to find good horticulture. Family nurseries established a generation ago may have a real-estate edge, but even they can become landlocked and find it easier to buy in somebody else's plants. That's why it's a welcome delight to encounter a nursery in the big-city orbit that still grows most of its own stock. As any gardener knows, nursery-grown plants are like homegrown tomatoes—they're always better than the ones in the grocery store.

Nabel's Nurseries in White Plains operates with 5 acres and 13 green-houses, backed by a 43-acre growing facility in Dover Plains, 50 miles north in Dutchess County. In season, nursery trucks deliver fresh material every day from the upstate farm. Owner Paul Nabel grew up in the business and took over after his brother Rudy retired. "When my mother and father started the nursery 60 years ago, it was an entirely different time," Rudy Nabel reminisced. "Westchester was still more country than city. None of us would be able to start a business like this today."

Nabel's commitment to freshness and quality attracts an appreciative following in metropolitan New York. Annuals, perennials, herbs, vegetables, ferns, grasses, and vines—some two-thirds of the inventory comes from Nabel's own farm and greenhouses. The Dover Plains farm has a high, cold location that is good for growing well-rooted plants with sturdy foliage. Prices are competitive. As a quality control measure, Nabel's upstate farm transports plants to Westchester only when they are healthy, happy, and finished for sale. Anything that isn't, is sent to a growing area called "the hospital," where it either recovers or is tossed into the compost heap.

Plant selection at Nabel's beats commercial garden centers hands down. Jazzy annuals are abundant in spring, just when window boxes (and their owners) are starving for color. A head-spinning selection includes apricot poppies, black fuchsias, wildly streaked and fringed coleus, angel's-trumpets in five colors, and even an electric-blue Chinese forget-me-not (*Cynoglossum* 'Firmament'). Container specimens are Egyptian papyrus, black elephant's-ear (alocasia), dwarf pink canna, dwarf navy-blue agapanthus, and tree-form flowering maples.

All sorts of hip vegetables are grown in the greenhouses, such as *edamame* (soybeans), frisée endive, husk cherries, alpine strawberries, broccoli raab, and grape tomatoes. Herbs feature real French tarragon, weeping rosemary, lemongrass, Egyptian walking onion, fruit-scented mints, and bay trees.

Almost 2000 perennial plant varieties form an equally impressive array, from early-flowering perennials such as poppies and creeping phlox, to mid-season performers such as dahlias and hardy hibiscus, to late-bloomers such as asters, perennial sunflowers, joe-pye weeds, and fall chrysanthemums. For shade gardens, Nabel's carries beautiful ferns, tiarellas, heucheras, epimediums, astilbes, violets, and wood anemones.

Tropical houseplants are sold all year in Nabel's greenhouses. Among them are many colorful so-called hot-mamas that perform well in dim apartments, such as showy flowering bird-of-paradise; bamboo palm (priced by the foot); and big, fleshy philodendrons in burgundy ('Black Cardinal') and orange-brushed chartreuse ('Painted Lady').

Directions: From Route I-95, take exit 18B/Mamaroneck Avenue and turn right off the ramp. The nursery is 2 miles on the right. From the Hutchinson River Parkway, take exit 23N and turn right onto Mamaroneck Avenue. The nursery is 0.5 mile on the right.

NORTH COUNTRY DAYLILIES

632 North Broadway, Saratoga Springs, NY 12866
Longlesson Farm, 444 Goosen-Regan Road, Buskirk, NY 12028
(518) 587-2156 (office); (518) 753-0356 (farm)
www.daylilies.netheaven.com; e-mail *melanie@netheaven.com*
Melanie and Bob Mason

Northern-grown daylilies. *Hybridizer's nursery. Free catalog. Catalog and photos on Web sites. Mail order April 15 to June 15. Open-garden sales, early July to mid-August, weekends, 10 to 4, and by appointment. Call for exact dates. Picnics and families welcome. Registered Black Angus cattle breeding stock. AHS Display Garden in Saratoga Springs, open by appointment. Articles and lectures.*

The Greek word for them, *hemerocallis*, means "beautiful for a day." In the early 1600s, Ben Johnson called them "flowers of light." Both pretty well sum up the delights of the daylily, the nation's most-admired garden plant. Popularity is expressed in numbers: the American Hemerocallis Society (AHS) recognizes thousands of registered daylily hybrids. Because most major hybridizers work in warm climates to accelerate breeding time, many new introductions are untested in cold zones.

Melanie Mason is an AHS national board member and daylily judge, known for her hardy daylily hybrids. In 2003, Mason won the AHS Region 4 Hybridizer's Award honoring her breeding achievements. Once an art teacher, Mason studied ornamental horticulture at SUNY Farmingdale and ran a landscaping business on Long Island for ten years.

"I got to know the great daylily wholesalers on Long Island," Mason recalls. "I started buying ten varieties for the landscaping business and one for me. Later, it became one for the business and ten for me." By the time Mason and her husband relocated to Saratoga Springs, she had a distinguished collection. Moving north three zones forced her to cull for hardiness. According to Mason, "Most Southern hybrids don't bloom and don't open in the north—they just 'sit and knit!'" She gave up landscaping and began what she calls "pollen dabbing," using her collection to inaugurate a breeding program for cold-tolerant hybrids. "Being a northern hybridizer is always slow work," Mason says. "The Florida breeders know in two years, but here it takes six years to evaluate the whole plant."

Today, North Country Daylilies grows some 1400 daylily cultivars derived from major breeders, inspired amateurs, and Mason's own hybridizing program. All plants are hardy to Zone 4, where they are field-grown. The inventory includes late bloomers, minis, doubles, spiders, and plants from other AHS Region 4 hybridizers. Color-coded landscape collections include "Fruit Salad," a collection of pastel peach, melon, strawberry, and coconut daylilies; a "Sunset" collection of yellows and oranges; an "Easter" collection of purples and yellows, and a "Rose" collection of coveted pink daylilies, ranging from ivory-pink to deep pink and blue-red.

As a breeder, Mason seeks large-flowered tetraploid daylilies with good branching and high bud count. "I make crosses with something in mind—lavenders, creams, picotees, and faded edges. Vision is important, seeing the plants you are trying to create," she says. "I tell people, 'Crossing daylilies is like making a stew. If you put in too much salt, it's the devil to remove!'"

As a collector, Mason has assembled what she calls "tall and small," a group of airy daylilies with small, bell-like blooms resembling the wild Asian species. The flowers of 'Itsy Bitsy Spider', for example, flutter like little yellow butterflies over its foliage. Another refreshing development is breeder Darrell Apps' "Fresh Air Kids," a prolific gang that includes coffee-colored 'Ernest' and pink 'Luther' (boasting 44 blooms per scape). Mason also appreciates the charm of miniatures, such as double-peach 'Bubbly', which she calls "a cute little corsage."

Mason's 'Longlesson' series is named for Longlesson Farm in Buskirk, where she and her husband raise daylilies and registered Black Angus cattle. Mason calls other series after Saratoga Springs business establishments. 'G. Willikers' evokes a local toy store, 'Soave Faire', a stationary store, and 'Lyrical Ballad', an antiquarian bookstore. A luscious newcomer, 'Mrs. London's Apricot Tart', honors a famous local bakery that makes extra fruit tarts during AHS Region 4 conventions.

In 2004, Mason began a new series called 'Old Field', bred from seedlings that came from her friend Patrick Stamile, the famous daylily hybridizer. "Without the early-on guidance of Pat and Grace Stamile, I doubt I'd be where I am today." Mason brought Stamile's seedlings north and used them in hybridizing. "After consulting with Stamile, Mason registered the best hybrids, using the 'Old Field' designation to acknowledge the debt. 'Old Field Wishful Thinking', the first in this series, is a big creamy daylily with rosy blush and lime throat, evocative of Stamile's most remarkable trademark plants.

Mason and her husband work their farm without help—digging, dividing, and replanting daylilies in the collection and breeding beds. Enthusiastic customers confirm that stock transplants well, without recovery problems in cold zones. The catalog provides a full account of origins, height, and bloom habits. Prices vary but are generally reasonable. Hard-to-find older varieties can be surprisingly affordable. Shipping of generous double divisions occurs in spring, followed by open-garden sales at Longlesson Farm. A separate display and hybridizing garden is located at the Masons' home in Saratoga Springs.

At peak bloom open-garden sales are the most fun. Fans are freshly dug on the spot. Family outings are encouraged. Longlesson Farm occupies 385 acres of hills, meadows, and ponds, enlivened by Black Angus calves and yellow Labrador retrievers. The Web site posts photos of both the daylily stock and Black Angus herd. Each year, the Masons cull the herd in much the same manner as daylily seedlings. "The herd and the lilies both take a good eye," Mason says, chuckling.

Directions: To visit the Masons' garden in Saratoga Springs, call or write for an appointment and directions. Longlesson Farm is 45 minutes southeast of Saratoga Springs. From Route 87, take exit 12 onto Route 67 east. In Schaghticoke, turn at the traffic light, staying on Route 67 east. In 5.4 miles, bear right onto Marpe Road (paved). At the stop sign, turn left onto Goosen-Regan Road and in 0.3 mile turn right into the Longlesson Farm drive. The nursery is at the top of the hill. From Route I-90, take exit 3B and turn onto Route 22 north. Pass Hoosick Falls and in Eagle Bridge turn at the blinking light onto Route 67 west. In about 9 miles, the road passes under a trestle. Make the next hard left (almost a U-turn) onto Marpe Road. At the stop sign, turn left onto Goosen-Regan Road, and follow directions above.

Nearby attractions: Saxton Daylily Gardens, 1 First Street, Saratoga Springs, NY 12866 (518-584-4697; Peter Saxton), specializes in 'Adirondack Strain' hybrids of breeder Stanley Saxton, who pioneered the development of super-hardy daylilies. D & M Country Gardens, 57 Rowe Hill Road, Hartford, NY 12838 (518-632-5752; http://daylily.net/gardens/dmcountrygardens), is a hobby daylily nursery with lovely display gardens, 30 minutes north of Saratoga. Mrs. London's Bakery, 464 Broadway, Saratoga Springs, NY 12866 (518-581-1652 or -4652; www.mrslondons.com; mail order), is an exceptional French café/bakery owned by Wendy and Michael London, "baking geniuses" who provision Manhattan's most expensive French restaurants. Saratoga County Chamber of Commerce (518-584-3255; www.saratoga.org) has links to the region's attractions.

ROSEDALE NURSERIES

51 Saw Mill River Road (Route 9A), Hawthorne, NY 10532

(914) 769-1300; fax (914) 769-8770

www.rosedalenurseries.com; e-mail *info@rosedalenurseries.com*

The Taylor family

Trees, shrubs, evergreens, perennials, fruits, vines, roses, tropicals. Family-owned horticultural farm and garden center. Retail and wholesale. Open year-round, daily, 9 to 5:30; closed Sundays in winter. No catalog. Plant list and planting guides on Web site. Call for specific availability. No mail order. Local delivery by arrangement. Landscape design services. Visitors welcome.

Rosedale Nurseries is the *grande dame* of Westchester County. Founded in 1898 as a rose nursery and acquired by the Taylor family in 1929, Rosedale has been, for as long as anyone can remember, the area's paramount source for trees and shrubs. Its retail center, greenhouses, and tree yard are sited on a 15-acre parcel in Hawthorne, in the heart of Westchester County, with a stream running along the edge. (Out back, Rosedale even has its own private exit off the Sawmill Parkway.) Its 600-acre Hudson Valley horticultural farm supplies nursery headquarters with hardy, field-grown trees and shrubs of a diversity unique in the New York metropolitan area.

Rosedale is recognized as one of the country's most successful retail nurseries in both volume and revenue. Its Web site posts a 175-page inventory of needled evergreens, broadleaf evergreens, shade trees, flowering trees, ornamental shrubs, fruit and nut plants, antique and modern roses, flowering vines, and perennials. Virtually everything in this rich cornucopia is on hand in spring, though stock usually thins out by late summer—it's best to call for specifics.

Prices are typical of refined nursery stock in Westchester County. Special orders are accepted, especially for large-caliper trees and shrubs, some hefty enough to fill a single truck. Most trees and shrubs are field-grown on the upstate farm, except for the smaller stuff, which is bought in. Some 1300 perennials for sun and shade, sold in gallon-size pots, are bought as well-rooted stock and repotted in the Westchester greenhouses.

While such wide-ranging inventory defies easy synopsis, it is fair to say that Rosedale's trees and shrubs are selected with a landscaper's eye for colorful foliage, flower power, and elegant garden-size forms. Excellent varieties of Japanese maple, exotic maple, hornbeam, magnolia, stewartia, and ornamental beech are offered. Someone has taken the trouble to select the best-performing flowering crabs and cherries. Native trees and shrubs are chosen for maximum ornament—the prettiest redbuds, serviceberries, witch hazels, buckeyes, and dogwoods. Many woody plants are available as attractive multistem or pruned-up specimens. The hydrangea and viburnum lists are extraordinary. Tree roses and espaliered apples are supplied. Particular treasures include the white form of redbud, 'Arnold Pink' silver-bell, double-flowered horse chestnut, columnar English oak, and the rare Korean evodia.

The evergreen collection is well suited to polished suburban gardens. Broadleaved evergreens are strong in cultivated forms of azalea, rhodo-dendron, camellia, holly, and boxwood. Dwarf, weeping, and birds-nest conifers provide visual interest in smaller spaces. Needled evergreens are strong in juniper, spruce, chamaecyparis, cedar, and pine. Marvelous pinetums and dramatic screens might be made with such items as purple-coned Korean fir, golden dawn redwood, and fastigiate yew. Refined ground-cover shrubs include Japanese skimmia, dwarf cotoneaster, and compact leucothoe.

Rosedale's main business is serving retail customers and their gardens. The nursery has a significant presence on prestigious Westchester estates. A busy staff of landscape designers oversees 15 work crews for residential garden installations. Rosedale is a major contributor to the Rockefeller Center Flower and Garden Show. Under landscape designer Russell Page, it provided the original plantings at PepsiCo's world-famous sculpture gardens, and has since supplied renovation efforts under François Goffinet. The PepsiCo gardens are an apt emblem, not only of Rosedale's preeminence in Westchester gardens, but also of what such sumptuous displays are all about.

Directions: From the Cross Westchester Expressway/Route 287, take exit 2 onto Route 9A north; the nursery is 3 miles on the right. From the Sawmill Parkway north, pass exit 25, keep right, slow down, and in 0.2 mile, turn right into the nursery's private entrance. From the Sawmill Parkway south, take the Eastview exit, turn left under the parkway, left again onto the parkway northbound, and in 0.2 mile, turn right into the nursery's private entrance. From Route 87 west, take exit 7A to the Sawmill Parkway north and follow directions above. From Route 87 east, cross the Tappan Zee Bridge, take exit 8A, follow signs to the Sawmill Parkway north, and follow directions above.

Nearby attractions: The Donald Kendall Sculpture Gardens at PepsiCo World Headquarters, Anderson Hill Road, Purchase, NY (914-253-2000), display monumental modern sculptures in a vast ornamental park (open to visitors; maps at parking lot kiosk). Across Route 9A from Rosedale, the Zagat-rated Oriental Diner, 58 Saw Mill River Road/Route 9A, Hawthorne, NY (914-769-0038), serves fresh sushi and gourmet Chinese food.

RUSLYN NURSERY
107 Mountain Rest Road, New Paltz, NY 12561
Vern and Barbara Palmateer

Rare dwarf conifers, Japanese maples, grafted trees and shrubs. *Small specialty nursery. Mostly wholesale. Open April to November, Saturday, 9 to 3 (weather permitting). Open weekdays by appointment only until 2. Closed Sundays and holidays. No plant list or mail order. No credit cards. Arrange for an appointment in advance.*

Ruslyn Nursery is a specialty grower of rare and unusual dwarf conifers, Japanese maples, and other grafted nursery stock. Owner Vern Palmateer is a grafting expert who propagates special items for eminent nurseries. Together with his wife, Barbara, he has operated Ruslyn Nursery for more than 30 years out of their home in New Paltz. The farmstead was built by an early Huguenot family from which he is descended. (The Huguenots were French Protestants who founded New Paltz in the 17th century.)

Ruslyn is best known for its dwarf and unusual conifers. Over the years, Palmateer has introduced a number of unique discoveries to the nursery trade. His distinctive Japanese umbrella pine (*Sciadopitys verticillata* 'Golden Parasol'), for example, has the virtue of flushing yellow in spring, white in summer, and green in winter. An unusual dwarf Fraser fir (*Abies fraseri* 'W. B. Rawls') was discovered at a Dutchess County nursery and named for the nurseryman. Other Ruslyn introductions include a reliably golden form of white pine (*Pinus strobus* 'All Season Gold'), dwarf blue forms of limber pine and Colorado fir, and a contorted Eastern hemlock (*Tsuga canadensis* 'Shawangunk') discovered by a friend on a local hike. A dwarf blue Colorado spruce is named 'Blue Moon', says Palmateer, "because this happens only once in a blue moon." All the stock is expertly propagated and, considering its rarity, reasonably priced.

Ruslyn grows 80 varieties of grafted Japanese maple, sold as mature trees. One of the nursery's best introductions, 'In the Pink', is a color-shifting Japanese maple Palmateer found in another nursery—a twiggy, upright, 15-foot tree whose foliage is shrimp-pink in spring, plum in summer, and bright tomato in autumn. Esteemed hybrids from Japan include flat-topped 'Kinyo Hime', small red 'Emperor One', and luminous scarlet 'Oshio beni'. Several Japanese maples are of the 'nisiki' type, richly variegated in pink and white. Small seedlings of the straight green Japanese maple, which Palmateer uses for grafting, can be purchased for a nominal sum.

Ruslyn grows excellent grafted witch hazels *(Hamamelis × intermedia)*, whose odd, ribbon-like flowers are first to bloom in February. Its most unusual witch hazel, *Hamamelis purpurea,* is a purple form all but unknown in the East. The nursery carries fine varieties of hardy boxwood, ornamental birch, Chinese dogwood *(Cornus kousa),* and unusual beech. Responding to the needs of landscaper clients, Ruslyn stocks good perennial plants from Lorjon Nursery (see profile) and other local growers.

In recent years, Palmateer has chosen to buy in the more common plant material and concentrate on growing plants of increasing rarity. "A lot of this stuff used to be a novelty. Now there's more on the market, even in the Big Box stores," says Palmateer. "We specialize in a few varieties that are still pretty unusual." Palmateer's virtuosity as a grafter can be seen in his double grafts, which he calls "the weird stuff I sometimes do"—such as a novelty Japanese maple with weeping green dissected foliage under a red-foliage canopy.

Although Palmateer no longer takes custom orders, he'll occasionally graft an exceptional new plant. "If someone found a rare variety, such as a *Pinus* or *Abies* witches'-broom, we'd do those," he says. "We introduce plants that would otherwise go by the wayside." He recently propagated a prostrate silver Fraser fir found at Shemins Nursery. "Manny Shemin gave it to me, but he didn't know it was silver," he recalls. "You just don't see a Fraser fir growing as a spreader with silver foliage."

Though wholesale sales are Ruslyn's bread and butter, the nursery is open to the public one "retail day" per week, on Saturday, strictly from 9 to 3. Visitors may peruse the retail yard independently or tour the eight holding houses under escort. Gardeners seeking plants must respect the terms on which the Palmateers open their nursery. Ruslyn is not listed in the phone book and is inaccessible by e-mail. An exasperated sign at the gate reads, "Please do not knock on our door with nursery questions when we are closed. Please respect our privacy as we would yours." As Barbara Palmateer, who runs the office, explains, "We're a small nursery for people who really love plants. We've been at it for over 30 years and it's hard work."

Like many old Huguenot families in the New Paltz area, the Palmateers are faithful to the religious traditions that sustained their forebears. Ruslyn's business card cites the Gospel of John. An "Upper Room" over the garage is a place of worship for a gentle group of believers. "God put it here," says Vern Palmateer. "It's all part of creation."

Directions: From Route 87, take exit 18, turn off the ramp onto Route 299 west, and proceed through New Paltz (5 lights). Cross the bridge, turn right onto Springtown Road, and turn left at the fork onto Mountain Rest Road; the nursery is up the hill on the right (#107).

Nearby attractions: The New Paltz Hostel, 145 Main Street, New Paltz, NY 12561 (845-255-6676; www.newpaltzhostel.com), has decent accommodation for $22 per night. In Rosendale, The Cement Company, 419 Main Street (845-658-3210), is a kicky little place with delicious food. For local produce, try Meadow View Farm, 105 Philles Bridge Road (845-255-6093; organic) and Walkill View Farm Market, 15 Route 299 West (845-255-8050; plants). Deborah Goldman Porcelain, 387 Springtown Road, New Paltz, NY 12561 (845-255-0417; www.goldmanceramics.com) produces luminous fine porcelain in a local studio.

Historical interest: New Paltz's Huguenot Street is the oldest original street in the country. Its ancient stone houses are overseen by the Huguenot Historical Society, 18 Broadhead Avenue, New Paltz, NY 12561 (845-255-1660; www.hhs-newpaltz.org). The town was founded in 1677 when six Huguenot families arrived in three wooden carts reading the 37th Psalm. They bought 40,000 acres along the Walkill River from the Esopus Indians and settled the town.

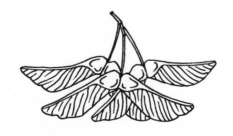

SARATOGA TREE NURSERY
2369 Route 50, Saratoga Springs, NY 12866-4738
(518) 581-1439
www.dec.state.ny.us/website/dlf/privland/nursery
New York State Department of Environmental Conservation

Seedlings for wildlife conservation and soil stabilization. State-run conservation nursery. Bare-root stock. Open year-round, Monday through Friday, 8 to 5. Free brochure. Catalog on Web site. Mail order. Orders due January 1 through March 31. Shipments mid-April through mid-May. Optional pick up in many counties. Regional offices listed on Web site. Nursery visits by appointment, groups preferred.

Since 1902, New York State has operated a nursery program to encourage the planting of trees and shrubs on public and private lands. Saratoga Tree Nursery is a publicly run tree nursery that produces seedlings for low-cost conservation plantings. The nursery's 300 acres are mostly devoted to seed orchards and production areas; state foresters also operate a large seed extractory. Over the years, the Saratoga Tree Nursery has churned out 1.6 billion seedlings, adding considerably to the state's wild lands and forests.

In the early days, Saratoga Tree Nursery grew conifer seedlings to stop erosion from all the lands cleared for farming, logging, and canals. Old-time state foresters once collected their grafting stock by blasting high branches with .22-caliber rifles. Today, wildlife support plants are in sharp demand and firearms no longer used. A free plant list is published annually by the state Department of Environmental Conservation and is also posted on its Web site.

Because wildlife conservation plantings are so popular, the state has amassed a small arsenal of plants intelligently chosen to support wild birds and animals through the year. Shrubs like highbush cranberry produce such delicious fruit that it's consumed right away. But others, like the sour toringo crab, offer important late-season "emergency food" that wildlife only eat in hard years, when they're desperate.

"We sell about 1.5 million seedlings a year in all," says David Lee, the nursery's principal forester. "We're up to about 45 or 50 species, with 95 percent of our seed coming from native New York trees." Inventory expands and contracts to meet demand. "Right now we're trying to figure out what wildlife plants we should keep growing," says Lee, "but the hardest species to figure out are our customers."

The plant list is short and sweet. Native white oak, sugar maple, black cherry, and black walnut count among the best hardwoods. Conifers include Eastern red cedar, white pine, and pitch pine. Of the dozen wildlife species, most are suited to moist areas—buttonbush, swamp rose, and red-osier dogwood, for example. Sandbar and pussy willows help with streambank stabilization, bayberry and beach plum with dune protection.

In recent years, the state has begun growing "wild apple" seedlings escaped from old orchards. Special plant mixes have been assembled for wildlife support, stream banks, and the Long Island shore. By private arrangement, the nursery also grows American chestnuts for the American Chestnut Foundation and black ash seedlings for the Mohawk tribe.

Seedlings cost very little and are easily planted in dormancy. Most are 2- or 3-year bare-root plants in well-packed bundles of 25, 100, or 250. Hard-to-grow conifers (such as Eastern hemlock, tamarack, and red spruce) come as 2-year tubelings. As a rule, seedlings cost $30 per 100, which means you can afford to lose a few plants. Plants are shipped bare-root (with advance notice of the shipping date) or can be picked up by arrangement in many counties.

Public nursery stock is intended strictly for conservation uses, not ornamental gardening or resale. Customers are mostly New York residents and landowners. Stock is also sold to people in nearby states (including New Jersey, Pennsylvania, and Connecticut) who cannot get the same plants from public sources. Besides wildlife support, conservation seedlings are used for windbreaks, erosion control, Christmas tree plantings, and hardwood forest establishment. Some landowners plant willows as snow fencing along busy highways.

Hedgerow plantings even work well in urban wastelands and city lots not usually associated with conservation planting, where wildlife has a tough time finding food. If each of us owes to the earth a debt of oxygen consumed in our lifetime, it's worth considering that trees and shrubs absorb carbon dioxide and exhale pure oxygen. Why not plant a Wildlife Mix Species Packet (20 plants for $24) at the back of your property—or maybe in the vacant waste next to the supermarket parking lot?

Directions: The nursery is located on Route 50 in Saratoga Springs, 30 miles north of Albany. Visitors welcome in groups; call ahead for an appointment.

Related sources: Croshaw Nursery, P.O. Box 339, 113 Mill Lane, Columbus, NJ 08022 (609-2978-6388; www.croshawnursery.com), grows tree seedlings for ornamental and conservation use. Founded in 1926, The New Jersey Forest Tree Nursery,

*37 East Veterans Highway, Jackson, NJ 08527 (732-928-0029; www.nj.gov/dep/park
sandforests/forest/njfs_seedling_nursery.html), supplies conservation plantings to
New Jersey landowners of at least 3 acres; grade-school planting programs. Bare-root
seedlings: pitch pine, green ash, chestnut oak, pin oak, persimmon, tulip poplar, arrowwood viburnum. Plastic tubes: Atlantic white cedar. Minimum order: 100 seedlings or
50-tree mix.*

SCHROON FALLS FARM, GARDENS, AND NURSERY

2002 Route 9, Schroon Lake, NY 12870

(518) 532-9492

www.schroonfalls.com

Ginni and David Campbell

**Hardy perennials, vines, trees, and shrubs. Adirondack natives. Container
annuals.** *Small specialty nursery. Open May 1 through Columbus Day. Hours from
May through Labor Day, daily, 9 to 6, Sunday, 9 to 5; from Labor Day to Columbus
Day, daily, 9 to 5. Catalog $3 (or a plant donation). No mail order. Minimal pesticides.
Landscaper discounts. Containers, organic supplies. Display gardens. Visitors welcome.*

One of the greatest services a nursery can provide is to screen good plants
for local conditions. This is true with special force in the Adirondacks, where
a chilly alpine environment and the warming presence of large lakes pose
strange challenges and opportunities. Gardeners in such areas can blow the
budget just testing survival rates.

Schroon Falls Farm, Gardens, and Nursery is the Adirondack's foremost
plant testing-ground. Owners Ginni Campbell and her son, David, operate
in Zone 3 to 4 conditions, so everything they grow is well hardened. This
toughness, combined with the Campbells' love of things innovative, makes
for an inventory that is at once practical and cutting-edge.

Ginni Campbell describes herself as a "certified plant nut" who founded
the nursery in 1995 as a weekend operation. It became full-time in 1998,
when David, a Cornell-trained horticulturist and talented landscape
designer, decided to join the effort. Writer Vita Sackville-West described
such impassioned gardeners as "always optimistic, always enterprising, and
never satisfied. They always look forward to doing something better than
they have ever done before."

Schroon Falls' most numerous plants are perennials—sorted for dry sun, dry shade, moist sun, and moist shade. This diverse, appealing inventory is cleverly chosen to refresh gardens without making them look too trendy. We found good collections of miniature hostas, ferns, lilies, daylilies, ground covers, and grasses. Lovely old-timers, such as peonies, chrysanthemums, and clematis, seem just right for cold country gardens.

Herbs are Ginni Campbell's first love, and the nursery is a source of 100 desirable aromatics—lavenders, sages, ground-cover thymes, and specialties such as gold oregano and variegated peppermint. A long list of Adirondack natives for woodlands and coarse meadows includes yellow bead-lily *(Clintonia borealis)*, New York ironweed *(Vernonia noveboracensis)*, Carolina thermopsis, and various wild butterfly weeds.

Like most nurseries run by plant lovers, Schroon Falls grows a few charming oddballs. Parrot's beak impatiens (*Impatiens niamniamensis* 'Congo Cockatoo'), for example, bears spectacular red-and-yellow flowers on a 4-foot stalk. Rocky Mountain dandelion *(Oenothera flava)*—a yellow sundrops with dandelion-like leaves—is, according to the nursery catalog, "prized for its ability to amuse young and old alike, if you are lucky enough to be watching when the flowers tremble and then burst open in the evening." One customer waited years to witness this miniature explosion, nightly, over cocktails.

Schroon Falls' tree and shrub stock complements the local flora with hemlocks and birches. Woody ornamentals are chosen to strike a sympathetic chord in area gardens: rhododendrons, azaleas, hydrangeas, dogwoods, Griffith Buck roses, lilacs, and golden elderberry. The ornamental fruit bushes are edible—blueberry, beach plum, service berry, and hardy wine grapes.

Taking cold-hardiness seriously, Schroon Falls offers some arctic plants (Zone 2): cut-leaf sumac, Canadian lilac, and five-stamen tamarisk from Siberia, for example. Some plants considered invasive elsewhere—barberry, burning bush, and Norway maple—are offered here because they can't get away with anything in the Adirondacks. It's just too cold.

"We're seeing Adirondack people who aren't afraid to grow things their grandparents didn't grow," says Ginni Campbell. "And the summer people take our hardy plants home when they leave because they're absolutely positive they *will* grow."

The nursery's display gardens stimulate adventurous plant choices and offer a taste of David Campbell's design skills. Campbell spent two years in historic garden restoration at The Mount (Edith Wharton's mansion in the Berkshires) and his work shares its calm sense of classicism. Displays include a shade garden, proving that plants *do* grow beneath pine trees; an herb and knot garden; an Asian garden of exotic maples surrounding a teahouse and pond; a 200-foot perennial border; daylily and grass gardens in full sun; a *potager* for decorative vegetables and cut flowers; and a native woodland walk terminating in a stone labyrinth. A small coffee bar allows visitors to pour a cup of java and relax among the gardens. Even the occasional after-hours visitor is allowed to wander here, courtesy of the Campbells' sympathy for plant fanatics.

Schroon Falls propagates most of its own annuals and perennials in on-site greenhouses; others are bought in as plugs and grown to size. Perennials come in 1- and 2-gallon pots at unassuming prices. Herbs in 4-inch pots are usually $3 each (4 for $10). Rock-garden plants in small quarts are also a bargain. Well-priced trees and shrubs come from specialty growers in upstate New York, Vermont, and Canada; the nursery grows a few local natives. While woody plants are good sized, nothing is so huge that it can't fit in a car or truck.

If attitudes are any prediction, Schroon Falls promises to become a magnet for horticulture north of Albany. Its cold-zone adventurism already qualifies it as a mini-arboretum of sorts. The catalog costs either $3 or a plant donation—any plant that "you think we may not already have in our gardens, or that you would like us to donate to a local garden club for a public garden project." As the nursery expands, one can readily imagine afternoon cream teas, moon-viewing evenings in the teahouse—not to mention an assembly of elegant plants, toughened for any eventuality.

Directions: The nursery is 90 minutes north of Albany. From Route 87/Adirondack Northway, take exit 28 and turn left onto Route 9 north. The nursery is 2 miles on the right at Miller Road.

Nearby attractions: Pitkins Restaurant, Route 9, Schroon Falls, NY 12870 (518-532-7918; in the village), is a local favorite with exceptional fried chicken. The Owl at Twilight, Olmstedville Road, Olmstedville, NY 12857 (518-251-4696) is a creative, chef-owned café, definitely worth the jaunt (take exit 26 off Route 87 and follow signs to Olmstedville).

SHEPHERD HILL FARM

200 Peekskill Hollow Road, Putnam Valley, NY 10579-3217
(845) 528-5917; fax (845) 528-8343
www.shepherdhillfarm.com; e-mail *myra@shepherdhillfarm.com*
Gerry and Myra Bleyer

Rhododendrons and azaleas. Small specialty nursery. Open by appointment. Free catalog. Catalog on Web site. Mail order. Seasonal display garden. Visitors welcome.

Shepherd Hill Farm is a rhododendron nursery in the lower Hudson Valley, 50 miles north of New York City. Gerry Bleyer and his wife, Myra, operate the nursery from their home on a rural hillside, overlooking her father's old Putnam Valley chicken farm. After departing from work in his family's candy packaging business (they make paper cups for Reese's Cups), Gerry Bleyer worked as a landscaper for private clients, including writer Sara Stein of *Noah's Garden* fame, before opening a nursery dedicated to growing unusual cold-hardy rhododendron and azaleas.

Bleyer became besotted with rhododendrons in San Francisco in 1978, at the same time he fell in love with his wife. "We used to spend our time in Golden Gate Park. The first time I ever saw a rhododendron collection in full bloom was in late May that year," he says. "We were together by July."

Shepherd Hill's stock is beautifully grown and well rooted. Bleyer uses "the slow but time-proven methods of raising healthy disease-free stock," propagating it fresh from rooted cuttings, seeds, or grafts. No tissue-culture material is used, avoiding the virused stock that plagues mass-production horticulture. Plants are sold at the farm or by mail order. Shepherd Hill's rhododendron display, abloom from April to June, is set off by a distinguished collection of mature dwarf conifers that are worth study in their own right.

Breadth is the hallmark of the specialty nursery. Shepherd Hill Farm focuses exclusively on rhododendrons and azaleas (a class of rhododendron). These handsome ericaceous shrubs are organized in four groupings: large-leaf rhododendrons, small-leaf rhododendrons, evergreen azaleas, and deciduous azaleas, including some wild forms. In all, Shepherd Hill grows some 120 different plants.

The nursery's chief treasure is a rare collection of cold-hardy Dexter rhododendrons, from which Bleyer takes rooted cuttings each year. These large-leaf rhododendrons are named for their breeder, Charles Dexter, a wealthy aristocrat who hybridized them on his estate in Sandwich, Massachusetts (now Heritage Plantation), from 1921 to 1943. The Dexter hybrids were breakthrough plants of larger stature, denser foliage, and more refined color than the crude "ironclad" rhododendrons that preceded them. Dexter used unusual Asian breeding stock from the Arnold Arboretum and other cutting-edge sources. Shepherd Hill's collection comes from Dexter's original plants; it's the most complete in existence. In appreciation, Bleyer donates several hundred plants each year to Heritage Plantation's plant sale, held in May, when its magnificent corridors of mature rhododendrons are in bloom.

Shepherd Hill offers Dexter's most celebrated hybrids, 'Scintillation' and 'Janet Blair', as well as some stunning but lesser-known varieties. These include red-flowered varieties and some Dexter pinks with contrasting throats and speckles. Some Shepherd Hill plants were chosen by wealthy friends from seedlings Dexter donated to their gardens. Henry Dupont chose 'Dexter's Cherry Red' from plantings at his Winterthur estate in Delaware, while 'Ben Moseley' was a Dexter seedling given to a Phipps on Long Island (now Old Westbury Gardens).

Bleyer also labors to grow elusive Dexter rhododendrons not yet in the trade, such as 'Dexter Champagne' and haunting 'Ashes of Roses'. Bleyer himself introduced 'Coxe Dexter' for its pale lavender-white flowers and perfect habit. The rarest hybrids prove difficult to propagate, such as 'Dexter Spice', a warm, cream-colored rhododendron of extraordinary beauty. "I've tried every year," Bleyer says determinedly, "and I'm going to try again."

Besides Dexter rhododendrons, Shepherd Hill offers a collector's choice of hardy big-leaf and small-leaf rhododendrons from major hybridizers. Bloom colors range from white and yellow to pink and purple, often set off with colored blotches and polka-dots. Many have beautiful leaves with silver or bronze *indumentum* (fuzz) on the underside of the foliage, making them handsome plants even after their spectacular trusses have ceased to flower.

Shepherd Hill also grows 45 varieties of evergreen azaleas from eminent American and Japanese breeding programs. Several were gathered from arboreta and private gardens (such as Winterthur) noted for their superior collections. The nursery's deciduous azalea collection offers eight hard-to-find wild azaleas from North America and Asia. The yellow-flowered Japanese azalea *(R. japonicum)*, for example, is delightful for its warm loveliness, as is the American flame azalea *(R. calendulaceum)* from the Appalachian Mountains. The royal Korean azalea *(R. schlippenbacchii)* is considered one of the world's most beautiful shrubs.

By combining delicate azaleas with larger rhododendrons, gardeners can achieve a magnificent shrubbery with a long bloom season, lush summer presence, winy fall foliage, and winter interest (rhododendron leaves roll up like cigars in the cold). Indeed, rhododendrons and azaleas are best grown together in a dedicated garden, where their beauty and diversity can be breathtaking.

The urge to acquire rhododendrons seems to have no logical stopping point. Bleyer labors continuously to increase the nursery's collection. "I've talked to other rhododendron specialists, and we agree," Bleyer says. "It's a disease."

Directions: From New York City, take the Taconic State Parkway north and exit onto Route 6. At the light, turn onto Route 6 west. At the fifth light, turn right onto Mill Street. At the next light turn hard left onto Peekskill Hollow Road. The nursery is a mile on the left, atop a shared driveway. From Route 84, take exit 16/Taconic State Parkway south, exit onto Route 6 west, and follow directions above.

Related source: Heritage Museums & Gardens, 67 Grove Street, Sandwich, MA 02563 (508-888-3300; www.heritageplantation.org), has 125 of Charles Dexter's 145 named hybrids, acres of rhododendron gardens, a labyrinth, miles of walking trails, and three American museums (open May through October); it's worth a pilgrimage in bloom season.

SPRAINBROOK NURSERY

448 Underhill Road, Scarsdale, NY 10583

(914) 723-2382; fax (914) 723-1677

www.sprainbrook.com

Alfred Krautter

General nursery stock. Trees, shrubs, annuals, perennials. Family-run nursery and garden center. Open year-round, Monday through Saturday, 8 to 5:30, Sunday, 9 to 4:30. Closed major holidays. Catalog on Web site. No mail order. Plant reservation with advance payment. Local delivery (fee). Seasonal items. Christmas trees and decorations. Garden supplies on separate Web site. Design and installation services. Christmas open house. Visitors welcome.

Sprainbrook Nursery is a family-run nursery in the heart of Westchester County, just north of New York City. The business was founded in 1944 by Alfred Krautter, who studied floriculture in Dresden, Germany, before emigrating to New York with his wife, Hermine. (Now in her 80s, she still works at the nursery.) Sprainbrook today is operated by their son, Alfred Krautter, a Cornell-trained horticulturist, with the help of his wife, Heidi, who runs the office.

From its inception, Sprainbrook's focus has been on plants—propagating, growing, testing, researching, and selecting plants of superior merit for garden use. The nursery basically grows everything—annuals, perennials, vegetables, houseplants, vines, woody plants, roses, fruit trees, and evergreens. Sprainbrook offers one of the area's largest and most discriminating plant assortments. An acorn logo is the symbol of this flourishing business.

"There are thousands of new varieties to choose from each year, many of them very beautiful, others dismal failures. Each year we become more selective weeding out old varieties and adding new gems proven to be superior," says Krautter. "For over 50 years we have dedicated ourselves to testing, visiting trial grounds, informing ourselves of new material and new trends, substituting better varieties but holding onto old timers that are longtime favorites."

In keeping with its progressive attitude, Sprainbrook recently dispensed with its popular printed catalog in favor of a comprehensive online catalog (downloadable from the Web site) of plant descriptions, photographs, and current prices. Customers can inquire of availability, place orders online, and even request digital photos of particular specimens. Sprainbrook is proud of its horticultural expertise and responds readily to questions. The Web site contains a message board, a lecture series list, and a monthly newsletter with updated gardening advice.

Information is also available the old-fashioned way, by telephone, which the nursery assures will be "answered by knowledgeable and courteous people, not by a machine." A photo album with color prints of new and classic plant varieties is available at the office.

It makes all the difference that Sprainbrook is a grower, not just a handler, of plants. The nursery grows virtually all of its own annuals and perennials from seed, cuttings, and transplants. Starter plants are hand-planted in sterilized soil mix and shipped to the nursery's upstate farm in Stephentown, to be finished for high-season sales. Mature perennials are wintered over in unheated outdoor frames, hardening to Westchester's climate. Plants are short, stocky, and bursting with new growth and buds—healthy evidence of natural exuberance rather than the result of force-feeding with commercial fertilizer. The stock looks healthy through the season. Fresh stock is brought down from Stephentown regularly, even in August and September when most nursery yards look tired. Specimen-grade trees and shrubs are buried in mulch and watered regularly. Prices are reasonable, reflecting the absence of the middleman.

Sprainbrook distinguishes itself by the depth of its inventory. "We have the largest selection of annuals in Westchester County," boasts Krautter. Many are colorful container plants. Scores of pansies and geraniums move out of the nursery, along with boatloads of petunias (including doubles, grandifloras, fantasies, minis, and the new kind that stands up to heat). For bold foliage there's burgundy perilla, pink-striped basket grass (*Oplismenus hirtellus* 'Variegata') and chocolate caricature plant (*Graptophyllum pictum* 'Chocolate'). Garden perker-uppers include larkspur, angelonia, Mexican sunflower, purple millet, and purple bell vine. For everything else, there's a mass of impatiens.

The perennial list is also rich. Plentiful supplies of iris, phlox, and hosta go without saying. Collector's items include horned violet, raspberry-pink mullein, red-stemmed meadow rue (*Thalictrum* 'Elin'), lavender bee balm, variegated cranesbill, a less-thorny form of hardy cactus, and hose-in-hose primroses, to name a few. The ornamental grasses are so numerous that they have to be sorted by height. Native perennials of good demeanor include Carolina lupine (*Thermopsis*), celandine poppy (the good kind, not the weed), and white obedient plant (*Physostegia virginiana* 'Miss Manners'). New

Yorkers should delight in oriental poppies such as 'Brooklyn' (raspberry with black polka-dots) and 'Central Park' (crinkled purple with black throat)—making great cut flowers if the cut stem is cauterized with a Zippo lighter.

If perennial gardening is comedic, decorative herbs are the straight men. Here are useful fillers such as germander, lavender cotton, a non-flowering lamb's-ears (*Stachys byzantina* 'Silver Carpet'), a compact Russian sage, peach verbascum, and lots of lovely creeping thymes. A separate shade plant list, including many ferns, demonstrates the possibilities in woodland. Vines include small and large-flowered clematis. There's a good suite of aquatics and bog plants.

Sprainbrook's tree and shrub collection provides ornament adapted to local conditions—cedar, holly, paperbark maple, weeping katsura, Japanese skimmia, and so on. Three cheers for stocking native rosebay rhododendron (*Rhododendron maximum*) and a hardy form of Southern magnolia (*Magnolia grandiflora* 'Edith Bogue'), along with hardy cherries and apricots, blueberry, compact boxwoods, topiary, useful little heathers and daphnes, scores of roses. The nursery's "garden center" (in an old red barn) has a welter of Felco pruners, leaf bags, books, and bird feeders.

Sprainbrook turns the garden center into a "Christmas Shoppe" in December. The botanical material is lovely: loose greens and berries, handmade balsam wreaths, fresh Fraser firs, and, for the overwhelmed, hand-decorated live Christmas trees.

Important work is still going on behind the sales area. Evergreens and woody plants are being hilled in, mulched, and sprayed with antidesiccant. Perennials are being cut back, covered with salt hay, and bedded down for the winter. The swimming pool is being transformed into a bulb cellar, from which potted bulbs will be drawn for forcing each week, as the year turns in the pale winter light. Then when the days brighten, the nursery again becomes an exhilarating hive of activity, even employing a night crew to fill the greenhouses with new varieties in time for spring.

Directions: From the Cross Westchester Expressway (Route 287), take exit 4 and turn left onto Route 100A. In 1.7 miles, after the blinking light, turn right on Ridge Road (becomes Sprain Road); proceed 2 miles to the nursery. From the New York State Thruway (Route 87), take exit 7, turn east off the ramp, and in 0.2 mile, turn right on Ashford Avenue. In 0.9 mile, turn left on Sprain Road and proceed 0.5 mile to the nursery. From Sprain Brook Parkway, take the Jackson Avenue exit and turn west onto Jackson Avenue; pass one traffic light, turn right onto Sprain Road, and proceed 1 mile to the nursery.

Nearby attractions: Sprainbrook's separate online shopping site, Garden Things (www.gardenthings.com), offers manufacturer-direct prices on garden tools, light tables, pond liners, and greenhouses.

ST. LAWRENCE NURSERIES

325 State Highway 345, Potsdam, NY 13676

(315) 265-6739

www.sln.potsdam.ny.us; e-mail *trees@sln.potsdam.ny.us*

Diana and Bill MacKentley

Hardy fruit and nut trees. Edible landscaping, timber, and hedgerow plants. *Family-run nursery. Open by appointment. Free catalog. Catalog on Web site. Mail order. Pick up by arrangement. Order deadlines May 1 (spring shipment) and September 30 (fall shipment). Custom grafting. Books on home orchard cultivation. Visitors welcome. Call ahead.*

Cultivated since ancient times in the world's cold regions, apples are called the "reliable soldiers of the seasons" on account of their stalwart facility to withstand temperatures of 30 degrees below zero and still bear fruit. An old tree's ability to rejuvenate probably accounts for pagan faith in the apple's immortality. Sauce apples, pie apples, cider apples, dessert apples—age-old varieties retain the dense, winy, sweet-tart flavors all but lost in modern commercial fruit.

St. Lawrence Nurseries is a family-run nursery specializing in cold-hardy fruit and nut trees. The nursery is in Potsdam, a small college town in northern New York, not far from the St. Lawrence River. The nursery occupies open acreage beside the owners' delightfully quirky farmhouse. A remarkable orchard of heirloom apples is supplemented by hardy pears, plums, and berry shrubs, along with hedgerow plants, nuts, and timber trees.

Bill and Diana MacKentley founded St. Lawrence Nurseries in 1977 on a farm acquired from their friend and mentor Fred Ashworth, a noted collector of edible plants for the north. The MacKentleys inherited Ashworth's hardy fruit and nut collection when they bought the nursery. "Fred farmed here for 50 years and got to know all the old-time plant breeders before they died—people like E. M. Meader, George Darrow, and Professor L. H. MacDaniels at Cornell. He was extremely knowledgeable about plants, yet humble and generous," recalls Bill. "He collected scion wood for 100 heirloom apples and sent trees to Old Sturbridge Village. Fred survived the Great Depression—he called it the 'Thirsty Thirties'—and became a founding father of the North American Fruit Explorers." On Ashworth's death, the MacKentleys resolved to continue his work of growing and preserving edible landscape plants for northern climates.

St. Lawrence Nurseries is best known for its vigorous old-fashioned apple trees, grown on a "standard" rootstock *(Malus × 'Antonovka')*. In his book, *Apples*, Frank Browning describes the classic old-fashioned orchard: "Full spreading trees, their open limbs as thick as thighs, were planted in steady rows, one every 40 feet." Because they can live for a century, standard trees are favored by heirloom fruit gardeners and traditionalists seeking to ensure the continuity of historic landscapes. St. Lawrence is the only propagator of standard apple trees in the Northeast.

The nursery's 150 apple varieties include colorful antiques with evocative names, such as 'Blue Pearmain', 'Red Astrachan', 'Ashmed's Kernel', 'Pound Sweet', and 'Westfield Seek-No-Further'. New York State heirlooms survive in 'Adirondack Crab', 'St. Lawrence', 'Piece Pasture', and 'Purdy'. Hardy cider apples (increasingly popular with home brewers) are 'Bullock' and 'Empire'. Newer varieties suited to small commercial orchards include juicy 'Liberty', aromatic 'Macoun', and crunchy 'Honeycrisp'. The nursery catalog contains detailed information on each tree's hardiness, disease resistance, ripening, and culinary characteristics.

Besides apples, St. Lawrence's hardy-plant inventory includes pears (the melting 'Nova' pear was named for the MacKentley's daughter); bush cherries, pie cherries, sand cherries, chokecherries, and ground cherries, many of which make excellent wildlife hedges; seedling plums, grafted plums, and cherry plums; blueberries, raspberries, and lingonberries; and grape varieties for jam, dessert, juice, and wine. Some heirloom plums may derive from trees sold in the 1770s by the country's earliest nurseryman, Long Island's William Prince. In *A History of Agriculture in the State of New York*, Ulysses P. Hedrick wrote, "[t]he Princes for a hundred years sold fruits in every town and hamlet, almost to every farmer, in the Hudson River Valley," making "the first attempt in America to breed new varieties."

St. Lawrence's medley of "edible landscaping plants" includes such gastronomic forage as Scottish black currant, Manchurian apricot, Siberian pea shrub, hardy white currant, and sand pear (good for vinegar). Sea buckthorn is a silver-leaved Siberian shrub noted for edible orange fruit. Like the rugosa roses, native *Rosa virginiana* makes a handsome hedge. Fruits once relished by the Iroquois—the bog cranberry, buffalo berry, nannyberry, and juneberry *(Amelanchier alnifolia)*—remain valuable in wildlife gardens.

Hardy nut trees can be planted for their luxury of shade as well as for lumber, edible nuts, and wildlife sustenance. St. Lawrence's native inventory includes shagbark hickory, black walnut, red oak, and 'Ashworth' bur oak (an oak with sweet acorns discovered by Fred Ashworth in the 1920s). The hazelbert (a hazelnut-filbert cross) makes a good hedgerow. Timber and yard trees include thornless honey locust, *Maackia amurensis,* Ohio buckeye, 'Sweet Sap' sugar maple (with twice the sugar), and native hackberry *(Celtis occidentalis)*, a seldom-offered elm relative rich in wildlife value.

The MacKentleys take special satisfaction in their plants' ability to withstand abusive cold. In winter, the nursery's average minimum temperature reaches 30 to 40 degrees below zero (Zone 3). Temperatures occasionally reach 50 below zero, not counting wind chill. The catalog confirms, "If we can't grow it here, we won't sell it." As a result, all the nursery's plants have heavy roots toughened to climatic stress.

St. Lawrence's inventory comprises some 300,000 plants, organically field-grown in open orchards and tangled hedgerows. No herbicides, pesticides, or artificial fertilizers are used to boost growth. The result, according to the nursery, is "a smaller but 'tougher' tree with a more balanced proportion of root to top." The average fruit tree is 4 to 5 feet tall at shipping—intentionally small, because such trees transplant better than large ones.

"We consider ourselves to be the best-kept secret in America," says Bill MacKentley. "We sell more plants than anybody else, and we squirrel in a lifestyle, too." Unlike large commercial operations, the MacKentleys and their seasonal staff do all planting, weeding, and digging by hand. Bill MacKentley grafts an apple scion with lightening accuracy—his deftness is sheer wizardry. "We sell 30,000 trees a year and I graft 15,000 of them," he says. "I can do four a minute, except on really cold days." These include custom grafts for customers who want to perpetuate irreplaceable old fruit trees. In the last thirty years, MacKentley estimates that he has grafted "over a third of a million trees."

Plants are usually shipped bare root by mail order but with notice can be picked up at the nursery. Although some trees and shrubs are dug in the spring, most are dug in the fall, when dormant. Plants are then either shipped for fall planting or stored in cold bunkers in the barn, buried in damp sawdust for early spring shipment. Shipping practices are excellent, as are growing and planting instructions accompanying each order.

While too distant for most casual travel, St. Lawrence Nurseries is well worth a visit from gardeners dreaming of the northern frontier. (We came in August after a wild ride through the Adirondacks in a freak snowstorm forced us to overnight at Lake Placid.) Visitors are welcome and there's much to see. Bill MacKentley is justifiably proud of his nursery and, as time allows, enjoys showing people around and giving grafting demonstrations. His favorite recreation is creating farm buildings from what he calls "scrounge materials," an imaginative practice that raises recycling to high art. MacKentley's scrounging skills are the subject of a popular course at the Northeast Organic Farming Association (NOFA). His latest storage shed was crafted ingeniously from disused billboards, scrap lumber, supermarket pallets, an abandoned ice box, and a discarded meat locker.

Nursery visitors should pause to admire the stately stone Buddha in the MacKentley garden, flanked, like angels, by a pair of Bechtel crabs (*Malus ioensis* 'Floro Pleno'). The nursery is a rare source for this enchanting native prairie crab, graced with double shell-pink flowers and silver bark—Tasha Tudor's favorite tree.

Directions: Potsdam is south of the St. Lawrence River and north of the Adirondack Forest Preserve. From Route 11 in Potsdam, turn onto Route 345 north; the nursery is 2 miles on the left. Visitors welcome; call ahead.

Nearby attractions: Named for a European capital following the War of 1812, Potsdam is a college town with many good B & Bs. American elms line Main Street, too far north to be ravaged by Dutch elm disease. Northern larch forests and remnant orchards are visible in the area. Various scenic byways through the Adirondack Mountains follow Routes 3, 30, 28, and 78; Route 12 is a scenic byway along the St. Lawrence River. Canadian Public Radio is FM 93.1. Hailed as "the Smithsonian of the Adirondacks," the Adirondack Museum (518-352-7311; www.adkmuseum.org) has a lumber camp, hermit's hut, private railroad car, boats, view, food, and folk art. The Six Nations Indian Museum, Onchiota, NY (518-891-2299), houses important Iroquois artifacts. The

Robert Louis Stevenson Cottage, Saranac Lake, NY (518-891-1990), has a quaint collection of Stevenson memorabilia. Great Camp Sagamore (315-354-5311; www.sagamore.org) is an 1897 Vanderbilt family retreat of the Gilded Age; open for tours, camping, and retreats. With rustic elegance, the Lodge on Clear Lake, Clear Lake, NY (518-891-1489), serves old-world German food and a martini menu.

STONECROP GARDENS
81 Stonecrop Lane, Cold Spring, NY 10516
(845) 265-2000; fax (845) 265-2405
www.stonecrop.org; e-mail stncrp@bestweb.net

Rock garden and woodland plants. *Nonprofit botanical garden. Open by reservation only, April through October, Tuesday, Wednesday, Friday, and 1st and 3rd Saturdays, 10 to 4. Admission $5, members free. Plants propagated from species and cultivars in garden. No catalog or mail order. Free seed lists and seed to members. Seasonal display gardens. Garden overview on Web site. Weekly photo archive of garden at www.gardenweek.org. Horticultural education. Professional internships. Group tours by arrangement. Write or call ahead to schedule visit.*

Rock-garden plants exert a curious fascination. Compact and gravel-friendly, their chief enchantments are diminutive scale, abundant bloom, and an appealing neatness that seems almost supernatural. This diverse group includes some of the most attractive plants in horticulture. Their very minuteness allows greater variety in a small area than any other type of gardening.

Stonecrop Gardens in Cold Spring, a beautiful town in the Hudson Highlands, contains one of the region's most revered rock gardens. Stonecrop originated as the 63-acre private landscape of Frank Cabot, a visionary garden-builder and horticultural dignitary whose summer garden in Quebec is the subject of his delightful book, *A Greater Perfection.* Cabot is also the founder and force behind the Garden Conservancy, a garden preservation organization whose national Open Days program unlocks the gates of hundreds of America's best private gardens each year. With his wife, Anne, he began developing Stonecrop in 1958, over the decades experimenting with garden forms and collecting rare plants from all over the world.

Today, Stonecrop's remarkable display gardens cover 12 acres of wind-swept outcrop in hardiness Zone 5. As its name implies, Stonecrop offers a perfect habitat for "stonecrop" (sedum) and such other rock-garden plants as thrive on grits and gravels. Stonecrop's extraordinary collection includes true alpines, native to the cloud zone above the timberline; dry-land plants from stony regions of desert and drought; peat plants from rocky heaths and shallow bogs; and other miniatures of the exposed ledge, sand bed, or stone wall. Some are robust and easily grown; others specialized and difficult. Many are simply unavailable to the ordinary gardener, except through discriminating private collections such as the one assembled at Stonecrop.

In common with Cabot's garden-preservation goals, Stonecrop is now a nonprofit garden open to the public by reservation through the growing season. Garden supporters are invited to join Stonecrop's membership for an annual fee. Members receive free admission, invitations to open house events, and free packets of seed collected from the gardens. Regular members select 10 spring seed packets from the garden's *Index Seminum*, or seed list, with extra packets awarded for cleverness to those who solve an acrostic word puzzle. Higher-level donors are allowed seed from the garden's *Index Rarium*, or rare-plant seed list. The mere whiff of access to the garden's extraordinary collections is enough to attract subscribers.

In addition to seed distribution, Stonecrop sells offsets from its collections in little pots set on covered sales benches behind the potting shed. Here members and visitors can purchase well-labeled rock-garden specimens, as well as a few perennials, the odd daphne, and other choice horticultural miscellany. Plants are propagated from seed or cuttings taken from the gardens, a legacy of the mail-order alpine nursery once operated here. Offerings consist mainly of overage the gardens cannot absorb. Stock is necessarily limited and unpredictable, changing with the seasons. There is neither catalog nor mail order; only the list of the garden's own plants offers a clue to what might be available. The authority of Stonecrop's rare-plant collection, however, guarantees interest in anything set on the sales bench.

Stonecrop employs an energetic staff of professional gardeners who labor to ensure the garden's ongoing horticultural richness. The garden's director, English horticulturist Caroline Burgess, once worked for Rosemary Verey and trained at Britain's prestigious Royal Botanic Gardens, Kew. Under her direction, Stonecrop has diversified its garden spaces and developed an encyclopedic flora. A well-coordinated staff propagates new plants, maintains established plantings, and constantly improves the collections with wonders seldom seen in gardens. Stonecrop is intended to demonstrate what can be achieved by horticultural enthusiasts, as well as to serve as an educational resource for plant study and practical horticultural training. In 2004, for example, the staff planted 45,000 bulbs at Stonecrop, adding to an already capacious trove of choice dwarf bulbs in the pit house.

Outside the potting shed, Stonecrop's hypertufa troughs and raised stone beds offer a jeweler's window of exquisite miniatures. Geoffrey Charlesworth, noted rock gardener, once dismissed the typical trough garden as "a cross between a Japanese landscape, a toy alp, and a doll house back yard." Others find them irresistibly charming. Stonecrop's troughs and sinks demonstrate the underused art of growing hardy miniatures—such as encrusted saxifrage, bunlike *draba*, and tiny alpine gentian—in outdoor containers. An alpine house functions as a collector's paradise, displaying alpine prima donnas that are desirable, beautiful, rare, and difficult.

Stonecrop's value as a garden far exceeds the sum of its plant list. Seldom do naturalistic design and sophisticated plantsmanship combine to produce such soul-moving results. Any gardener interested in rocky habitat should make a priority of visiting Stonecrop through the seasons, notepaper in hand. Natural and man-made ledges support intricate alpine plant colonies. Rock-garden plants in vast numbers follow stratums and faults, creep over rigid edges, and establish themselves in a thousand charming ways. Their miniature clusters, dense cushions, and slow-creeping mats offer extraordinary visual variety. Some alpines are small succulents, others minute flowering perennials, and still others, on inspection, reveal themselves to be tiny shrubs or trees. Adding to this magical landscape are life-size gardens of woodland and water, a Himalayan slope, bamboo tunnels, a wisteria pavilion, an English-style flower garden, and a tropical conservatory floating on a lake. "Miss Gertrude Jekyll," as scarecrow, watches over the vegetable garden. Inspiration may be found in every season.

Directions: Cold Spring is 55 miles north of New York City in the lower Hudson Valley. Stonecrop is located on Route 301, 3.5 miles west of the Taconic Parkway and 2.5 miles east of Route 9. A turn-off on the north side (signposted) leads to the parking area and garden entrance. Visitors by reservation only.

Nearby attractions: A superb photographic archive of Stonecrop's 1999–2000 plant collections is posted by Garden Week (www.gardenweek.org). The Garden Conservancy's Open Days Program publishes an annual directory of open gardens in many states, including New York and New Jersey (www.gardenconservancy.org). A nice little café in Cold Spring is East Side Kitchen, 124 Main Street (845-265-7223; www.eastsidekitchen.com; open 12 to 9). Foxgloves, elegant spandex gardening gloves invented by Cold Spring landscape architect Harriet Zbikowski, are sold at The Country Goose, 117 Main Street, Cold Spring (845-265-2122). Just south on Route 9D in Garrison, Manitoga, the home and woodland garden of pioneer industrial designer Russel Wright, is open for hikes, picnics, and guided tours of Dragon Rock, Wright's experimental home on the rock ledge (845-424-3812; www.russelwrightcenter.org.). Boscobel, Route 9D, Garrison, NY 10524 (845-265-3638; www.boscobel.org), is an historic home with gardens overlooking the upper Hudson. Across the river, the Storm King Art Center, Old Pleasant Hill Road, Mountainville, NY 10953 (845-534-3115; www.stormking.org), is a 500-acre museum whose landscaped grounds serve as exhibition space for modern sculptures by renowned artists, including the famous Wall That Went for a Walk, constructed by Andy Goldsworthy in 1998 (open Wednesday through Sunday, April to November; tours daily at 2). The Storm King Lodge, 100 Pleasant Hill Road, Mountainville, NY 10953 (845-534-9421; www.stormkinglodge.com), is a pleasant old carriage house turned guest lodge.

SYLVAN BOTANICALS NEW YORK GINSENG

P.O. Box 91, Cooperstown, NY 13326

(607) 264-8455

www.catskillginseng.com; e-mail *ginseng@telenet.net*

Scott and Sylva Harris

Ginseng and goldenseal. *Woodland-based horticultural farm. Plant and seed list on Web site. Mail order only. Ginseng farming information and advice. Lectures. Closed to the public except by appointment.*

Sylvan Botanicals is a ginseng farm near Cooperstown whose specialty is growing and distributing American ginseng planting stock. Founded in 1991 by Scott and Sylva Harris, Sylvan sells hand-harvested ginseng roots and seeds to amateur and professional growers seeking to establish ginseng as a forest crop. Scott Harris is president of the Empire State Ginseng Growers Association and the region's preeminent ginseng farmer and booster. His published monograph on American ginseng demonstrates a keen knowledge of its history. Sylvan Botanicals is the largest distributor of live American ginseng and goldenseal roots in the northeast.

American ginseng *(Panax quinquefolius)* is a handsome understory herb native to the great upland forests of eastern North America. After 300 years of over-collection, American ginseng is rare, threatened, or endangered in the states where it grows wild. Appendix II of the Convention on International Trade in Endangered Species (CITES) treaty ranks this plant as vulnerable to federal endangerment, owing to the pressures of international trade. Global trade in ginseng roots and rhizomes is now regulated.

The nursery's principal product is "New York Wild Catskill Mountain Ginseng Roots," derived from an especially palatable strain of local ginseng. A Cooperative Extension agent has called Catskill Mountain ginseng "the finest ginseng in the world." Sylvan Botanicals is certified organic by NOFA-NY, assuring that no artificial chemicals or pesticides are used in production. Each fresh root comes with a certificate from the New York Department of Environmental Conservation confirming legal harvest, age, and origin of the root. Roots of "select premium grade" ginseng stock range from 16 to 50 years old, priced according to age. Roots aged 10 years or more are ready to be planted in shade or woodland. To make it interesting, the nursery suggests choosing a root that was "born" the same year you were.

All sales of ginseng root are by mail order, accompanied by detailed planting instructions. Besides roots, Sylvan sells "premium grade" stratified seed from wild and wild-simulated ginseng populations. Seeds and roots of goldenseal (another medicinal forest herb, now threatened or endangered in the wild) and a dozen other native woodlanders are also for sale, along with books on ginseng cultivation. Scott Harris offers on-site consulting services and lectures on establishing ginseng plantations, from backyard plots to large woodland acreage. A "seed market update" posted on the Web site provides harvesting news and lecture notices.

The Harrises grow their nursery stock in a sugar maple forest whose exact location is a guarded secret. Other roots and seeds are purchased from six local ginseng growers in wild-simulated settings, as well as from wild harvesters during the legal picking season. As the Harrises explain, "We work with a small select group of responsible and ethical wildcrafters and provide them with free seed for replanting. As long as there is a legal season for harvesting wild ginseng, it will continue to be dug, dried, and exported from our country. Our 'adopted' wild roots remain alive and are returned back to the woods for the production of seed."

As part of its mission to support wild populations of ginseng, Sylvan Botanicals urges dealers and wildcrafters to replant seed from wild populations, as required by law in New York and many states. Each year the Harrises themselves plant 25,000 seeds in remote locations in New York State and donate seed to the United Plant Savers for planting in the wild—practices that are beneficial when seed is derived from local genotypes. They also sponsor replanting projects at nonprofit organizations, colleges, and universities as a way to counter irresponsible wild digging. Illegal poaching, normally a federal or state felony, is now beginning to be controlled with marking programs that apply an invisible calcium-laced dye to protected plants—making it easier to find and prosecute poachers, even if it doesn't save plants that have already been dug and prepared for export.

How ginseng is cultivated greatly affects the commercial value of its roots. "Wild-simulated" ginseng, grown in uncultivated woodlands for 9 to 12 years, is the closest thing to wild ginseng and has the highest commercial value and lowest production costs. Cultivating ginseng is no get-rich-quick scheme, if only because of the plant's slow growth and palatability to deer. Nevertheless, because many woodland landscapes serve few other productive purposes, ginseng culture could prove to be a valuable agricultural supplement, like maple sugaring, contributing to the well-being of rural farms.

The jury is still out on whether threatened native herbs such as ginseng and goldenseal can be grown as forest crops without disturbing remnant gene pools. Ginseng is under collection stress and goldenseal is on New York's "rare" list, with less than 20 known populations in the state. Preservationists worry that introduced plants will weaken surviving strains and narrow an already compromised genetic base. To avoid contamination, conscientious growers can limit plantings to areas that don't house known wild populations. Woodland farmers can be effective preservationists when they employ growing practices that take pressure off wild populations and preserve genetic diversity. Ironically, the woodland grower's imitation of wildness may prove to be an important means by which real wildness can be preserved.

Nearby attractions: In Cooperstown, the Farmer's Museum, Route 80 /Lake Road (888-547-1450; www.farmersmuseum.org), maintains period gardens and sells old-fashioned seed packets in the 19th-century store.

Related source: A 1999 USDA Forest Service study, "Economics and Marketing of Ginseng" (www.unl.edu/nac/afnotes/ff-4), analyzes the profitability of ginseng farming.

TURTLE TREE SEEDS
Camphill Village, Copake, NY 12516
(800) 620-7388; (518) 329-3038; fax (518) 329-7955
www.mamasearth.com/turtletreeseed.htm; e-mail *turtle@taconic.net*
Nathan and Beth Corymb, Seed Production Managers

Biodynamic garden seed. *Community-run horticultural farm. Free catalog. Mail order. Orders by mail, phone, or fax through May 31. Web page shows availability; no online orders. $10 credit card minimum. Seed packets. Bulk seed. Books. Gift certificates. Camphill gift shop catalog (518-329-4511).*

If a secular, scientific society had to choose one sacred symbol, surely it would be the seed. For it is said that we are "the guests of plants" on earth; without them, the web of life on which we depend would perish.

Turtle Tree Seeds is a small organic seed enterprise specializing in open-pollinated, biodynamically grown garden seed. "Biodynamics" is a USDA-approved farming process articulated by Dr. Rudolf Steiner, an Austrian scientist and philosopher, in his Agriculture Lectures in 1924. Biodynamic agriculture emphasizes living soil, the farm as a holistic organism, and a healthy, diverse ecosystem. According to the Demeter Association, "Biodynamic agriculture is the oldest certified ecological farming system and has been an assurance of quality since 1928."

Turtle Tree seed is produced biodynamically by farmers who are committed to caring for the land. Much of the seed is grown at Turtle Tree's biodynamic farm at Camphill Village, a socially enlightened community located in Copake, in the northern Hudson River Valley. The remaining seed is procured from contract growers, including many community-supported agricultural farms (CSAs). The catalog identifies seed suppliers and their practices. While all use biodynamic methods, some are certified biodynamic by the Demeter Association *(www.demeter-usa.org)*

and some are certified organic by the Northeast Organic Farming Association (NOFA) *(www.nofa.org)*.

In the beginning there were beans: Bush beans, soup beans, pole beans, runner beans, soybeans—you can always judge a vegetable seed catalog by the richness and curiosity of its beans. Turtle Tree offers a wonderful collection, including such lively heirlooms as 'White Aztec Half Runner', 'Maine Yellow-Eye', and 'Aunt Ida's Italian Pole Bean'. Corn comes next in the vegetable lineup: sweet corn, popcorn, flour corn, and field corn. Turtle Tree offers all these, along with blue corn from the Hopi Tribe and a new biodynamic corn bred for low-input farming.

After corn and beans, squash is the Third Sister of the Iroquois: zucchinis, pumpkins, summer squash, and winter squash. Turtle Tree is also a source for a delicious striped sweet-potato squash called 'Delicata', an improved heirloom developed by the Public Seed Initiative. This important project is a cooperative program between NOFA-NY, the Farmer's Cooperative Genome Project, the USDA Plant Genetics Unit in Geneva, New York, and the Cornell Department of Plant Breeding. The Public Seed Initiative supports organic farmers by breeding improved vegetable varieties suited to small-scale agriculture in the Northeast.

The rest of Turtle Tree's seed list is diverse enough to gratify the most ardent vegetable lover: shell, snap, and snow peas; cherry, paste, and stuffing tomatoes; sweet and hot peppers; cantaloupes, watermelons, celeriac, fennel, and kohlrabi. Seeds include French carrots, Russian kale, German cabbage, Taiwanese eggplants, Swiss storage beets, and Boston pickling cucumbers. Exotic vegetables are Japanese burdock, Chinese broccoli, and 'Hon Tsai Tai', a yellow-flowered purple pak choi. The list includes gastronomic lettuces, cresses, and greens, including a corn salad (or "rapunzel") proven cold hardy to upstate New York. For small commercial growers, 'New York Early' is a globe storage onion well adapted to the Northeast.

Turtle Tree's herb and flower seeds are equally suited to ornamental potagers, kitchen gardens, and family farms. Herb seeds include tea herbs, strewing herbs, edible seeds, salad flowers, potpourri ingredients, and medicinal herbs such as *Arnica montana* (miraculous for bruises), and milk vetch (a Chinese tonic). Flower seeds include blue flax, cockscombs, castor beans, pinks, poppies, and sunflowers. Cover crops, grains, and forage plants suit small-scale farmers. Books include Dr. Rudolf Steiner's *Agriculture* and *The Woodchuck's Guide to Gardening*.

Turtle Tree's seeds are sold in small, medium, large, and extra large packets, as well as in bulk. The catalog gives "days to maturity" guidance on when a crop should be ready to harvest, calculated to upstate New York. (Actual maturity dates, of course, vary widely.) Seed orders must be placed by May 31; after that, packets are sold through Peaceful Valley Farm Supply *(www.groworganic.com)*, a California-based mail-order source for organic seeds and supplies.

Founded in 1961, the Camphill Village Community at Copake *(www.camphillvillage.org)* is the oldest independent Camphill community in North America. This intentional community allows people with special needs and volunteers to live and work together. Its members receive "the warmth and stability of extended family homes shared with co-worker families; dignified meaningful work and training options; and a rich array of cultural, educational, and artistic opportunities." Camphill Village work includes biodynamic farming, cheese making, forestry, vegetable and herb gardening, woodworking, stained glass, weaving, book binding, candle making, and baking.

The name "Turtle Tree" derives from a creation story of the Onondaga Tribe. The Turtle symbolizes the American continent; the Water in which it swims, the Tree of Life; and Life itself, as it branches across the Turtle's back, the great Mississippi River system. This beautiful legend, recounted in Turtle Trees' catalog, tells the fate of Sky Woman, who fell to earth in the crevice of a great uprooted tree. Perceiving that she could not swim, a little muskrat retrieved earth from the watery depths and deposited it on the back of the Great Turtle; "Almost immediately it began to grow and grow, until it became the whole world." Seeds dispersed from Sky Woman's hands became trees and grass and flowers: "Life on Earth had begun."

Directions: Copake is in the upper Hudson River Valley, southeast of Hudson on Route 22. Write or call ahead for an appointment to visit the Camphill community and its biodynamic farm.

Related sources: Eastern Native Seed Conservancy, P.O. Box 451, Great Barrington, MA 01230 (413-229-8316; www.enscseeds.org), seeks to preserve regionally adapted heirloom and Native American seed, including beans of New York's Six Nations tribes. The Nature Institute, 20 May Hill Road, Ghent, NY 12075 (518-672-0116; www.natureinstitute.org), is a small nonprofit organization seeking to re-vision science and technology so as to realign humanity with nature; classes and seminars.

UNION SQUARE GREENMARKET

East 17th Street and Broadway, New York, NY

(212) 788-7476

www.cenyc.org

Council on the Environment of New York City

51 Chambers Street, Room 228, New York, NY 10007

Annuals, perennials, herbs, houseplants. *Farmers' market. Open year-round, Monday, Wednesday, Friday, and Saturday, 8 to 6. No catalog or mail order. Regional growers. Seasonal. Plant selection changes. Fresh local produce, dairy products, artisanal breads. Visitors welcome.*

Thirty years ago, when the city's first green markets were formed, it was hard to get produce farmers to agree to set foot in New York City—"Gotham," as it was known. Some plucky farmers, lured by the chance to sell produce at a decent profit, gingerly began attending open-air markets, which the City had located in grungy parks in the hope of displacing drug dealers.

The people who live here may be New Yorkers—tough, resilient, and mouthy—but there has never been anything wrong with their taste buds. When fresh-picked vegetables and fruits hit the stalls, along with homemade pie and grass-fed lamb, it didn't take Manhattan residents long to show up and form lines. Farmer distrust melted. Produce grew sophisticated. Restaurants opened. Neighborhoods revived. Today, New York City's green markets are among the most successful in the country, occupying 31 locations in 5 boroughs and attracting some 250,000 visitors per week.

The queen of these markets—the oldest, largest, and fanciest—is the Union Square Greenmarket in lower Manhattan. This 35,000-square-foot open-air market is open year-round, four days a week. Market activity clusters at the north end of Union Square Park. Technicolor vegetable stalls vie for attention with mushroom farmers, cheese makers, artisan bakers, beekeepers, and cut-flower vendors. The farmers and their families do their own selling—right off the truck. Vendors are required to grow, can, or bake everything they sell, ensuring an array of fresh, often unique, produce. A chalkboard at the city's official booth (at the park's western entrance) posts the day's specialties. Freshness can be smelled a block away.

In the horticultural circles, it's now pretty well agreed that the Union Square Greenmarket is the best place to buy live plants in Manhattan. Here, at last, city dwellers can shop for fresh plants at a decent price without getting a car and driving two hours. The journey itself feels like an outing. As *New York Times* writer Regina Schrambling wrote of the Union Square Greenmarket, "A Saturday morning there is like a cross between a mind massage and a trip to the country, without the shrink or the jitney."

Horticultural regulars huddle in close proximity on 17th Street at the corner of Park Avenue. The Stokes Farms' truck rumbles in early from Old Tappan, New Jersey, with a well-grown assortment of bedding plants, hanging baskets, and cooking herbs. Spring vegetable transplants include jalapeño peppers, 'Sweet 100' tomatoes, and everbearing strawberries. Martha Washington geraniums are a day's bargain, but zonal geraniums are more popular. "They're the standard low-maintenance New York plant," the stand attendant cracks. "All you need is sun."

Van Houten Farms sells flowering annuals in small pots under the Proven Winner label—including African daisies, flowering tobacco, geraniums, asters, lobelias, dahlias, herbs, and seven kinds of marigold. A few nice perennials, grasses, and woody plants are parked beside the truck. (A typical day might reveal dwarf fothergilla, red Japanese maple, tree lilac, silver-lace vine, and gold-variegated euonymus; the nursery will take orders for particular plants.) It's always fun to ponder whether buyers' personalities match their rose choices—'Feisty' (scarlet), 'Sultry' (yellow), and 'Carefree Delight' (hot pink).

Another grower, Fantastic Gardens of Long Island, sells indoor plants propagated in its greenhouses in Patchogue. A day's finds may include black caladium, variegated Swedish ivy, miniature jade plant, and several kinds of hens-and-chickens (*Sempervivum* spp.). When available, the nursery's rhapis palm, cardboard palm, and variegated calathea show unusual flair. Barrel cactus and white moth orchids were on sale when we stopped by.

The Blew family of Oak Grove Plantations, Pittstown, New Jersey, offers wonderful culinary herbs in 4-inch squares or mix-and-match flats. Selection is unusual: French sorrel, English lavender, Greek oregano, Roman chamomile, Mexican epizote, bronze fennel, chervil, a dozen mints, and a coriander-like herb called papalo (short for Aztec *papaloquelite*). Eight basils include a purple Armenian variety called 'Ararat'. A dozen heirloom tomatoes include 'Black Brandywine', 'Green Grape', 'Yellow Plum', and 'Orange Oxheart'.

Potted sunflowers and nasturtiums aren't really a bargain as they are grown easily from seed, but they look fresh and pretty. Bags of raw heirloom popcorn are sold next to a locker holding frozen farm sausage.

At a small stand nearby, the East Side Ecology Center offers "New York City Pay Dirt"—compost and worm castings—at $1 per pound. Worm castings are superb for jump-starting small plants. An advertisement for a starter red-worm composting kit declares, "You can do it in a one-bedroom." The center also accepts "compostable vegetable waste," in case you want to donate some fresh garbage on your way to the market.

The Greenmarket's colorful flux seems to inspire a playful, chance-taking attitude. What's here one day is gone the next. Things aren't always where expected. Vegetable vendors sell peonies; plant vendors offer fresh maple syrup. Plant inventories shift as the seasons progress, with spring transplants giving way to summer perennials, fall mums, and aromatic Christmas greens. Vendors themselves shift around; Saturday's regulars may differ from Wednesday's.

The affection with which New Yorkers cherish their green markets gives them near-cult status, second only to community gardens. The city estimates that green market farmers cultivate some 10,000 acres of regional farmland, 1300 acres of which is protected from development. The lure of green markets—farm-fresh produce at affordable prices in prime urban locations—reflects not merely the positive economies of truck farming, but the imaginative use of public space for beneficial purposes. Green markets are the town greens of New York City.

Directions: Union Square is located on Manhattan's lower east side, from 17th Street to 14th Street and from Park Avenue to Union Square West.

Nearby attractions: Union Square Café, 21 East 16th Street, New York, NY 10003 (212-243-4020), uses premium green market produce. Olives, 201 Park Avenue South at 17th Street (212-353-8345) has a Green Market Tasting Menu. The Jefferson Market Garden, Greenwich Avenue at Sixth Avenue, is a beloved community garden at the heart of Greenwich Village, on the site of a demolished 12-story prison. Neighborhood fund-raising, matched by the city, supports this remarkable oasis of tranquility, encircled in a wrought iron fence (open afternoons, except Monday).

Related sources: A list of farmers' markets in the five boroughs of New York City is available from the city's Greenmarket Program (212-788-7476; 212-477-3220; www.cenyc.org). Farmers' markets and produce farms in New York State are posted at www.agmkt.state.ny.us. State-certified nurseries are listed at www.agmkt.state.ny.us.

ZENA GREEN NURSERY
403 Zena Road, Kingston, NY 12401
(845) 679-0300; fax (845) 679-0269
www.zenagreen.com; e-mail *tskyler@hvc.rr.com*
Toby Skyler

Unusual container plants, alpines, and grasses. *Small specialty nursery. Open May 1 through June 1, Friday, Saturday, and Sunday, 9 to 5, and by appointment. No catalog or mail order. Custom growing from plant list; orders due by February 1. Garden design. Visitors welcome.*

As most of us come to know, gardens are ephemeral. Some gardeners deal with this by envisioning their gardens as movements in time, experiments in form, compasses, homing devices, and ways of thinking about things. Such creative folk usually can't stay still, though, any more than their gardens.

Zena Green is an experimental nursery near Woodstock with a varied repertoire of choice and often little-known garden plants. Owner Toby Skyler is a zealous gardener whose plant list changes each year to reflect new interests. She's studied biology, taken seminars at the New York Botanical Garden, and undergone an 18-month internship at Stonecrop Gardens (see profile), one of the hemisphere's most illustrious rock gardens. She's also a hands-on garden designer and maintainer whose client list includes the Woodstock Golf Course and some of the area's wealthiest people.

Skyler started the nursery in 1997 as a way to experiment with interesting plants. "I'm always trying the odd seed," she says, "looking for plants that do well in gardens but that people don't know about."

Like many gardeners with a restless interest in what each seed will reveal, Skyler keeps an eclectic plant list—annuals, grasses, alpines, and container plants—the kind of plants that materialize, jump around, and behave unexpectedly. Many are plants for a season, tender fare that blooms like mad and is replaced with something else next year. Random examples are thistle-like cardoon, Malabar spinach vine *(Basella rubra),* and a black-podded form of Apple-of-Peru

(Nicandra physalodes). Zena Green is known to grow a gold form of jasmine nightshade *(Solanum jasminoides* var. *aurea),* small-flowered morning-glory relatives (*Convovulus cneorum; Evovulus* 'Blue Daze'), and a few well-chosen dahlias and verbascums.

The stock is innovative but never preposterous. A good deal of it serves in container displays—European 'Balcon' geraniums, coral diascia, and cut-leaf lavender from the Canary Islands, for example. Even familiar plants come in startling colors, such as dark red African daisy, purple pineapple lily, and yellow and papaya impatiens. Finding what deer and woodchucks don't eat has become a local imperative, which surely accounts for Skyler's capacious supply of ornamental grasses and herbs.

The nursery is small by most standards—one owner, two polyhouses, a vine-covered potting shed, and a good-sized nursery yard. It's open for the month of May, when demand for floral experiments is keenest. Skyler grows everything from seed and cuttings, sourced from friends, connoisseurs, and sophisticated European seed houses. She'll even custom-grow plants if you get your order in on time.

Customer reports confirm the fun of shopping here. "You'll go in looking for something specific and get sidetracked by six things you've never seen before," one customer said. "I guess that's why they provide wagons."

Gardens evolve, and so do their owners. Skyler's taste has moved from what she calls "froufi" toward a green canvas with swaths running through. "You can't hold onto gardens," Skyler says. "They're a revolving thing and have to be started anew—that's how you keep them fresh."

Directions: From the New York State Thruway (Route 87), take exit 19/Kingston and turn west on Route 28. In 5.7 miles, turn right onto Zena Road; the nursery is 2 miles on the left.

Nearby attractions: Bowen House/Roseland Cottage, 556 Route 169, Woodstock (860-928-4074; www.historicnewengland.org), is an 1846 Victorian summer "cottage" with plantings inspired by landscape designer Andrew Jackson Downing. The chef-owned Blue Mountain Bistro, 1633 Glasco Turnpike, Woodstock, NY 12498 (845-679-8519; www.bluemountainbistro.com), has a fine wine list and great tapas using local produce.

LONG ISLAND

LONG ISLAND

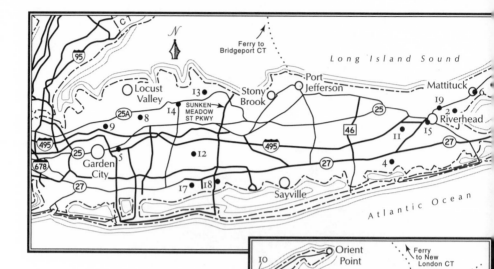

1. The Bayberry Nursery

2. Beds & Borders

3. Fort Pond Native Plants

4. Henry Leuthardt Nurseries

5. Hicks Nurseries

6. Landcraft Environments

7. Marders Garden Shop

8. Martin Viette Nurseries

9. Old Westbury Gardens

10. Ornamental Plantings

11. Peconic River Herb Farm

12. Roslyn Nursery

13. S. Scherer & Sons

14. Smirnow's Son's Peonies

15. Talmage Farm Agway

16. Trimble's of Corchaug Nursery

17. Van Bourgondien Bros.

18. Van Dyck's Flower Bulbs

19. VerDerBer's Garden Center

Long Island

THE BAYBERRY NURSERY

P.O. Box 718, 50 Montauk Highway, Amagansett, NY 11930
(631) 267-3000; fax (631) 267-6332
www.thebayberry.com; e-mail *bayberry@thebayberry.com*
David Seeler

Fine trees, shrubs, and perennials. Landscape architect's nursery. Open daily, March through November, from 8:30 to 5. Call for exact dates. No catalog or mail order. Fine garden ornaments and furniture. Landscape design year-round. Display arboretum. Visitors welcome.

The Bayberry Nursery is an elegant supplier of landscape plants in Amagansett, just east of the Hamptons. It was founded 35 years ago by owner David Seeler, a sophisticated landscape architect who's designed many important estates in the Hamptons and beyond. His style is at once relaxed and refined; Anne Raver of the *New York Times* called him "a garden guru who knows when to stop." He clearly understands and cares about plants, even when installing trophy trees and dream gardens for the likes of Paul Simon, Ralph Lauren, Edward Albee, Billy Joel, Lauren Bacall, and Helmut Lang. By showing respect for living landscapes, his designs ease into their settings with unusual rightness and grace.

Seeler's esteem for plants informs all aspects of the nursery. "We're blessed with a boss who gives us an enormous latitude—so we buy just about everything," says Paige St. John, the nursery's tree and shrub buyer. There's no plant list, because the stock changes every year and, indeed, every season. The inventory combines tried-and-true performers with exotics, hard-to-finds, and collector's items—all the plants needed for refined garden design.

The Bayberry was one of the first East End nurseries to enter the big-tree game, sourcing trophy stock for instant landscaping projects. Each specimen is unique, of course. A perfectly matched group of eight weeping copper beeches, for example, came from the 1962 Seattle World's Fair. (There are only three left.) Caroline Kennedy Schlossberg's discarded boxwoods were revitalized to supply another garden. The 23 varieties of spruce include "an old allée of Hoopsii that are to die for," says St. John.

Yet the odds are high that any large, expensive specimen—a Japanese stewartia or thunderhead pine, say—will be available as well in affordable, smaller-size plants of equal quality. It's part of a deliberate policy to make great garden plants available to everyone. "We're all plant fanatics," says St. John. "It's like a drunk becoming a bartender. We can't help ourselves—we absolutely love great plants."

The nursery's beautiful woody ornamentals are a plant lover's dream. Magnolias, for example, include 'Big Pink', which lives up to its name, and 'Caerhays Belle', a magnolia from a Cornish castle whose large cup-shaped flowers are called "the richest pink imaginable." Among the 40 or 50 roses are top-rated climbers and exotic species such as *Rosa omeiensis.* Other plants include golden rain tree, Hinoki cypress cultivars, hedging hollies, colorful forms of American smoke tree, and choice blue and white hydrangeas.

Native trees and shrubs also make up part of the inventory—native witch hazels, viburnums, and azaleas, for example—valued by site-sensitive gardeners to complement the area's natural beauty. There's even a 'Tiger Eye' variegated staghorn sumac. The vines include fancy-leaved schizophragmas and a peachy-pink trumpet vine called 'Morning Calm'.

Perennials are bought in fresh from first-rate local growers. Handling practices honor good horticulture over commercial demands. The staff won't buy forced perennials, for example, even though they make other garden centers look good in early spring—it's bad for the plants and misleading to gardeners. By spreading plant choices out over the season, gardeners are given a diversified choice of plants blooming in their proper season.

Among the perennials, a day's rough sampling revealed many grasses, peonies, salvias, and monardas—not to mention the orange echinacea, yellow foxglove, double white campanula, and immense purple joe-pye weed. Numerous shade perennials are present, thanks to a staffer whose garden is all shade: hostas, ferns, paint-leaved heucheras and heucherellas, yellow and striped forms of Japanese forest grass *(Hakonechloa macra),* and a wide selection of sedge (carex). According to the staff, short-toothed mountain mint *(Pycanthemum muticum)* was a failure, "but we wouldn't have known without trying it."

Two stone boars at the nursery's entry gate are emblematic of its refined garden furnishings, urns, and sculptures—especially animals. Page Dickey's book, *Dogs in Their Gardens,* shows the Seelers' pet canines lying in the backyard among howling stone coyotes.

The Bayberry's costly appearance is misleading when it comes to prices. "We look like we're expensive, but we're not," says St. John. "We have a lot of the same stuff as Marder's but at better prices, and our nursery is beautiful." A half-price plant sale in October is one of the area's most competitive horticultural events. People come early, wait for the gate to open, and make a beeline for specimens they've admired all year.

Set in a large handsome show garden, The Bayberry is named for the wild shrub whose presence typifies East End coastal thickets. Most mature ornamentals are up for grabs in landscaping projects, but in the meantime, they ground the nursery (and the Seeler summer house behind it) in a lovely, if somewhat mobile, series of outdoor rooms.

Seeler's wife, Ngaere Macray, founded Sagapress to publish the works of her friend, English gardener Graham Stuart Thomas—and there's something quite English about The Bayberry's aesthetic. Perhaps it's the mild climate, the polished style, and the English-like love of countryside. A grassy meadow behind the nursery, punctuated with junipers, seems like an ancient grazing ground leading down toward the sea.

Directions: The nursery is on eastern Long Island's South Fork. From Montauk Highway (Route 27) in East Hampton, go east and it's on the right, just before the town of Amagansett.

Nearby attractions: Hampton Chutney Company, Amagansett Square, 74 Montauk Highway/Route 27, Amagansett (631-267-3131), makes delicious dhosa pockets (open Wednesday through Sunday, 10 to 5). Two of Long Island's finest preserved gardens are the 16-acre Long House Reserve, 133 Hands Creek Road, East Hampton (631-329-3568; www.longhouse.org) and 2-acre Madoo Conservancy, 618 Main Street, Sagaponack (631-537-8200; www.madoo.org). Mecox Gardens, 257 County Road 39A, Southampton (631-287-5015) and 66 Newtown Lane, East Hampton (631-329-9405), sells chic high-end garden ornaments and furniture. Whitmore's Tree Farm, 80 Route 114, East Hampton, NY 11937 (631-329-0446), is a wholesale/retail grower of large specimen-quality trees. Whitmore's Garden Shop, Montauk Highway, Amagansett (631-267-3182), is a florist with a small selection of woody ornamentals.

BEDS & BORDERS
P.O. Box 616, 600 Laurel Lane, Laurel, NY 11948
(631) 298-1836; fax (631) 298-1834
www.bedsandborders.com; e-mail *info@bedsandborders.com*
Kevin Cande

Innovative bedding plants and container collections. Unusual annuals, biennials, and tender perennials. Large commercial greenhouse nursery. Catalog $10. No mail order. Open to garden clubs and groups by prior arrangement. Mixed flat surcharge 15%. Display gardens. Mid-summer and fall garden tours by appointment.

Beds & Borders is the region's preeminent wholesale grower of specialty container and bedding plants. Founder Kathryn Pufahl, a biomedical researcher turned horticulturist, began the nursery in 1987 with a lone plastic greenhouse beside her father's adhesive factory in Riverhead. She cannily chose to focus her energies on specialty annuals and tender perennials—plants then largely unobtainable on the wholesale market.

Pufahl's talent for creating unique container combinations earned her the title of "Queen of Containers" from writer Tovah Martin. She treated containers as miniature gardens, employing what she called "the same principles of design and seasonal change that are valued in the garden." Pufahl died of cancer in 2003 at age 44. Her husband, Kevin Cande, now manages Beds & Borders with the help of a dedicated staff. In 2004, Cornell University instituted the Kathy Pufahl Container Design Competition to honor her triumph in revivifying the horticulture industry's spring-container business.

Largely because of her inventive leadership, Pufahl's business came to dominate the container-plant trade in garden centers from Maine to Maryland. Plant production today takes place in a state-of-the-art complex erected in 1997 on 17 acres on Long Island's North Fork. This 90,000-square-foot growing facility includes a computerized glass greenhouse, a flexible open-roof structure, and 2 acres of outdoor production.

Beds & Borders grows 400 varieties of specialty plants and sells a million of them a year. Selection is innovative. To pass muster, plants must be vigorous and show outstanding design qualities, with fruity, forward colors and dramatic textures. The tender salvia list is outstanding. Even common annuals appear in unusual forms: pink-and-salmon lantana, miniature lavender impatiens, and double petunia with strawberry veins.

It was Pufahl's vision to champion high-scoring foliage plants that can handle heat and drought. The nursery continues to be an excellent source of these plants—caladiums, sweet potato vines, purple heart (*Tradescantia pallida* 'Purpurea'), plectranthus, and even heat-tolerant coleus. New plants come from sources high and low. Beds & Borders discovered Helichrysum 'Limelight' in an herb nursery and was first to grow it as an ornamental. It popularized a pink species petunia *(P. integrefolia)* obtained from a local landscaper, who got it in Queens.

Beds & Borders' main customers are garden centers and design professionals. (It also supplies more than 30 municipal and botanical gardens, including Manhattan's Bryant Park and the Central Park Conservatory Garden.) For wholesale customers, the minimum reserved order is $750 and minimum delivery $1500. Container collections have been assembled to provide mixed-planting material in a single unit. Professionals often come in person to select plants.

While not exactly encouraging retail traffic, the nursery will sell available (non-reserved) plants to Master Gardeners, garden clubs, and other interested groups that come for a greenhouse tour. Group visits are easier to schedule after peak shipping season is past. Purchases are allowed by the flat, with a surcharge for mixed flats; no minimums apply. It is not necessary to tiptoe, but visitors should obey the rules of commerce and keep things businesslike and brief.

A visit to Beds & Borders is worthwhile just to see 2 acres of ornamental annuals grown under glass. The light inside the greenhouses is strangely clear, brightening tonalities like the light in a jeweler's window. Multicolored flats extend from wall to wall like a psychedelic lawn. Among the tropical succulents, notices in Spanish warn the Hispanic maintenance crew. "*No agua! Mantenir un poco seco!*"

All new varieties are tested before being included in the catalog. In the trial gardens, an alert observer can spy new introductions from Proven Winners, Flower Fields, and Ball Horticultural at least a year before their release. As Cande says, "Our network of avid plant nerds offers us a tremendous number of new varieties. Picking which of them to offer is the hard part."

A stunning 4-acre garden streams around Beds & Borders' greenhouse complex and can be visited by anyone who calls ahead. This unusual display argues in favor of revived bedding-plant gardens, updated with looser forms to suggest informality and wildness. Whole sweeping flower borders have been planted lushly, structurally, as if they were containers. *Newsday* writer

Irene Virag rightly calls these "compositions created not with oil paints or watercolors, but with verbenas and bacopa and scaveola and coleus and caladiums." The effect is extraordinary.

Directions: From New York City, take the Long Island Expressway (Route 495) to exit 73. Turn east on Route 58/Old Country Road, which turns into Route 25, passing through the town of Riverhead. Continue at the traffic circle on Route 25 east. After passing the intersection of Route 105, in 4.8 miles, turn right onto Laurel Lane. The nursery is 500 feet on the left.

Nearby attractions: Jamesport Country Kitchen, Route 25, Laurel, New York, 11948 (631-722-3537; www.northfork.com/catering/jck.htm), is a terrific little chef-owned restaurant not far from the nursery. Beds & Borders' staff like the Mexican fare at Amazon Grill, Route 25, Mattituck (631-298-5400).

FORT POND NATIVE PLANTS
P.O. Box 5061, 26 South Embassy Street, Montauk, NY 11954
(631) 668-6452; fax (631) 668-6439
www.nativeplants.net; e-mail *info@nativeplants.net*
James C. Grimes

Native and uncommon perennials, grasses, ferns, and woody plants. *Small specialty nursery. Open year-round, Monday through Saturday, 8 to 5, Sunday, 9 to 2. Closed major holidays. Free catalog. Catalog on Web site. Mail order. Call to check availability. Large quantities by arrangement. Internet specials. Online advice and garden calendar. Tours, workshops, and classes. Books, pottery, accessories. Christmas trees and greens. Landscape design and construction. Wetlands restoration. Display garden. Visitors welcome.*

Fort Pond Native Plants is a specialty nursery in Montauk, a luminous town on the easternmost tip of Long Island with windswept dune grasses and views out to sea. Fort Pond is uniquely tuned to Long Island's natural environment, specializing in fine native grasses and uncommon plants that fit well in a naturalistic landscape.

Owner Jim Grimes is a visionary landscape architect whose practice focuses on native landscape restoration. His approach is at once simple and sophisticated. "Our native vegetation is something in which we take pride. I try to arrange landscapes based on plant communities—not a museum of

plants without cohesiveness, but groups of plants that are found in association," he says. "I'm not a purist, though. Just because it's a native doesn't
mean it's a good landscape plant. Some of the flora from Asian woodlands
looks just right in our environment."

Nursery ambitions support this refreshed approach to garden-making.
"One of our constant goals is to promote the use of native
vegetation," says Grimes. "Another is to seek out the
unusual, less common plant varieties, including
specimens, new or rare perennials, annuals, trees, and
shrubs." This is not a rejection but an embrace of
Long Island's garden traditions. As Grimes says, "I
love the older estates on Long Island. They
don't need a lot of alteration, because the
shake-out of plants has already occurred."

Fort Pond Native Plants offers elegant perennials and
woody plants for use in landscapes, restorations,
driveways, ponds, and gardens that agree to settle
down (as the older estates have done). Grimes began
the nursery in 1994 as a means of supplying his clients
with unobtainable native plants. The nursery still grows
some items but buys most in from local growers who can stock appropriate
species. Prices are competitive, even for plants that are hard to source. While
the retail nursery serves an appreciative public, its landscaping arm, James C.
Grimes Land Design, remains the driving force behind the business. Not all
plants are native, of course. "We're plant guys," Grimes admits. "We're suckers
for the unusual."

Fort Pond's catalog lists nearly 900 perennials and vines vetted for their
landscaping skills. Most are chosen for durability: yarrows and butterfly
weeds for bony soils; hardy cyclamen for planting under trees; and rock
cresses, heathers, and sea pinks for gravelly patches. The nursery always has
something unheard of, such as a silvery evergreen *(Gomphostigma virgatum)*
from Zimbabwe, and sunwheels *(Buphthalum salicifolium)*, which turns out to
be a little yellow daisy useful for hiding other plant's underskirts.

Some 80 ornamental grasses, the great swishers and fillers of naturalistic
landscapes, include a dozen stylish miscanthus hybrids (with invasiveness
warnings) and little bluestem *(Schizachyrium scoparium)*, a once-neglected
poverty grass now embraced by Mid-Atlantic highway departments. Of the
24 sedges, Pennsylvania sedge *(Carex pennsylvanica)* makes a no-mow shade

ground cover. Crinkled hair grass *(Deschampsia flexuosa)* produces a shimmering haze of flower spikes.

Most of Fort Pond's native plants are recognizable and uplifting, like the blue and white baptisias and airy meadow rues. For natural meadows, Fort Pond uses sneezeweeds, coneflowers, joe-pye weeds, and a zillion asters. Maryland golden aster *(Chrysopsis mariana)* is an East End wildflower described as "a real drought buster." Long Island coastal-thicket plants include Northern bayberry, sheep laurel, and edible hedge (such as beach plum and blueberry). If they really want them, English flower-border lovers can still have delphiniums, foxgloves, and cranesbill geraniums (31 kinds).

It seems no Long Island nursery can stay in business without hydrangeas. Besides blue *Hydrangea macrophylla* classics, Fort Pond carries two white-flowered natives: oakleaf hydrangea (*Hydrangea quercifolia* 'Alice'), with handsome fall foliage, and smooth hydrangea (*Hydrangea arborescens* 'Annabelle'), which makes a good hedge.

Fort Pond's plants are suitable and practical, giving gardens an uncomplicated grace. "I hate gardens that are on life support, with chemicals and spray schedules," Grimes says. "Mulch this, spray that, wrap it in newspaper—it takes all the fun out of it."

Such complaints echo the century-old objections of Sir George Sitwell against the English archetype of today's typical garden: "the mown grass, and the rather undecided gravel path, and the scentless roses, and the rich and startling masses of horticulturists' flowers, and the unhappy blotches of subtropical foliage." Instead, Fort Pond seeks to furnish gardens with enduring, locally adapted plants of beauty, authenticity, and presence—instruments of what Sitwell called "the music of the landscape."

Directions: Montauk is at the tip of Long Island's South Fork. From the Hamptons, take Montauk Highway/Route 27 east. In Montauk, come over a hill where the ocean and a yellow motel come into view. Turn left at the Exxon Station onto Embassy Street; the nursery is the second block on the right.

Nearby attractions: Montauk Daylily Garden, 136 Second House Road, P.O. Box 518, Montauk (631-668-2964; www.choicemall.com/daylily), grows 450 daylily varieties, including some local hybrids. The local breakfast hangout is Mr. John's Pancake House, Montauk Highway, Montauk (631-668-2383). When the Rolling Stones were Montauk regulars, visiting their friend Andy Warhol in the 1970s, Mick Jagger wrote "Memory Motel" at the Memory Motel, 692 Montauk Highway (631-668-2702), where you can still get a drink and listen to live music.

HENRY LEUTHARDT NURSERIES

P.O. Box 666, 607 Montauk Highway, East Moriches, NY 11940
(631) 878-1387; fax (631) 874-0707
www.henryleuthardtnurseries.com; e-mail *Leuthardtnursery@aol.com*
John M. Leuthardt

Dwarf fruit trees and espaliers. Berry fruits and grape vines. Family-run horti-
cultural farm. Open March 15 through May 30 and September 1 through December
20, Monday through Saturday, 9 to 12 and 1 to 4. Open Sunday, 10 to 12 and 1 to
3, for pick up only. Digging season mid-October through mid-December and mid-
March through mid-May, depending on weather. Free catalog. Catalog on Web site.
Mail order. Call for current availability and price sheet. Handbook on dwarf fruit tree
culture $2. Planting and landscaping services. Display garden. Visitors welcome. Call
ahead for an appointment.

Henry Leuthardt Nurseries has been growing dwarf fruit trees on Long
Island since 1920 and fruit-tree espaliers since 1937. The nursery's founder,
Henry Leuthardt, was a Swiss horticulturist descended from a long line of
fruit-tree propagators. (The family coat of arms, dating to 1653, shows a
triple-U-form pear espalier.) Leuthardt spent 50 years growing dwarf fruits,
using skills that have passed down through his family. John Leuthardt, the
founder's great-grandson, continues the family tradition today. "The
Leuthardts love shapes and craftsmanship," he says.

Fruit-tree espaliers are evocative products of an old-world horticultural
skill, employing pruning styles dating to the Middle Ages. The technique is
to prune trees to grow flat against a garden wall or structure, which not only
saves room but also warms the tree and fosters superior fruit. Long valued by
old-garden connoisseurs, espaliers are becoming increasingly popular—
doubtless because they look wonderful in small gardens, planted against
walls, in containers, and along wire trellises. With proper care, a fruit-tree
espalier can last 100 years.

Henry Leuthardt is one of the few American nurseries producing
espaliered fruit, and many consider it to be the country's best source. The
nursery's most intricate espalier is a 6-arm Palmette Verrier, which takes at
least five years to grow and looks like a candelabra. The 4-arm Palmette
Verrier takes four years and looks like a big pitchfork. A "Belgian fence"
involves planting a line of Y-shaped espaliers two feet apart to create a
diagonal lattice. Apple and pear espaliers are the easiest to maintain, but fan

shapes are available in peach and cherry, too. "It's both an art and a science," says John Leuthardt. "People don't realize the hard work it entails."

Besides espaliers, Henry Leuthardt is known for its excellent dwarf and semi-dwarf fruit trees—apple, pear, European and Japanese plum, cherry, peach, and nectarine. "Rare and choice" varieties include "the apple that used to make such unequalled pies and sauces; the apple you saved for the teacher, hoping the memory would last until examination time." Antique apples are 'Lady', a small-fruited variety dating to ancient Rome, and 'Fameuse', from the Middle Ages. Jane Austen fans will fancy 'Improved Moorpark' apricot, the same variety planted by Fanny Price's aunt in *Mansfield Park*. The nursery grows an unnamed pear that survives salt spray and produces luscious fruit. Berry fruits and grape vines are also listed.

"We grow all the fruit trees ourselves on high-quality rootstock," says John Leuthardt. "We bud in August, graft in January, and plant them out in spring." Mature plants are freshly dug (not held in storage) and pruned before shipment. Espaliers are custom crated and shipped at affordable rates, though it's cheaper to pick up trees at the nursery. Espalier prices are based on the tree's size. Considering the hand labor involved, prices are reasonable.

There's a picturesque orchard behind the Leuthardts' Greek Revival farmhouse in East Moriches, on Long Island's south shore. Stone walls, a wishing well, and an elegant 1840s barn give the nursery yard a quaint charm. An 8-sided "garden house" (comprising eight 4-arm espaliers) replicates the one Henry Leuthardt exhibited at the 1938 World's Fair in Flushing Meadows. In the 1930s, Leuthardt espaliers graced many of Long Island's Gold Coast estates, including J. P. Morgan's place. Today, mature Leuthardt espaliers can be seen at Mount Vernon, The Cloisters, Monticello, the Governor's Palace in Old Williamsburg, and the Delegate's Garden at the United Nations.

Garden writers can't seem to resist writing about Henry Leuthardt Nurseries. Leslie Land, Linda Yang, and Barbara Damrosch have all praised the nursery in the *New York Times*. Ken Druse recommended Leuthardt espaliers for "taking the screen of landscape art one step further." Katharine White spoke glowingly in *Onward and Upward in the Garden* in 1962. "Just in from planting a Henry Leuthardt double-horizontal cordon apple tree against the north brick wall of the terrace," she wrote. "The Leuthardt tree is a 'Chenango Strawberry' summer apple, a perfectly trained specimen and in perfect condition on arrival—the fulfillment of a dream."

Directions: The nursery is on Long Island's south shore, 10 miles west of Westhampton. From the Long Island Expressway (Route 495), take exit 68 onto the William Floyd Parkway south. Turn left onto Montauk Highway/Route 80. The nursery is on the north side, halfway between Center and East Moriches.

Nearby attractions: Hulse's Potting Shed, 45 Bank Street, Center Moriches, NY 11955 (631-878-7463), is a small family nursery selling spring annuals, vegetables, and herbs in old-fashioned wooden flats (small deposit), wrapped up with newspaper and twine. White Truffle Inn, 578 Montauk Highway, East Moriches (631-874-0757), serves French food. Buckley's Irish Pub, 368 Montauk Highway, Center Moriches (631-874-6083), has good pub grub.

HICKS NURSERIES

100 Jericho Turnpike (Route 25), Westbury, NY 11590
(516) 334-0066; fax (516) 997-2532
www.hicksnursery.com
The Hicks family

Perennials, annuals, aquatics, trees, shrubs, houseplants. *Family-run retail garden center. Open year-round, daily, 8 to 6, Fridays, 8 to 8. No catalog or mail order. Events and seminars. Flower Show in March. How-to information sheets. Children's events. Seasonal newsletter. Gardener's Advantage discount program. Display gardens. Visitors welcome.*

A 35-year-old Quaker farmer named Isaac Hicks purchased a wagon load of trees in 1850 and, three years later, started a nursery that still thrives in western Long Island. His genius was to buy mature trees and work out a way to move them. Hicks' son, an engineer, invented a horse-drawn device that could move large trees in full leaf. By the late 1800s, shade trees from Hicks Nursery lined the streets of Great Neck and Garden City. The ability to move large trees was vital in landscaping Long Island's great estates, where many Hicks trees still flourish.

Hicks Nurseries is Long Island's oldest nursery and garden center. Each generation has left its stamp, adding improvements that far exceed the original tree business. In the early 20th century, Hicks specialized in new plants from Asia and Europe suited to Long Island's environment, securing collector's specimens (along with the Arnold Arboretum) from the era's cutting-edge plant hunters. A trophy that has survived from its own breeding program is the Hicks yew *(Taxus media hicksii)*. In the 1960s, the family converted its 245-acre nursery into a family-oriented retailing and growing operation. Thousands of feet of greenhouse space were added in the 1970s and overhauled by a Dutch specialist in 1996. Hicks Nurseries today functions as a full-service up-market garden center and continuing magnet for area horticulture.

Spring begins with Hicks' Annual Flower and Garden Show, a two-weekend-long commercial blast with spring bulbs, free seminars, and family events. Summer offers tomato-growing contests and a weekend farm stand. Autumn is enlivened with a fall festival, hay rides, and "Otto the Ghost" appearances. Halloween begins two months before the holiday and sells 75,000 pumpkins. At Christmas, the nursery fills with holiday greens and glitter.

It's not just fun and games, though. Hicks combines customer service from a knowledgeable staff with a complete selection of fine garden plants and supplies. Throughout the year, Hicks puts on workshops and seminars to acquaint gardeners with the latest plants and gardening techniques. How-to flyers are available on-site and online. Plant lists address deer-resistant perennials, seaside gardens, fall-color shrubs, figs, and houseplants. These lists aren't just useful, they're backed by live plants sold in the garden center.

It took this long to get around to the plant list because that's the garden-center experience. You have to trudge through a lot of retailing, but Hicks has the goods.

Hicks carries fine perennials for local conditions and is the Long Island Horticultural Society's official source for its designated Gold Medal Plants— mainly garden plants that can take sand, salt, and drought and still look good. Yarrows, mugworts, chrysanthemums, heathers, poppies, coneflowers, flowering herbs—they're ornamental and (for deer) unpalatable. The greenhouses abound with pre-planted patio pots, Proven Winner annuals, and combination hanging baskets. An aquatic center houses water lilies, pond plants, and fish. The greenhouses display diverse tropical houseplants and indoor bonsai.

Hicks hasn't given up on trees, either. Dwarf fruit trees and hide-that-neighbor conifers (white pine, yew, and Leyland cypress) are nursery specialties. You can get your soil tested in the fertilizer section, which includes good organic supplies.

Display gardens at Hicks Nurseries are conceived as "idea laboratories" packed with inspiration for home gardeners. There are gardens for spring bulbs, vegetables, aquatics, cut flowers, and perennials. There are gardens for children. If you're sick of gardening, there are silk flowers and florist supplies. If you'd rather see someone else's garden, Hicks is a civic-minded promoter of two Gold Coast estates now open to the public—Old Westbury Gardens (see profile) and Planting Fields Arboretum, both nearby, and both still growing trees Hicks planted a century ago. Come to think of it, the nursery logo (a horse-drawn cart filled with trees) remains a good symbol of customer-oriented capitalism—Hicks' business model for more than 150 years.

Directions: From New York City on the Long Island Expressway (Route 495), take exit 39, turn right at 3rd light onto the service road, and then onto Old Westbury Road. Turn left at 1st light onto Jericho Turnpike (Route 25 east). Hicks is on the right. Coming west on the Long Island Expressway, take exit 40W onto Route 25 west, and in 2 miles, Hicks is on the left. From the Northern State Parkway, take exit 32 and follow signs to Old Westbury. Turn north on Post Avenue and left on Jericho Turnpike (Route 25 east). Hicks is on the left.

Nearby attractions: Two white pines on the terrace at Old Westbury Gardens (see profile) were planted by Hicks in 1907. Planting Fields Arboretum State Historic Park, P.O. Box 58, Oyster Bay, NY 11771 (516-922-8600; www.plantingfields.org), Long Island's foremost public arboretum, is the former Coe estate, landscaped by the Olmsted Brothers. It has an excellent plant collection and 409 acres of formal gardens, lawns, woodland paths, and greenhouses (open Monday through Friday, 9 to 5). Cornell Cooperative Extension of Nassau County, 239 Fulton Ave, Hempstead, NY 11550, maintains a horticulture hotline (516-228-0426, Monday through Thursday, 10 to 12:30).

LANDCRAFT ENVIRONMENTS

1160 East Mill Road, Mattituck, NY 11952
(631) 298-3510; fax (631) 298-3514
www.landcraftenvironments.com; e-mail *info@landcraftenvironments.com*
Dennis Schrader and Bill Smith

Innovative tropical and container plants. Specialty wholesale nursery. Open by appointment, year-round, Monday through Friday, 8 to noon and 1 to 5; Saturdays in spring. Free wholesale catalog. Minimum shipping $2500, minimum pre-order $1500. After June 1, plants sold first-come-first-served. Lectures and events. Garden design. Display gardens. Photos on Web site. Visitors welcome by arrangement.

Tropical plants have rhythm. Languid, hot, and hip-rolling—they're the horticultural equivalent of ukulele music. Their seductive presence transports cold-climate gardeners on fleeting escapes to steamier climes—Hawaii, say, or Jamaica. They're bright and colorful and they like to party.

Landcraft Environments is the region's preeminent wholesale grower of exotic tropical and half-hardy plants—plants for an island paradise. Owners Dennis Schrader and Bill Smith began Landcraft in 1982 as a garden design-build firm and found themselves spiking their designs with tropical exotics for seasonal color. Their only problem was finding plants that seemed exciting enough—for their clients' gardens or for their own. When they tried growing rarities from seed, an epiphany struck: "Growing things was more fun!" So in 1992 they bought a gentleman's farm, built a 100-foot greenhouse, and started an exotic-plant nursery—a taste of the tropics in Zone 6.

Today, Landcraft is at the forefront of a tropical-gardening trend. The nursery propagates and grows 750 varieties of tropical and tender perennials in an acre of greenhouse space, supplemented by generous outdoor displays and growing areas. It supplies hundreds of thousands of plants every year to garden centers, landscape designers, botanical gardens, and public parks throughout the Northeast. Its plants and gardens have been featured in *Horticulture, Fine Gardening,* and *Country Living Gardener.* Schrader, a noted lecturer who's appeared on *Martha Stewart Living TV,* is the author of *Hot Plants for Cold Climates,* an engaging reference on using tropical plants in the temperate zones.

Landcraft's tropical plant inventory is innovative and near-encyclopedic. Plants are valuable for bold texture, brawny structure, bright flowers, and shiny or painted leaves—often all at once. Some put out more flowers in a season than a hardy perennial does in a lifetime. A lot of them look like cool '60s party dresses. And unlike hardy plants, heat doesn't faze them. "All the plants we grow thrive in our hot, humid summers, and many perform well into the autumn months," boast the owners. They offer a stylish solution to what Schrader calls "the sorry appearance of the August garden."

Most of Landcraft's plant material is sold wholesale in spring and early summer, though some fall material is now being added. In April and May, the nursery is too busy with big orders to deal with walk-ins. But beginning in June, when things quiet down, it gently opens its doors to individuals who want to pick up leftover stock. Because inventory is so diverse, there's plenty left to enjoy. The catalog is reserved for wholesale customers, but the entire plant list is found on Landcraft's Web site. Plants generally come in flats and quarts. Be sure to call ahead.

"Hardly any plant in the whole plant kingdom," designer Joe Eck once remarked, "is as impressive as a well-grown banana." Landcraft grows bananas—Japanese fiber banana, blood leaf banana, rare Chinese yellow banana—even Royal variegated banana, once reserved for Hawaiian royalty (fruit and foliage are striped cream and white). Logical neighbors are any number of elephant's-ears, tropical gingers, and verdant ferns—not to mention *Lee amabilis* 'Splendens', a red-leaved shrub from Borneo, or *Oenanthe javanica* 'Flamingo', a ferny pink-variegated ground cover from Java. A few tropicals, like the nursery's dwarf palmetto palm, are actually hardy (with care) to Long Island. There's even a native plant: variegated pokeweed.

Many tropicals are well-known container subjects, such as hibiscus, impatiens, lantana, begonia, and geranium. Landcraft grows all these in voguish forms, such as burgundy-leaved hibiscus and yellow impatiens with black stems. Also on hand are dramatic collections of brugmansia, canna, flowering maple (*Abutillon* spp.), and coleus in many freaky varieties. Among the succulents, the agaves are notable for their purple and mottled forms. Tropical topiaries (columns and standards) offer instant garden panache. As far as we know, Landcraft is the sole regional source for dwarf pomegranate standards.

Don't miss strolling in Landcraft's lavish 2-acre garden, a jungle paradise wrapped in 14 acres of fields. Decks, porches, and patios brim with flamboyant containers. Perennials borders, dwarf fruit orchards, arbors, trellises, woodland walks, and papyrus ponds grace the grounds. But the big payoff is the Tiki hut, a bravura allusion to equatorial heat, palm trees, Hawaiian shirts, and cocktails garnished with parasol-skewered cherries. Bring a camera so you can write yourself a note on the back of a photo: Having a wonderful time, wish you were here.

Directions: From New York City, take the Long Island Expressway (Route 495) east to exit 73. Take Route 58 east/Old Country Road for 4 miles and turn left onto Route 43/Northville Pike. At the end, turn right onto Sound Avenue east. In 7 miles, in Mattituck, turn left at the light onto Wickham Avenue. Bear left at the fork onto Grand Avenue, turn left onto East Mill Road, and the nursery is 500 feet on the left. From Laurel, take Route 25 east to Mattituck, turn left onto Wickham Avenue, and follow directions above. Call ahead.

Nearby attractions: Right next door is an excellent wholesale grower of ground-cover perennials: Glover Perennial Growers, P.O. Box 1587, Mattituck, NY 11952 (631-298-1492; gloverper@aol.com; Jim Glover). In Greenport, Salamander Café, 2530 Manhasset Avenue (631-477-8839), serves delicious homemade lemonade and informal food.

MARDERS GARDEN SHOP AND NURSERY
P.O. Box 1261, Snake Hollow Road, Bridgehampton, NY 11932
(631) 537-5000; (631) 537-7023
www.marders.com
Charlie and Kathleen Marder

Large-caliper trees and shrubs. Premium nursery stock. *Specialty garden center. Open year-round, daily, 9 to 5. No catalog or mail order. Seminars. Garden shop. Organic garden supplies. Landscaping services. Organic property care. Display gardens. Visitors welcome.*

Marders Garden Shop and Nursery is a fine-plant purveyor in Bridgehampton, Long Island. Owners Charlie and Kathleen Marder established the business in 1977 for the purpose of transplanting large trees, using Long Island's first truck-mounted spade. An important early customer was Alfonso Ossorio, an artist and sugar magnate then converting The Creeks, his 64-acre East Hampton estate, into an arboretum. Marders is now a multimillion dollar nursery on 18 acres, brimming with big-tree specimens of a stature most gardeners wait a lifetime to see.

Our first experience of Marders began in the parking lot, where we confronted a perfect small-leaf azalea the size of a traffic rotary. Tiny leaves, rosy buds, immaculate condition. An immense root ball, expertly wrapped and strapped. Price tag, $12,500.

A woman attendant appeared, dressed in cashmere. Is this azalea, we inquired, your most expensive plant? No, Madam, it's the 90-foot bald cypress specimen, over there—$99,500. Does that include planting? No, planting is an additional 50%, with a 2-year warranty. Oh. So that tree, planted, with sales tax, actually costs about $150,000? No, Madam (extracting a slim pocket calculator). As a capital improvement (dunk-dunk on the calculator), assuming the highest tax bracket (dunk-dunk)—the actual cost would be about $120,000.

Wow, we thought, stunned. This is the first nursery we've ever visited that offers tax advice.

The woman in cashmere graciously offered a nursery tour in a spiffy electric cart. By then, $4950 for an admirable 18-foot *Magnolia grandiflora* 'Bracken's Brown Beauty' started to look reasonable. We'd always wanted a big beech tree, though not necessarily a 12-inch caliper round-leaf beech for $18,500 or a pair of 50-year-old copper beeches at $55,000 apiece. A perfect vase-shaped green Japanese maple, tagged at $850, seemed a bargain.

Pristine high-caliper trees are like expensive garden sculpture—they confer instant status and panache. Marders secures its many specimens through a national network of high-end tree brokers. Hefty price tags reflect the technical challenges and horticultural skill involved in handling such trophy stock—and the fact that nobody but the rich can afford it.

The telltale sign of what writer Richardson Wright called "gardeners that are just too rich" is their plants—"plants that are always on their best behavior, having been groomed, tubbed, and manicured since birth."

This pretty well describes the entire nursery stock at Marders: fine plant varieties, faultlessly presented. Not only trees but also stylish annuals, perennials, tropicals, orchids, topiary, roses, and conifers—the full range of sophisticated nursery stock, all in premium condition. Prices, too, tend to be premium. Marders once grew its own garden plants, but now they're all bought in from the area's top organic growers, including Talmage Farm (see profile). The staff is unfailingly polite.

A major part of Marders' business is custom-designed landscaping. Demand is high. The estates of New York's cultural elite require first-rate embellishment; developers' spec houses cry out for distinction from their neighbors. Marders specializes in supplying local land barons with aesthetic, site-sensitive landscaping, flower-pot maintenance, and organic property care.

Visitors to Marders naturally gravitate to its Garden Shop, housed in a handsome Amish barn that Charlie Marder had transported from Pennsylvania. Bulbs, books, bouquets, and elegant housewares fill the store. Japanese ikebana shears, slate plant tags, and natural jute-leaf bags typify the contents. Garden supplies are 100 percent organic, reflecting Marders' strong commitment to earth-friendly products.

Outdoor plants are so artfully arranged along curved walkways that there's almost no need for display gardens. "Potscapes at Marders" offers refined pre-planted container gardens in large pots; much of their coifed contents comes from Beds & Borders (see profile). Thanks to bulk purchasing, the stunning lead planters and Haddistone urns are more affordable than you'd expect, especially during Marders' fall sale.

Of course, there *are* display gardens, expertly designed and executed. Don't miss the Zen garden, with its huge evocative boulders. Plans are afoot to develop the pond at the back of the property as a natural water garden and picnic site. It's hard for any display to compete with the magnificent tree specimens, though. We're still thinking of the statuesque ginkgo, the lovely twisted willows, and the row of six perfectly matched holly trees.

Directions: The nursery is on eastern Long Island's South Fork. From Montauk Highway (Route 27) in Bridgehampton, turn north at the bank onto Snake Hollow Road. Marders is on the left.

Nearby attractions: Della Femina, 99 North Main Street, East Hampton (631-329-6666; reservations a must), is a smart, celebrity-packed restaurant owned by a famous ex-ad exec. Nick & Toni's, 136 North Main Street, East Hampton (631-324-3550), is a casual, gourmet Italian place-to-be-seen, popular with celebrities in sneakers and baseball caps. To ogle the local estates, drive down Lily Pond Lane, the "Park Avenue" of East Hampton, famous for what writer Steven Gaines calls "Gatsbyesque man-

sions set on towering dunes, with green lawns so vast that the semicircular driveways look like small racetracks." Bridge Gardens Trust, 36 Mitchell Lane, Bridgehampton (631-537-7440; www.bridgegardens.org), is a pretty 5-acre preserve with specimen trees, roses, topiary, a bamboo room, and that emblem of local gardens, a 750-foot-long double privet hedge.

MARTIN VIETTE NURSERIES

P.O. Box 10, 6050 Northern Boulevard (Route 25A),

East Norwich, NY 11732

(516) 922-5530; fax (516) 922-3801

www.martinviettenurseries.com; e-mail *info@martinviette.com*

Russell Ireland and family

Fine garden plants. *Horticultural garden center. Open year-round, April through October, daily, 8 to 6, November through March, daily, 9 to 6. Extended hours, Friday and Saturday, May and June. Closed major holidays. No catalog or mail order. Online shopping and customer service, Monday through Friday, 9 to 5 (203-894-9368 or by e-mail). Free "garden rewards." Children's activities. Containers. Books. Seasonal items.*

Martin Viette Nurseries bills itself as "Long Island's Leading Horticultural Center" with good reason. This garden center has the island's largest overall selection of trees, shrubs, annuals, and perennials. It offers diagnostic services, planting services, statuary, pottery, outdoor furniture, seasonal displays, a Christmas shop, a florist, home-conservatory installation, and a prodigious landscaping service, including home golf course design and installation. This all takes place on a 42-acre garden center whose groomed grounds resemble those of a country club—indeed, there's a putting green on-site and a country club right across the street.

Martin Viette is owned by Russell Ireland, a horticultural heavy hitter who was born into the nursery business. His father graduated from SUNY Farmingdale's ornamental horticulture program and ran a mom-and-pop nursery in Oceanside. He endured a year's apprenticeship in a Dutch wholesale nursery before buying his parents' business, establishing a landscape division, and expanding into growing facilities in East Norwich and Stony Brook. He purchased Martin Viette Nurseries in 1976, grooming its inventory and displays to their present state of near perfection.

Martin Viette Nurseries itself was founded in 1920 by a Swiss immigrant who once worked on the Havemayer estate; his business specialized in provisioning Gold Coast estates through his contacts with estate gardeners. His son, Andre Viette, sold the business to Ireland before founding Andre Viette Nursery in Virginia. (He still sometimes returns to lecture on daylilies, his specialty.)

Most of Martin Viette's nursery stock today is "Home Grown & Harvested by Hand"—a trademarked name for the field- and container-grown stock produced on Ireland's growing facilities in Jamesport and East Hampton. Ireland plays an eminent role in the national garden-center industry, lecturing extensively, judging flower shows, and traveling abroad to source the best plants and products. His business empire's participation in an upscale network of leading garden centers assures the high quality of Martin Viette's stock and goods. Smaller nurseries may penetrate specialized plant groups in greater depth, or grow things that aren't susceptible to commercial production, but it's fair to say that Martin Viette represents the best of what mainstream horticulture has to offer.

Though the garden center stocks practically every plant imaginable, it's best to start with the ornamental trees and shrubs. According to garden writer Josephine Neuse, "evergreens offer more beauty per inch than almost any other form of plant life." Just seeing the nursery's extraordinary collection of holly trees, boxwoods, and choice conifers in one place is inspirational. The black shiny berries of *Ilex excelsa,* for example, contrast handsomely with the red-berried hollies. Needled evergreen trees are so prettily shaped that, inground or in proper pots, they'd make great outdoor Christmas trees. A similar glow is achieved in the woody ornamentals area, where a gold-leaved *Cornus mas* might interweave with a long-blooming crape myrtle, or a mature autumn cherry might set off the fire in a flame-colored hedge maple. Landscape and garden roses are well stocked, and the perennial yard is known for its comprehensiveness, especially in daylilies. Flowering annuals and pre-planted containers are one of spring's spectacular pleasures.

While the Disneyfication of garden centers has its drawbacks, Martin Viette transcends commercial models to provide a truly enjoyable "shopping experience." The grounds staff outdoes itself with displays on a grand scale—a vintage truck might be used as a whimsical spring planter, for example. Staff members are knowledgeable and friendly. Attractive pamphlets offer advice on such things as roses, butterfly gardens, and compost piles. Signage is good, labels informative, and prices, while not low, aren't nearly as high as the elegant setting might suggest. Free "garden club" membership offers special sales and services. Periodic specials and clearance sales, including a "daylily dollars" program, serve the needs of customers on a budget.

The garden shop has an extensive supply of organic and nontoxic garden supplies. Classy urns and containers are in exceptional supply. The award-winning landscape division designs and builds everything from finished perennial borders to entire landscapes; all planting services come with a generous guarantee.

The serene, park-like grounds with their mature ornamental plantings are a treasured resource for professional photographers—as well as for home gardeners seeking to emulate even the smallest corners of Long Island's great estates. If you can't go in person, a virtual tour on the Web site offers a remote vision of the garden center and its handsome grounds.

Directions: The nursery is on Northern Boulevard/Route 25A, south of Oyster Bay. From the Long Island Expressway, take exit 41N and follow signs to 106N, stay right when the road splits, and follow Route 106 north for 3 miles. Turn left onto Northern Boulevard/Route 25A; the nursery is a mile farther on the left, across from the country club.

Nearby attractions: The John P. Humes Japanese Stroll Garden, Oyster Bay Road at Dogwood Lane, Mill Neck (516-676-4486), is a 4-acre gem of contemplative garden design, supported by The Garden Conservancy. Brookville Nurseries, 5300 Northern Boulevard/Route 25A, Brookville (516-626-0018; open year-round, daily, 9 to 5, extended spring hours), also called "The Rose Farm," is known for its top-graded potted roses and perennials. It's run by the Izzo sisters, who wear flowered dresses and sunbonnets; one is even named Rose.

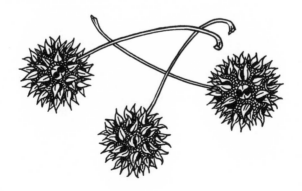

OLD WESTBURY GARDENS
71 Old Westbury Road, Old Westbury, NY 11568
(516) 333-0048; fax (513) 333-6807
www.oldwestburygardens.org
Peter J. Grant, Director of Horticulture

Specialty garden plants. Nonprofit organization. Open daily, except Tuesday, mid-April through October, 10 to 5. No catalog or mail order. Plant Shed near parking lot. Plant sale in early May. Formal display gardens. Admission fees, free to members. House tours, separate admission. Gift shop. Books. Café in the Woods. Wildflower walks. Holiday celebrations and open hours. Extensive English gardens. Visitors welcome.

Old Westbury Gardens is a Long Island country estate modeled on an English manor house. With 88 acres of landscaped grounds and 25 acres of formal gardens, it's considered the most beautiful English-style garden in America. John Shaffer Phipps built this aristocratic manor in 1904 as a wedding present for his English bride, to remind her of her stately home in Sussex. Now a nonprofit estate that welcomes the public, Old Westbury is famous for its rose gardens—a romantic parterre brimming with roses and an All-America Rose Selection Test Garden. Mrs. Phipps loved roses and tended them herself; her favorite color was pink. We like to imagine that she followed the advice of a Southern lady to make them flourish: "Cut off their heads and feed 'em like hawgs."

Old Westbury Gardens attracts 80,000 visitors a year to tours, lectures, and concerts, but for gardeners, its strongest lure is garden plants. A Plant Shed, located near the parking area, sells English-flower-border plants—the same sophisticated perennials and container plants, in fact, that are chosen for Old Westbury's own urns and gardens. You may even find extras from the vegetable garden, whose produce is donated to a local soup kitchen. Well-priced perennials come in 5-inch squares or gallon pots, vines and peonies in 2-gallon pots, and herbs in 4-inch pots. Plants are all grown in Old Westbury's own greenhouses or bought in fresh from the best local growers.

Because the garden is constantly renovating and improving its own collections, Plant Shed shoppers get the benefit of the staff's experience choosing plants for beauty and bloom succession on Long Island. Rare and cutting-edge varieties are preferred, for the garden has no original cultivar records and is therefore not bound by history. "Every year, we try creative new things," says Assistant Director of Horticulture Kim Johnson, who supervises the walled garden. Prices are good, too, so there's no reason not to follow the brochure's suggestion and "take home a little of the gardens."

Old Westbury's celebrated plant sale, held the first weekend in May under a large tent, offers even more outstanding plant selection—huge, innovative variety at less-than-retail prices. Esoteric annuals, tropicals, tender perennials are big sellers, as are hardy perennials, herbs, clematis, and David Austin English roses. Choices may extend to English daisies, wisteria, tree peonies, hellebores, ornamental onions, and flowering vines. The Long Island Rhododendron Society holds a sale here the same day (ask about 'Phipps' Yellow', an admired rhododendron bred on the estate). Master Gardeners and Bartlett Tree Experts are on hand for soil testing and advice.

The plant sale is an excellent incentive to become an Old Westbury member, for members get exclusive admittance to the plant sale two days before public opening—and free access to the gardens all year. As any collector knows, the plant-sale preview is just the time to troll for horticultural gems. There's also an Arbor Day plant sale for the winter weary. Plant sales on Mother's Day and Father's Day are a great excuse to bring your parents for lunch.

Gardeners acquiring plants at Old Westbury should take time to admire its horticultural wonders. The magnificent walled garden has the oldest yellow tree peony on Long Island. The bronze peacocks near the Ghost Walk splay fantails of trained yew. The boxwood parterre's shrubs are two centuries old. Lead urns on the balustrade are planted with ivy-leaf geraniums, propagated from cuttings each year since 1959.

Many of the patrician amenities that helped an English lady banish wistfulness also remain, for Old Westbury's grounds are deliberately maintained in the style of the original owners. Formal allées of linden and beech trees line the entry lanes. A noble American beech occupies the west terrace. The cutting garden provides constant fresh flowers for the house. A half-timbered thatched tea cottage, built for a Phipps daughter, evokes an English fairy tale. Occasional puppet shows and maypole dances are held, to the merriment of children; picnic lawn concerts and musical evenings amuse the adults. Inscribed on the gates is a blessing that might apply in even the smallest garden: *Pax Introentibus, Salus Exeuntibus*— Peace to those who enter, good health to those who depart.

Directions: Old Westbury is 20 miles east of New York City. By train, take Long Island Rail Road to Westbury Station, then a taxi to Old Westbury Gardens (2.5 miles from the station). By car from the Long Island Expressway (Route 495), take exit 39/Glen Cove Road, turn east onto the service road, and in one mile, turn right onto Old Westbury Road; the gate is 0.4 mile on the left. (Traveling east on the LIE, cross over the expressway to access the service road.) From the Northern State Parkway, take exit 32/Post Avenue, turn north onto Post Avenue, turn left onto Jericho Turnpike (Route 25), and turn right at the first light onto Old Westbury Road; the gate is on the right.

Nearby attractions: Old Westbury Gardens' Café in the Woods is the place to lunch, or in fine weather, bring a picnic. The 12-acre Clark Botanic Garden, 193 I.U. Willets Road, Albertson, Long Island (516-484-8600; www.clarkbotanic.org), holds a lively plant sale on Mothers' Day weekend. Meadow Croft, the John E. Rockefeller Estate, 138 Bayport Avenue, Bayport (631-472-9395), is a 75-acre woodland and wetland preserve with circa-1910 gardens surrounding a Colonial Revival home.

ORNAMENTAL PLANTINGS
41000 County Route 48, Southold, NY 11971
Mailing address: 229 Fifth Avenue, Greenport, NY 11944
(631) 765-2614 (nursery); (631) 477-2410 (office);
fax (631) 477-0201 (from 9 to 3)
www.ornamentalplantings.com; e-mail *ltlbny@peconic.net*
Jack Weiscott and family

Ornamental grasses, herbs, and ground covers. Roses and shrubs. Seashore plants. *Small specialty nursery. Open from late April through Columbus Day, daily, 10 to 5. Free catalog. No mail order. Early-bird order discounts. Landscape design and maintenance. Newsletter.*

Ornamental Plantings is a small retail nursery on Long Island's North Fork specializing in unique and unusual grasses, herbs, ground covers, and seashore plants. Owner Jack Weiscott is a passionate and attentive plantsman with a college degree in nursery management. He worked at several East End wholesale growers (including The Plantage, Long Island's preeminent wholesale perennial nursery) before starting a fledgling nursery in 1984.

Fifteen years later, he bought a parcel of vacant Southold farmland, erected greenhouses and a gravel driveway, and moved the nursery to its present site.

Ornamental Plantings stocks unique, unusual, and high-quality plants that work well in Long Island gardens. The 300-plant inventory is functionally much larger than it appears. Weiscott vets plants for rarity, beauty, weirdness, and all-around horticultural interest. Collections of locally valuable plants—such as herbs, sedums, ground covers, and roses—must not only grow well but also repel deer, tolerate drought, and withstand salt spray and buffeting ocean winds. What's left standing is a small band of extremely good garden plants.

One of the distinguishing marks of talent is discernment—the ability to notice what others ignore. Weiscott keeps an experimental daylily bed and has introduced several fine plants uncovered as chance seedlings in his nursery. His best known is a miniature fountain grass *(Pennisetum alopecuroides)* that cropped up in a flat of liners. He named it 'Little Bunny' for its cute habit and soft flower heads.

"I had a hard time selling 'Little Bunny' until the Perennial Plant Association convened on Long Island," Weiscott recalls. "Five busloads of insane nursery owners and perennial maniacs visited Ellen Talmage's nursery and bought every pot in five minutes. It spread everywhere after that."

Another nursery introduction, 'Silver Lining', is a compact blue fescue with intense silver-blue foliage. By mid-July, says Weiscott, "it looks like aluminum." A further find he hopes to introduce soon is a large and lovely variegated miscanthus planted in the nursery's grass berm.

Unique grasses are not the only draw. Ornamental Plantings' first-rate lavender list, including popular 'Provence', is reflected in sweeping lavender displays along the driveway. One-of-a-kind ground covers include a New Zealand burr with foliage the color of grape jelly *(Acaena microphylla* var. *purpurea inermis)* and a little-known burstwort that resembles moss and takes foot traffic *(Hernieria glabra)*. Seaside plants include native bayberry and red juniper, several shimmering willows, and fine beach roses and climbers in 2- and 3-gallon pots.

Weiscott also stocks what he calls "strange little shrubs" in case any plant-crazed collector happens by. He hunts for "cool plants" at other nurseries. He's forever testing exotic seed from sources such as Chiltern Seed and Jellito Seeds, two renowned European suppliers.

Ornamental Plantings propagates virtually everything it sells, except for roses and the occasional dwarf conifer. Because it's a grower in an out-of-the way location, prices are sensible. Plants are propagated from seed and cuttings (mostly to 2-gallon size). Grasses come in 3- and 5-gallon pots so they'll establish quickly. The surrounding gardens serve as stock beds, plant displays, and garden design exemplars—a floral compendium of nursery activities. Exotic chickens provide atmosphere and keep the bugs down.

Weiscott has help on weekends from his wife, Roberta, a local teacher, and their two sons. The nursery's greenhouse manager, Clyde (Skip) Wachsberger, is an award-winning *sumi* brush painter whose illustrated book, *On Leaf and Flower*, sketches a home-garden experience that parallels the nursery's own work. "We like to experiment with unfamiliar plants; we like to grow from seed; we like to push hardiness limits," he says. "Most of all, we love continually to create new settings, preferably wild and complex."

Directions: From New York City, take the Long Island Expressway (Route 495) east to exit 73. Take Route 58 east/Old Country Road. In Mattituck, stay straight when Route 25 turns sharp right. In two blocks, turn right onto Route 48 east/North Road. In Southold, the nursery is just past Ackerly Pond Lane on the right.

Nearby attractions: North Fork Food, Route 48 at Horton's Lane, Southold, NY 11971 (631-765-6264), is a small gourmet take-out café, nearly next door to the nursery. The Harbes Family Farm, Sound Avenue/Route 48, Mattituck (631-298-0800; www.harbesfamilyfarm.com), is a genial family farm (8 kids) with hot roasted corn, fresh lemonade, and bedding plants.

PECONIC RIVER HERB FARM

2749 River Road, Calverton, NY 11933

(631) 369-0058; (631) 369-6179

www.prherbfarm.com; e-mail *info@prherbfarm.com*

Cristina Spindler

Herbs and perennials. Trees, shrubs, vines. Open April through June, daily, 9 to 5; July through October, daily, 9 to 4. No catalog or mail order. Workshops and classes. Cut flower bouquets. Tea Garden available for garden club meetings. Painters and photographers welcome. Picnics encouraged. Display gardens. Visitors welcome.

Peconic River Herb Farm is Long Island's preeminent retail herb nursery— among other things. It was founded in 1986 by Cristina Spindler after she and her husband tamed the land and used the downed trees to build themselves a log home. It's hard to believe that a modern couple could take up homesteading on Long Island, but that's exactly what the Spindlers did, and are still doing. Their farmstead is in Calverton, near Riverhead, on a sandy 14-acre site sandwiched between the Long Island Rail Road tracks and the Peconic River. Even today, locust trees felled from the land form the elaborate rustic arbors and trellises that give the nursery its romantic charm.

What started with a flat of herbs and a self-serve cash box by the roadside has become, through industry and effort, an inspired destination garden and nursery. Spindler is a goal-oriented plantswoman whose mission is at once horticultural, educational, ecological, and artistic. Although the farm has long since diversified into flowering perennials, annuals, and structural border plants, herbs were its logical starting point. Forget the prissy, English-tea-room image. Herbs here are recognized for what they are—handsome garden plants with multiple uses that aren't afraid of a tough job.

The farm is *the* place for lavender—English, French, and Spanish lavenders and all their delightful spiked cultivars, short and long, purple and blue, pink and white. Some have an oily perfume, others are fit for cut flowers or topiary. Basil is the second biggest seller, and here again, there's amazing diversity—Thai, sweet, holy, African blue, and so on. The thymes, too, come gold and silver, lemon and orange, creeping and wooly.

The remaining herb inventory is nearly encyclopedic. Here's where to find blue rosemary, lemon catnip, alpine strawberry, caraway, shiso, *Arnica montana,* and motherwort, for example. A special category of "everlastings" are grown for *potpourri* and dried flower arrangements. Many herbs (such as borage) are both edible and beautiful—as are the vegetables (such as gourmet peppers and salad greens), which look great planted decoratively among herbs. There's much of culinary, medicinal, and ornamental interest to choose from, even if you just want something that'll grow in sand.

Peconic River Herb Farm is an excellent source of cottage-garden plants, choice annuals and tropicals, and what are called "grandmother's garden" shrubs. Perennials are a cut above what's normally seen, such as blue-eyed phlox, white evening primrose, and such pretty natives as pink swamp milkweed and willow leaf amsonia. Plants that attract butterflies, repel deer, and do well in seashore conditions are prominent. Specialty annuals offer greatest bloom power, with larkspur, love-in-a-mist, sweet Annie, zinnia, sunflower, and broom corn, for example—even unusual morning-glories and a Mexican flame vine.

Old-fashioned roses feature David Austin hybrids, Meidiland landscape shrubs, highly rated beach roses, and gorgeous climbers such as 'New Dawn' and variegated pink 'Seven Sisters'. Gardenworthy trees and shrubs, the most recent addition, are simply terrific. There's river birch, Scotch heather, Irish heath, three-flower maple, lowbush blueberry, chaste tree, black pussy willow, dawn redwood, flowering crab, beach plum, and others, even tea plant *(Camellia sinensis)*—all of which can and should be grown in Long Island gardens.

Herbs and most annuals and perennials are grown from seed and cuttings in the farm's greenhouses, while woody ornamentals are all sourced locally. The stock is vibrant and readily fills its place in gardens. Because the nursery has limited growing space, it emphasizes proven plants that perform well over a long period.

Herbaceous plants come in plugs and small pots offering excellent value. In spring you can buy little plugs very reasonably—part of an overall effort to encourage gardeners to plant their herbs and flowers in generous drifts, even within a limited budget. "We'd like to help people have successful gardens, not just sell them things," says Spindler. "There are so many barren yards." Summer and fall clearance sales make purchases downright economical. Don't forget to check the "Wow $5 each" area for weary woody plants.

Peconic River is an obvious favorite of herb gardeners. The Herb Society of America's influential Long Island Chapter holds its Herb Fest here in late September. The farm's mission is strongly educational, so there's a busy schedule of classes and workshops on all sorts of subjects—lavender wreaths and container gardening being the most popular. Indeed, almost everything here, like herbs, is both decorative and useful, from the whimsical containers and garden art right down to the Garden Planning Guides (at the nursery and on the Web site) cataloging the season's inventory and each plant's best uses and growing conditions.

Any excuse will do to visit this enchanting place. A little dirt road leads in, past rows of lavender reminiscent of the south of France. Off the parking lot, rose pergolas beckon. The nursery is run out of two rustic barns beset with inventive flowering containers and capti- vating garden art (we loved the carved "Red Dahlia" birdhouse, barbed-wire roses, and Haitian art crafted from recycled oil drums). Herb and perennial borders are so pretty you'll want a notepad and camera. Picnic tables encourage whole-day trips.

"This whole business is an elaborate excuse to put in a garden and pay for it," says Spindler. Her fertile imagination leads her to beautify every nook—even the little wooden outhouse by the railroad tracks has its allée of honey locusts and formal herb plot.

Eventually you'll wander off toward the river, the "wild and scenic" Peconic River whose timeless presence gives the landscape its magic, like a page from *The Wind in the Willows*. Here's where homesteading is still active: witness the beehives, the prodigious compost heap, and the refreshingly messy cutting garden—proof that the owner's energies are human, after all.

Directions: From the Long Island Expressway (Route 495), take exit 21 onto County Road 24 north. In 0.2 mile, turn left onto River Road. In 0.2 mile, just before the railroad tracks, the driveway is on the left (signposted). From Route 25 or 25A, turn south on Edwards Avenue. After crossing the railroad tracks, turn right on River Road. The farm is 0.2 mile on the left.

Nearby attractions: Other Long Island sources of herbs and flowering perennials are Hart's Cove Herbary, 72 Woodlawn Ave, East Moriches (631-874-8095; www.hartscoveherbary.com); Daisy Garden, P.O. Box 801, Gillette Avenue and Rail Road Avenue, Bayport (631-363-2708; www.daisy-garden.com); and Porter's Color- ful Gardens, P.O. Box 75, Main Road (Route 25), Jamesport (631-722-5400; e-mail colorfulgardens@aol.com). In the quaint town of Stony Brook, the Museums at Stony

Brook, 1208 Route 25A, Stony Brook (516-751-0066), house an herb garden maintained by Herb Society of America volunteers. The Big Duck, Route 24, Flanders, NY 11937 (516-852-8292), is a circa 1931 duck-shaped building, built by a Riverhead duck farmer as a store to sell his Peking Ducks; considered a classic of roadside architecture, it now houses East End tourist information and exhibits on Long Island's age of early motoring.

ROSLYN NURSERY
211 Burrs Lane, Dix Hills, NY 11746
(631) 643-9347; fax (631) 427-0894
www.roslynnursery.com; e-mail *roslyn@roslynnursery.com*
Dr. Philip Waldman

Rare rhododendrons and azaleas, camellias, conifers, and distinctive ornamental plants. Small specialty nursery. Open year-round, Monday through Saturday, 9 to 5; Sundays in April and May. Mail order. Catalog $3; also posted on Web site. Fall sale list. Call for current availability. Advance orders for nursery pick up. Shipping from April 1 through June 15 and September 1 through November 15. Selective Gardener's Club membership. Gift certificates. Visitors welcome.

Roslyn Nursery is the region's most comprehensive source of rare rhododendrons and distinctive ornamental plants. Dr. Philip Waldman and his wife, Harriet, founded the nursery in 1984 when their passion for rhododendrons—ignited when landscaping their first home—exceeded all reasonable bounds. As plant lovers, they couldn't bear to discard the extras.

Now retired from dentistry, Phil Waldman is a talented plant propagator whose energy and organizational skills stun many horticultural pros. He began as a rhododendron hobbyist, became a collector and then an award-winning hybridizer, diversified into rare woody plants and evergreens, added unusual perennials, and now grows more than 2000 choice garden plants. Seldom does an amateur move so fast and make such a splash in the plant trade.

Today, Roslyn is a go-to source for starter-size collector's plants. It caters to plant enthusiasts, laboring hard to stay on the cutting edge. Garden magazines cite it more often in their source notes than any other nursery in this book. Its catalog is an important reference for rare-plant collectors, listing hundreds of rhododendrons and azaleas and hundreds of more uncommon trees, shrubs, and perennials. Prices are high for these small container-grown plants, but so is quality, and for many items, Roslyn is the sole source. New introductions sell out fast when publicity creates a run on orders.

The Waldmans' goal is to find and grow the most outstanding plants for the temperate zone. Their quest for superior new forms, especially cold-tolerant rhododendrons, is constant. Each year they introduce some 300 new cultivars, dropping others that have become mainstream or boring. Most of their stock is propagated from cuttings gathered from such public collections as Long Island's Planting Fields Arboretum, the U.S. National Arboretum, the Arnold Arboretum, Longwood Gardens, and the J. C. Raulston Arboretum. Of the generous collectors who've shared their discoveries, the best known is Dr. Nick Nickou, a renowned Connecticut rhododendron collector whose garden has long been a Roslyn resource.

Roslyn began as a rhododendron nursery and this genus dominates its plant list. Hundreds of rhododendron hybrids, rhododendron species, and deciduous and evergreen azaleas are offered in bewildering variety. Large-leaf rhododendrons come in every color and habit imaginable, as do many lesser-known lepidote (small-leaved) rhododendrons. Azaleas come as spring-bloomers, fall-bloomers, doubles, bicolors, and beautiful species. A fragrant double-flowered yellow azalea ('Narcissiflora') seems representative of their loveliness. Waldman's own hybrids include 'Purple Pinwheel', a compact rhododendron with strap-petal flowers, and 'Howard Epstein', a rock-garden azalea with double white blooms.

The Waldmans' basic selection criteria are hardiness and beauty. Over the years, their interests have broadened to include hundreds of unusual trees and shrubs—broad-leaved evergreens, flowering trees, deciduous shrubs, and conifers. Roslyn has notable holdings of camellia, holly, kalmia, pieris, boxwood, and daphne. Occasionally there's a true rarity, such as *Parrotiopsis jaquemontiana,* a small Himalayan tree with white flowers and yellow fall color, and *Elsholtzia stauntonii,* a little-known hardy Chinese shrub with lilac-pink flowers.

"Variegated plants," writes nurseryman Tony Avent, "add a welcome bit of insanity to any garden." Roslyn's taste for variegation is evident in such things as white-budded Japanese black pine and silver-highlighted Eastern hemlock.

A few variegated plants sound grotesque—the white-speckled, dwarf, globular form of giant redwood, for example. But many are delightful in rock gardens, such as the variegated cotoneaster and tiny-leaved Chinese elm ('Frosty').

Japanese maples leaf out in carnival colors, while other specimens come in bright yellow (Eastern white pine), chartreuse (pagoda dogwood), or mint-green (Chinese juniper). Weeping blue American larch and weeping *Juniperus squamata* 'Chinese Silver' might enhance the mood in a pet cemetery. Columnar forms of sugar maple, Japanese snowbell, flowering cherry, and Hinoki false cypress make good entry gates.

Although known for woody plants, Roslyn grows voguish perennials under hybridizing pressure, such as heuchera, tiarella, eupatorium, euphorbia, and ornamental grasses. It grows 55 varieties of perennial geranium. Hostas, too, are popular, along with plants like Japanese forest grass and ferns that do well in rhododendron shade.

Roslyn is a no-frills mail-order house that welcomes visitors who want to pick out their own plants. The nursery is plain compared to the exotica it turns out—a simple gravel parking lot and 25 greenhouses, with plants housed alphabetically, for ease of order filling. Visitors are sometimes surprised that it lacks elaborate rhododendron displays, but those are at the Waldmans' home, not their nursery. A "Selective Gardener's Club" allows member discounts on nursery pick ups. This is not a garden center and, while attitudes are generally affable, service is minimal. Reports on mail-order customer service are mixed.

What's at the nursery is what's in the catalog—starter-size plants in unsurpassed variety, occasionally supplemented with landscape-sized specimens. Visitors must sort through the mixed inventory on their own. Some specimens are bigger, healthier, better rooted, and more weed-free than others. One gardener likened it to a treasure hunt. Another appreciated the chance to "slow down and 'smell the rhodies.'"

Directions: The nursery is south of Huntington. From the Long Island Expressway (Route 495), take exit 50, turn left onto Bagatelle Road, turn left onto the LIE service road, and take the first right onto Burrs Lane. The nursery is 1 mile on the right. From Northern Parkway, take exit 42 and turn south onto Deer Park Avenue. Pass the LIE and turn right on Ryder Avenue; at the T-junction, turn left onto Burrs Lane. The nursery is 0.5 mile on the right.

Nearby attractions: Right next door is Suburban Water Gardens, 211 Burrs Lane, Dix Hills, NY (631-643-3500; www.suburbanpond.com), a source for aquatic plants and fish since 1947. An excellent wholesale source of larger woody ornamentals, evergreens, and perennials is Atlantic Nurseries, 691 Deer Park Avenue, Dix Hills (631-586-624; www.atlanticnurs.com)—send your landscaper.

S. SCHERER & SONS
104 Waterside Road, Northport, NY 11768
(631) 261-7432; (631) 261-9325
www.waterlilyfarm.com; e-mail *lilyfishpond@aol.com*
Robert Scherer

Water lilies and pond plants. *Family-run aquatic greenhouses since 1907. Open year-round, Monday through Saturday, 8 to 6, Sunday, 9 to 4. Holiday and winter hours vary; call ahead. Catalog $2. Mail order. Plants shipped bare root. Larger potted plants sold at the nursery. Pond supplies. Koi and goldfish. Gift certificates. Seasonal and Christmas items. Display garden. Visitors welcome.*

In the 18th century, the Duke of Devonshire built history's first aquatic greenhouse on his estate at Chatsworth, England, for the purpose of growing water lilies *(Victoria regia)*. It was viewed as outlandish. The first cold-hardy water lilies were bred by a Frenchman, Monsieur Marliac, in 1887—and so the outdoor lily pool was born. From these twin origins come modern water gardening, whose pleasures begin and end—as any dragonfly will tell you—with water lilies.

Scherer & Sons is Long Island's prime source for aquatic plants, and most especially water lilies. This 4th-generation nursery has been owned by "water lily people" since 1907. Nursery founder Sigmund Scherer, a native of Germany's Lake Constance, apprenticed at the Royal Botanic Gardens in Zurich before emigrating to Long Island at the turn of the 20th century. His grandson, Robert Scherer, now owns, and his great-grandson, Robert Walton Thomas Scherer (Bobby), manages, the largest aquatic nursery in New York State—and one of the largest in the nation. Because the family's name, Scherer, is German for "pruner," it is fitting that Scherer descendants continue to use clippers in pursuit of their *métier.*

The nursery is housed in a pleasantly old-fashioned wooden building, its interior orderly and clean. Healthy floating aquatics occupy whole rooms full of gurgling tanks. Winter dreamers may come off-season to think and plan, but the true water-gardening season lasts from mid-April to mid-October, when water lilies come alive and flower.

The Scherers pride themselves on propagating and growing their own water lilies. Hardy water lilies may look like delicate landing pads for Tinkerbell, but in outdoor gardens they're indomitable. All are beautiful—this is one of the few plants without any dogs in the family tree. Modern hybrids come in a stunning range of bloom colors, especially those from Perry Slocum, America's foremost hybridizer. It's hard to imagine going to all the fuss of pond gardening without water lilies.

The catalog lists 9 red, 11 pink, 6 white, 4 yellow, and 5 "changeable" (yellow-copper-pink) hardy lilies, but more varieties are available, so it helps to inquire before selection. Among the best water lilies are 'Attraction', a rich garnet-red with yellow-tipped mahogany stamens; 'Gladstone', the largest pure white (and fragrant); and 'Marliac Carnea', a soft flesh-pink with moody purplish leaves.

Heady perfumes and richer colors are virtues of the tropical water lily, which needs indoor protection to survive cold winters. Scherer grows 25 day-blooming tropicals and a dozen night-bloomers. Tropicals are the only water lilies with elusive blue and purple blooms; some have mottled foliage. One of the most popular, 'Pennsylvania' (a.k.a. 'Blue Beauty'), produces large azure flowers throughout the summer.

Not all tropicals are blue, of course. 'Panama Pacific' is the rosy-purple color of a Roman senator's toga; 'August Koch', a pale wisteria violet; and 'El Dorado', a deep yellow. Few can outperform 'Missouri', with its immense white flowers over coppery leaves. Best grown from June to September in cold climates, tropical water lilies need at least four hours of sunlight and daytime temperatures of 70 degrees to bloom.

The tropical miniatures are great for tub culture. We once grew violet-blue 'Pamela' in a whiskey barrel, where it bloomed all summer on a hot city street, much to the wonder of passersby. (Clean tub water was achieved with tiny oxygenating plants; passing children were fascinated by the hovering dragonflies.)

Hardy water lotus are like water lilies but more aggressive—a lotus plant in a barrel will eventually burst the barrel hoops. Scherer's 18-plant collection spans the ages, from the early Egyptian lotus *(Nelumbium speciosum)* to elegant modern hybrids. Tropical bog plants impart a sultry air—taros, water cannas, palms, Egyptian papyrus, water poppy, and bog lily. For cold pond edges, the nursery's 42 Louisiana iris offer handsome strap foliage and a rainbow of bloom color. Hardy shallow-water plants include sweet flag, marsh marigold, arrowhead, wild rice, and spiky cattails and rushes.

Scherer & Sons supplies water lilies, lotus, iris, bog plants, floaters, and oxygenators by mail order, bare root, at reasonable prices. Other plants (including large water lilies in outsize pots) are only sold at the nursery. A perennial yard houses plants for poolside landscaping, fresh from some of Long Island's best growers. Among them are flowering perennials, ornamental grasses, rare conifers, azaleas, heathers—even dwarf rock-garden plants for gravelly pond edges.

Scherer sells not only pond and pond-edge plants but also fish to go with them—ornamental goldfish and catfish. Lovely gold and silver koi, imported from Japan, are quite affordable. (As catfish scavengers, koi are forbidden in or near natural waterways, where they destroy native fish.) The nursery also sells fiberglass pools, heaters, pumps, liners, waterfalls—you-name-it for the water garden.

Staff courtesy accords every customer personal attention and advice, whether for a single plant or an entire ecosystem. Although Scherer does no waterscape contracting, he does keep a list of reputable outside firms. To occupy the nursery in the winter months, Scherer sells Christmas greens and European ornaments of the kind you get from people who love Christmas.

Directions: From the Long Island Expressway (Route 495), take exit 53N onto Sunken Meadow Parkway north, get off at exit SM5, and turn west on Route 25A. In 4 miles, turn right at Nocello's Restaurant onto Waterside Road. Scherer's is 0.7 mile on the right. From the Northern State Parkway, take exit SM1 onto Sunken Meadow Parkway north and follow directions above.

Nearby attractions: Pumpernickel's Restaurant & Lounge, 640 Main Street (Route 25A), Northport, NY (631-757-7959), serves bratwurst and German-American fare in an atmospheric setting.

SMIRNOW'S SON'S PEONIES

168 Maple Hill Road, Huntington, NY 11743
(631) 421-0836; (631) 421-0818
E-mail *smirnowb@ix.netcom.com* (use headline "peony")
Bill Smirnow

Tree Peonies. Small specialty grower. Catalog $3. Mail order only. Shipping from October through Thanksgiving. Early orders filled first. Grafted 3-year plants. Limited estate-size Japanese plants. Seasonal. Open only by appointment.

Smirnow's Son's Peonies is a mail-order supplier of exotic tree peonies based in Huntington. The nursery was founded in 1940 by Louis Smirnow, a noted hybridizer who introduced many Japanese tree peonies to America in the 1950s and Chinese varieties in the 1980s. His introduction of the first yellow inter-sectional hybrids, bred by Toichi Itoh of Japan, caused a sensation in 1974 and earned the American Peony Society's Saunders medal. After his death in 1989, much of Smirnow's stock was shipped to Australia, leaving behind a name, a garden, and a worldwide network of contacts.

The nursery's present owner, Bill Smirnow, is a grandson who employs these family assets to create a home-based nursery specializing in imported Japanese and Chinese tree peonies. Although these exotic grafted shrubs are more common now than 20 years ago, his plants stand out for two reasons: they represent named varieties still rare in this country and they're all 3-year nursery-grown plants and older, which means they're big enough to transplant successfully. (Many commercial tree peonies are unnamed one-year plants, which aren't.)

Smirnow imports grafted plants from sources in Japan and China but prefers the Japanese varieties. The nursery beds also hold a limited number of estate-size plants that he can occasionally be persuaded to part with. Also available are potluck collections of tree peony seed, presumably from plants in the collection, which might be fun to fool around with.

Smirnow's Son's uses two catalogs, one for named Japanese tree peony hybrids and the other for "Chinese Conquest" varieties. Both catalogs are a bit out of date, making it hard to tell exactly what's in stock. Shipping takes place in fall (as is proper with bare-root peonies), but it's a good idea to get your order in early so as to increase the odds of getting what you want. Tree peonies are never cheap, but considering what's offered, Smirnow's are an excellent value.

The catalogs list both Japanese and Chinese types by their Asian names. The Chinese varieties are assigned names of Sminow's family and friends for easier ordering—which means that white 'Yu Lan Piao Xiang' must be ordered as 'Dr. Lisa Smirnow' and 'Fen e Jiao' as 'Karen'. Japanese tree peonies are listed under their Japanese names, even red-and-white striped 'Shima-Nashiki', better known here as 'Island Brocade'.

More than 80 Japanese varieties are listed (including some gorgeous black-reds), alongside a few yellow *Paeonia lutea* hybrids. Because Smirnow is more interested in Japanese plants, it's probably better to order from this catalog if you're playing the odds. An intriguing group of "reblooming" Japanese plants is shown flowering in December under snow-covered straw huts in the Japanese mountains.

Tree peonies are garden aristocrats that have been popular in China for at least 15 centuries and in Japan for 12. Despite an ancient pedigree and royal appearance, they're easy Zone 4 plants that perform well in Northeastern gardens. Their magical appeal is partly exquisite coloring and partly the delicate crepe-paper-like texture of their blossoms. Long roots and shade tolerance makes them ideal in deciduous half-shade and in dappled nooks that rarely host anything this elegant. Planted properly, they'll live practically forever—we've heard of Chinese specimens that survived the Cultural Revolution (even imperial garden plants were purged for disapproved political associations) and are now 400 to 600 years old.

Smirnow's nursery is home-based and therefore not open to the public except by special arrangement. The most effective way to contact the owner is by e-mail (adding "peony" to the subject line to distinguish it from "spam" mail). A throat injury hinders speech and makes telephone contact difficult, but Smirnow is otherwise a cordial correspondent who's gallantly working his worldwide contacts to source these horticultural treasures. It's taken a millennium for Western connoisseurs to appreciate the full range of Asian tree peonies, and Smirnow's Son's remains an instrumental source.

TALMAGE FARM AGWAY

1122 Osborne Avenue, Riverhead, NY 11901
(631) 727-0124; fax (631) 727-0326
www.talmagefarmagway.com; e-mail *agway@talmagefarm.com*
The Talmage family

Perennials, annuals, trees, shrubs, roses, herbs, aquatics, and vegetables. Family-run garden center. Open year-round, Monday through Friday, 8 to 6; Saturday, 8 to 5; Sunday, 9 to 5. Shorter hours in winter. No catalog or mail order. Custom plant orders. Organic garden products. Animal feed. Workshops and seminars. Seasonal events. Visitors welcome.

Counted among Long Island's earliest settlers, the Talmages arrived in 1650 and have been farmers ever since. In 1850, a branch of the family bought a large farm in Riverhead's Baiting Hollow and used it to grow potatoes until 1963. Today, the farm comprises a 300-acre golf course, an 80-acre sod farm, and a 50-acre wholesale nursery that makes more money than the whole farm ever did in potatoes. In 2001, Talmage Farm bought the former Agway store in Riverhead as a retail outlet for its garden plants.

The Agway is a perfect fit. Henry Talmage, a 6th-generation farmer and former president of the Long Island Farm Bureau, oversees Talmage Farm's vast high-tech greenhouse operation. Its current wholesale output of disease-free geraniums is about 25 million plants a year. His sister, Ellen Talmage, a Cornell University-trained horticulturist influential in many professional organizations, spearheaded Talmage Farm Perennials on family land 15 years ago. She started with a small shed and a sign that read "Horticultural Goddess," for fun occasionally donning a toga and farm boots. The perennial farm now grows 850 varieties, including worthy native plants derived from Long Island genotypes that have been used in public reclamation projects. The Riverhead Agway is just down the street—close enough for plants to be delivered directly by tractor from Talmage Farm fields and greenhouses up the road.

Talmage Farm Agway is a 7-acre retail garden center with a large store (once a potato barn), an even larger nursery yard, and a warehouse. Unlike most Agways, it has unusually good garden plants, most of which come straight from Talmage Farm. Its strong suit is gallon-size perennials and native plants at great prices—fresh healthy stock that'll survive well in local gardens. A full complement of popular flowering perennials is ever in stock. And because they're so rare in the nursery trade, common native Long Island plants seem quite special: salt hay, American beach grass, white wood aster, seaside goldenrod, and naturalized beach wormwood. These natives can be ornamental, too—variegated cordgrass, double and white forms of marsh marigold, and a butter-yellow form of columbine. Even the cultivated shrub roses look a little brassy beside Virginia rose, found wild along Long Island's coastal dunes. If a plant isn't in the store, they'll bring it down for you from the farm.

Talmage Farm Agway stocks herbs, vegetables, woody plants, and seasonal greenhouse plants. New Guinea impatiens and 100 varieties of geraniums derive from Talmage Farm's greenhouses. The Agway is an excellent source for organic fertilizers and natural garden supplies. It's a real Agway, too, with 15,000 SKUs attached to such store items as animal feed, pet supplies, propane, and super-turf builder. Seasonal events tend to focus on animals, such as the "Equine Event" (horse weekend) and Pet Santa day when people bring their pets to visit Santa Claus. A chicken and a horse once showed up in Santa outfits.

Some time when you're here, take the short ride down Osborne Avenue to Talmage Farm—broad flat fields, good soil, a cluster of family houses, and the 4-acre greenhouse operation at the corner of Sound Avenue. It's an attractive but unsentimental working landscape, at once ancient and modern. It represents the way Long Island families plan to keep their agricultural land intact for six more generations. The little public library at Baiting Hollow, with its Indian arrowheads and books by Ellen Talmage on kids' horticulture, is open on Thursday and Saturday.

Directions: From New York City, take the Long Island Expressway (Route 495) to Riverhead, take exit 73 and turn west off the ramp onto Route 58. In 2 miles, turn sharp left onto Osborne Avenue; the Agway is on the right. From Riverhead, take West Main Street (Route 25) east past the Tanger Outlet Center. At the 4th light, turn right onto Route 58 and left onto Osborne Avenue; the Agway is on the right.

Nearby attractions: Briermere Farms, 4414 Sound Avenue, Riverhead, NY (631-722-3931), is a roadside apple stand where Ellen Talmage sent us for homemade pie. The Riverhead Grill, 85 East Main Street, Riverhead (631-727-8495; open 8 to 8, Sunday, 8 to noon), is a 1932 Kullman diner serving comfort food. Star Confectionery, 4

East Main Street, Riverhead (631-727-9873), is where everybody goes for chocolate and egg creams. Warner's Nursery, Garden Shop, Florist & Landscapes, 2669 Sound Avenue, Baiting Hollow, Riverhead, NY 11933 (631-727-8733), is an attractive 7-acre garden center stocked with fresh-dug trees from the family's former potato-chip farm. Hallockville Museum Farm & Folklife Center, 6038 Sound Avenue, Riverhead (631-298-5292), is a living history museum showing a typical North Fork farm from 1880 to 1910.

TRIMBLE'S OF CORCHAUG NURSERY
20985 Main Road (Route 25), Cutchogue, NY 11935
(631) 734-6494; (631) 734-6476
E-mail *trimbles@optonline.net*
Anne Trimble and Nancy Leskody

Unusual annuals, perennials, herbs, and woody ornamentals. *Small specialty nursery. Retail and wholesale. Open March through December, daily, 9 to 5. Free catalog. No mail order. Organic grower. Plant-request book. Pottery, organic supplies. Gardening advice and lectures. Open house. Tours. Gift certificates. Idea gardens. Landscape design and construction. Christmas lighting service. Visitors welcome.*

Trimble's of Corchaug is a small nursery of high plantsmanship and whimsical charm, located on Route 25 in the pretty town of Mattituck (of which Cutchogue, or Corchaug, is a hamlet). Voted the best garden center on Long Island's North Fork in 1998, Trimble's propagates and sells a fine assortment of annuals, perennials, herbs, and woody ornamentals, using organic growing methods. The ability to combine ecology and horticultural chic is in itself an impressive testament to the nursery's talents.

Owners Anne Trimble and Nancy Leskody began Trimble's in 1991 by acquiring an existing nursery, complete with four acres and two greenhouses. Trimble, a degreed horticulturist and landscape designer, has an extensive background in state and urban horticulture, including eight years as Director of Children's education at the Brooklyn Botanic Garden. Leskody, who oversees plant production, is a dedicated environmentalist and former playground inspector for the New York City Parks Department. Their combined energies have transformed a simple roadside nursery into a locus of plantsmanship and design, with sales yards, a large heated greenhouse, 11 hoophouses, in-ground trees and shrubs, and display gardens filled with mature specimens and amusing artifacts.

Trimble's plant list focuses on "winners"—unusual flowering plants not available in most garden centers. "As it takes as much labor and time to bring a mediocre plant to flowering as a winner," wrote Richardson Wright in *Greedy Gardeners,* "it is the better part of wisdom to begin with winners. That gives you a head start."

Among Trimble's annual and tender-perennial winners are front-runner varieties of flowering tobacco, lily-of-the-Nile, spotted nettle, crested cockscomb, duck's-foot coleus, and castor bean. Pretty container subjects include pot marigolds, California poppy, non-stop begonias, and all sorts of daisies. Voguish cannas and calla lilies add tropical grandeur to containers. The catalog lists impressive assemblies of salvia, verbena, viola, petunia (including "million-bells" mini-petunias), and pelargoniums of fancy-leaf, ivy, scented, and zonal habit. Even showy edible vegetables are on display, such as artichokes and bloody sorrel.

For perennial plant winners, Trimble's grows champions and old favorites that make good garden companions. Each perennial comes in many cultivars, with selection changing each year to allow experimentation and to build on past success. Examples for shade gardens are hellebore, Solomon's-seal, and goatsbeard; for streambanks, cardinal flower and turtlehead; for sunny meadows, bee balm and coneflower; for ground cover, cranesbills, alpine strawberry, heuchera, and rock cress; and for dry gardens, ornamental herbs, dwarf goldenrod, sea lavender, and hardy ice plant.

Because land-use regulations require Trimble's to grow almost everything it sells, fresh plants are the nursery's lodestone. A sign at the counter declares, "All we can grow here is plants, so we grow the best darn plants we can!" Most are grown from seed, vegetative cuttings, and divisions and are sold in quart, gallon, and 2-gallon pots. Mature hostas are grown to 3-gallon size. Pots are well rooted and well priced.

Outdoor horticulture is entirely organic, while inside the greenhouse, chemicals are minimized. Soothing jazz and soul music from a "surround stereo" system must affect plant happiness, for the nursery stock seems glossier and more vibrant than elsewhere.

Visitors are invited to consult Trimble's "idea garden," notable for its flea-market chic and frolicsome style. Offbeat artifacts, rustic trellises, and funky containers punctuate its convoluted paths. The color scheme favors blue, orange, purple, and aqua. Embedded pottery shards make crazy-quilts in stone walkways. Bottoms-up wine bottles form decorative edging. In the parking lot, flowers tumble from donkey carts. Shutters are painted with blue moons; old license plates are tacked on the check-out shed wall. In a kind of adult treasure hunt, customers who find "Trimble's turtles" (ceramic turtles concealed in odd places) are entitled to nursery discounts.

Such jollity shouldn't obscure Trimble's skill and originality. Anne Trimble directed landscape design at Central Park's Tavern on the Green in its glory years, and her gifts as a landscape artist are well recognized. (She all but invented the sophisticated practice of wrapping trees with Christmas lights—something she could probably be persuaded to do again.) The nursery has a special talent for designing deer-resistant perennial gardens, container plantings, and garden renovations. "Whether your vision of paradise is an English cottage garden, a Japanese tea garden, a sun-drenched meadow, or a little bit of wilderness," the owners write, "we can make your vision real." Trimble's is living proof that artistry and fun can be serious business.

Directions: The nursery is on Long Island's North Fork. From the Long Island Expressway (Route 495), take exit 73 onto Route 58 east, which becomes Route 25 east. In Mattituck, pass the high school, and the nursery is one mile farther on the left. From the Cross Sound Ferry at Orient Point, take Route 25 west through the hamlet of Cutchogue, pass Pellegrini Vineyards on the right, and after the road bends, the nursery is on the right.

Nearby attractions: Professional chefs frequent 225-acre Wickham's Fruit Farm, Main Road/Route 25, Cutchogue (631-734-6441; www.wickhamsfruitfarm.com), for fruit, vegetables, and fresh baked pies (open daily except Sunday). Cutchogue Village Green, Main Road, Cutchogue (631-734-7122), is a cluster of historic antique buildings showcasing North Fork history; the Old House, built in 1649, is the oldest English frame house in New York State. Cutchogue Diner, Main Street/Route 25, Cutchogue (631-734-9056), is a circa 1940 Kullman diner classic. Hellenic Snack Bar and Restaurant, Main Road/Route 25, East Marion (631-477-0138), serves terrific Greek food.

VAN BOURGONDIEN BROS.

P.O. Box 1000, 245 Farmingdale Road (Route 109), Babylon, NY 11702
(800) 622-9997; fax (800) 327-4268
www.dutchbulbs.com; e-mail *blooms@dutchbulbs.com*
Van Bourgondien family

Dutch bulbs and perennials. Family-run bulb enterprise. Office open Monday through Friday, 8:30 to 6, Saturday, 9 to 12. After-hours automated ordering service. Free retail and wholesale catalogs. Catalogs on Web site. Mail order only. Fall sales. Free Garden Guide with each order. Gift certificates. Fund-raising program for non-profits. Articles and photos on Web site. No visitors.

Van Bourgondien Bros. is a giant mail-order clearinghouse for Dutch bulbs and flowering perennials based in Babylon, on the western end of Long Island. The business is named for its founding family, the Van Bourgondiens, who began growing tulips in Holland 200 years ago and have published bulb catalogs since 1880. The family didn't come to America until 1904, when Carl Van Bourgondien was dispatched to New Jersey to sell his family's Dutch flower bulb crop. He set up a warehouse and, as they say, never looked back. The business today has a staff of 250 and is still firmly in family hands.

Although a pictorial history shows 7th-generation Van Bourgondiens assembled in a bulb field, the family bulb farm long since forfeited its place in the supply chain. Most of today's bulbs are purchased as commodities through the Dutch bulb auction. Other bulbs and perennials are sourced from growers in Japan, India, South Africa, and Israel. Van Bourgondien's real role is as bulk buyer and go-between, brokering bulbs to everyone from backyard growers to professional gardeners at the White House.

Van Bourgondien has made a name among bulb suppliers for its selection and customer service. Bulbs may be commodities, but nobody carries everything, so a great deal depends on the supplier's taste and quality control. Van Bourgondien offers an ever-changing array of healthy Dutch bulbs—brilliant satin tulips, crisp daffodils, gleaming crocuses, innocent snowdrops, and all sorts of minor spring bulbs—as well as dahlias, tuberous begonias, calla lilies, and flower-border perennials.

One of the great advantages of bulb gardening is that it's hard to screw up. "You could be an idiot and plant a bulb, and it will grow," says Debbie Van Bourgondien, the company's director of retail sales. Known by her trademark, "the Bulb Lady," Van Bourgondien is the company's greatest public relations asset, publishing a newsletter and answering bulb questions online. Her views are based on professional know-how and the experience of growing 60,000 bulbs in her home garden, which is open for virtual tours on the Web site.

The Van Bourgondiens make an obvious effort to stock uncommon items not readily sourced through other suppliers. A number of gorgeous "exclusives" include 'White Fire', a delicately red-striped *greigii* tulip with a warm center, and 'Monte Beau', a painterly lemon/white early tulip that looks like a chalice of sunlight. For years, gardeners yearned unrequitedly for *Tulipa violacea* 'Pallida', a diminutive wild white tulip with a metallic blue base—and here it is, in good supply, alongside 'Waterlily' colchicum and a beautiful white spider lily *(Lycoris albiflora)*. Van Bourgondien is an exclusive source for the first double-flowered Oriental lily, pale pink 'Miss Lucy', hardy to Zone 3.

Long participation in the tulip game may account for a certain baroque twist in family taste—represented by such oddities as ruffled double-cup pink daffodil, chocolate-colored poppy, and double tiger lily. The catalog touts a positively hideous brown-mustard-lavender bearded iris (called 'Brown Lasso') as "ideal for the front border." Most things are breathtaking, though—the fringed tulips that seem frost-encrusted, the dusky black fritillaria, the cream foxtail lily, the lovely little snow crocus, and of course the magnificent wild martagon lily.

Daffodils are the ultimate perennial. Being deadly poisonous and creature-proof, they live long and multiply, to the gladness of spring gardens. "There is only one way to plant daffodils," observed writer Richardson Wright, "—with a very prodigal hand." Van Bourgondien's bulk daffodils come in color combinations: orange and yellow, apricot and carrot, citrus and pink, white and salmon. Good landscaping collections are assembled for pink-cup daffodils and May-flowering tulips. The catalog favorite, though, is clearly a fragrant, long-flowering, award-winning, yellow/white narcissus, called 'Bulb Lady' after Debbie Van Bourgondien.

It bears mentioning that all Van Bourgondien bulbs ("wild" or not) are cultivated; none are actually dug from the wild. Bulbs are sold retail and (to qualified professionals) wholesale, with prices and sizes what you'd expect. A special program offers bulbs for nonprofit fund-raising efforts. The Web site, if somewhat ad-congested, is crammed with useful information for the home gardener. As any collector knows, you can get lost in bulbs. Their "diversity of color, flower form, size, habitat, and desirable growing conditions," writes John Bryan in *Bulbs*, "rival all other forms of vegetation."

VAN DYCK'S FLOWER BULBS
P.O. Box 430, Brightwaters, NY 11718
(800) 248-2852; fax (800) 639-2452
www.vandycks.com
Jan Van Dyck

Flower bulbs and perennials. Family-run bulb enterprise. Open year-round, Monday through Friday, 8:30 to 5, Saturday, 9 to 12. Closed major holidays. Free catalog. Catalog on Web site. Mail order only. Free bulbs with early and online orders. Online newsletter and Planting Guide. Gift certificates.

Van Dyck's is a mail-order supplier of Dutch flower bulbs and perennials based in Brightwaters, Long Island. For decades, it has supplied bulbs to garden centers, public parks, and landscapers at wholesale prices. A retail catalog now offers top-size bulbs in smaller quantities to homeowners, with prices reflecting "the same purchasing advantage as the professionals." The motto, stated in Van Dyck's free catalog, is "Highest Quality, Lowest Prices, Satisfaction Guaranteed."

Besides old standbys, Van Dyck's goes out of its way to feature new introductions and popular favorites. News-making tulips include a double form of 'Beauty of Apeldoorn', resembling a big orange ranunculus, and 'Antoinette', a "chameleon" tulip that changes color from primrose yellow to salmon pink. A new white narcissus called 'Rosy Cloud' has lavishly frilled double-pink cups. Yellow and white 'Minnow' is one of the prettiest miniature daffodils.

Several tulips are sold exclusively by Van Dyck's: 'Hot Lips', a white tulip with crushed rose coloring and a blue throat; 'Juice 'N Honey', a vibrant orange and yellow tulip; and 'Lemon Drop', a pale yellow tulip with bright highlights. Van Dyck's supplies the dazzling red crown imperial (*Fritillaria imperialis* 'Rubra') shown on this book's front cover.

Van Dyck's is also an excellent source for bulb classics, such as poet's narcissus, 'Thalia' narcissus, and parrot tulips. Species bulbs seldom available at these prices include hardy cyclamen, double snowdrops, spring snowflake *(Leucojum aestivum),* and martagon lilies. Novelty bulbs include a red-flowered spider lily *(Lycoris radiata),* a rust-colored Dutch iris, and a crazy-looking allium called 'Hair'.

Some of Van Dyck's best deals are on mixed-color collections of spring bulbs useful for naturalizing in drifts: yellow daffodils, double daffodils, dwarf iris, large-flowering crocus, wood hyacinths, mariposa lilies, and botanical tulips. (All bulbs are commercially grown, none collected from the wild.) For late-spring and summer flowers, Van Dyck's offers Oriental and trumpet lilies, tall bearded iris, Oriental poppies, and hellebores. The Chinese tree peonies, though small, are an unusual bargain. Giant Dutch amaryllis and paper-white narcissus can be forced indoors at Christmas.

Because Dutch bulbs are now auction commodities, a bulb house's connection to Holland growers matters less than it once did. Still, Van Dyck's sources some exciting things its competitors don't have. Selection is not exhaustive, but there's plenty to think about.

A barrel of spring bulbs planted at different depths, for example, can flower for two months. Van Dyck's daffodil mix (25 bulbs), tulip mix (25 bulbs), and soft-pink *Crocus sieberi* 'Firefly' (25 bulbs) will bloom from March into May. If you order online, they'll send 8 more tulips. Total credit card damage: $24.85, plus shipping. When the combustion ends, you can hoick out the bulbs and plant petunias.

VERDERBER'S GARDEN CENTER

P.O. Box 2265, Main Road (Route 25), Aquebogue, NY 11931
(631) 283-5753; fax (631) 722-4388
John and Maria VerDerBer

*Trees and shrubs. Perennials. Landscape nursery and retail garden shop. Open
year-round, Tuesday through Saturday, April through December, 9 to 6, winter hours,
9 to 4. No catalog or mail order. Local delivery. Custom design and installation. Trees
dug to order. Visitors welcome.*

VerDerBer's Garden Center in Aquebogue is a landscaper-owned nursery
located directly on Route 25 in Aquebogue on Long Island's North Fork.
John VerDerBer is a professional landscaper with a major landscaping
business, mainly in South Fork towns. He and his wife, Maria, who live on
the property, opened the garden shop to provide a retail outlet for their
nursery stock. Growing fields in Southampton supply field-grown trees and
shrubs to both businesses—they grow 90 percent of their own stock. A barn
and large polyhouses also produce plants on garden-shop grounds.

What customers like best about VerDerBer's is its freshly dug plants in
good sizes at good prices—especially plants for screening, hedging, and
specimen use. "I like everything, and they *have* everything," said a Garden
Club officer with a local summer home. Others praise the inventory as
"different from the run-of-the-mill." Trees range from small starter plants to
large-caliper specimens. Plants at the garden center are well organized and
well labeled, making this the equivalent of a user-friendly bargain outlet for
savvy gardeners.

Because the landscaping operation constantly digs tree and shrub stock,
it is no trouble for VerDerBer's to custom-dig plants. Retail customers can
choose in-ground trees and have them dug to order—a valuable service for
those seeking vibrant plants for fast transplantation.

VerDerBer's carries exceptionally good evergreens, especially Hinoki
false cypress and blue holly. Big rhododendrons are well suited to instant
landscaping projects. The beech tree collection (including red 'Spaeth' and
weeping beech) is excellent. Grafted trees include Japanese maples, weeping
cherries, and purple-osier willow standards. Deer resistance is a local imperative, translating into aromatics (such as boxwood) and inedibles (such as
dwarf Alberta spruce). Attractive ornamental trees include multistem river
birch, 'Edith Bogue' magnolia, and 'Forest Pansy' redbud.

Perennials in 2-gallon pots are the kind landscapers use for massing—Montauk daisies, heathers, astilbes, hostas, and daylilies. Ubiquitous Long Island landscaping plants, such as hydrangeas, rugosa roses, junipers, and crabapple trees, are, of course, present in great numbers.

Someone here has a collector's eye for conifers. On a stroll through the sales yard, we noted incense cedar, zebra arborvitae, blue Alaskan cedar, blue weeping Alaskan cedar, Irish juniper, birds-nest spruce, purple-moss false cypress, and Korean pine. Broadleaf evergreens are numerous, including variegated English holly and upright, dwarf, and gold forms of Japanese holly (*Ilex crenata*). A few viburnums and winter hazels offer a hint of naturalism.

VerDerBer's stock is sensibly priced—South Fork gardeners would call it wholesale. Perennials come in generous 5-gallon pots and containerized trees in 15-gallon pots: the perfect landscaping size. Handsome workhorse roses ('Sea Foam' and 'Carefree Wonder' come to mind) are a bargain, especially at the fall sale. We saw a 5-inch caliper variegated sweetgum being moved out the driveway. A magnificent 30-foot dawn redwood with no price tag must have been sold. That's the lesson at VerDerBer's: good stock at good prices moves fast. It's the ultimate commercial compliment.

Directions: The nursery is on Route 25, north of Riverhead. From the Long Island Expressway (Route 495), take exit 73 onto Route 58 east/Old Country Road; in 4 miles, continue when it becomes Route 25 east. Look for the nursery in Aquebogue on the right.

Nearby attractions: Modern Snack Bar, 628 Main Road/Route 25, Aquebogue (631-722-3655; www.modernsnackbar.com), is a North Fork diner with "great home cooking" (open 11 to 9; closed Monday).

CENTRAL
AND WESTERN
NEW YORK

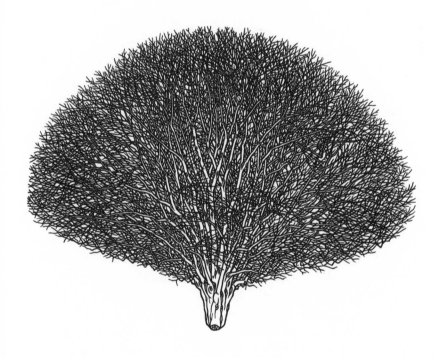

CENTRAL AND WESTERN NEW YORK

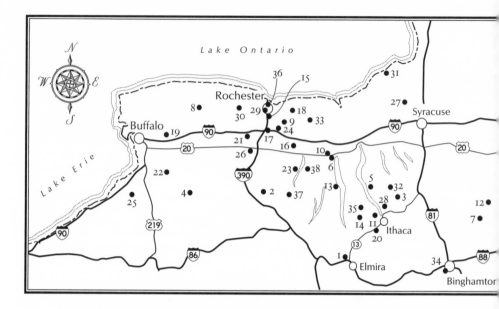

Central and Western New York

ALCHEMY WORKS SEEDS & HERBS
374 Latta Brook Road, Horseheads, NY 14845-3102
(607) 737-9250
www.alchemy-works.com; e-mail *admin@alchemy-works.com*
Harold Roth

Seeds for magick herbs. *Small seed house. Catalog on Web site. Mail order. Untreated seed, sourced internationally. Incense resins and medicinals. Open by appointment only.*

Alchemy Works Seeds & Herbs is a small seed house near Elmira specializing in hard-to-find seeds, herbs, and resins that play a traditional role in paganism, the nature cult of ancient Europe. The belief that plants have divine power is an important tenet of earth-based spirituality. According to the catalog, "the very best way to develop your *wortcunning* (knowledge of plants) is to grow your own magick herbs." Although focusing on plants used in witchcraft, the seed list includes perennials and self-sowing annuals of genuine interest to non-pagan gardeners. As might be expected, many plants are unusual, and some are poisonous.

Owner Harry Roth is an experienced organic gardener with longstanding interests in herbal medicine, alchemy, and paganism. Together they led him to the "plant path of alchemy," using alchemical techniques to mix plant-based medicines. "As far as I know, I'm the only business that caters to pagan gardeners," he says. While most seeds and resins come from outside sources, Roth uses some wild-crafted herbs and grows others for seed—white henbane, datura, costmary, and 20 species of foxgloves. Skilled research enables Roth to make historically accurate substances such as *kyphi*, the incense used by Egyptians in the Temple of Horus.

A primary attraction is Alchemy Works' superb inventory of poppy seed. The list features a number of coveted blue poppies (*Meconopsis* spp.) and several small yellow alpine poppies *(P. miyabeanum; P. rhaeticum; P. radicatum)* suitable for rock gardens The opium poppy *(Papaver somniferum)*, considered a moon plant for its sedative properties, is offered in many cultivated forms, including double 'Black Peony'; white red-fringed 'The Clown'; peony-flowered 'White Cloud', and single 'Persian White' (used in an Ayurvedic concoction called "bedtime chutney"). 'Hens and Chicks' is an outlandish opium poppy noted for its maternal seedpod surrounded by little pods. Blooming in Flanders fields during World War I, the red corn poppy *(P. rhoeas)*, once thought to spring from the blood of fallen soldiers, remains a wonderful meadow brightener.

Alchemy Works offers seed for many native perennials of therapeutic repute and intriguing garden potential. Swamp milkweed is a showy butterfly-support plant whose stalks were once used as dental floss. Canadian wood betony *(Pedicularis groenlandica)* was brewed by the practical Cheyenne to break up a cough; today's pagans use it for astral travel. An attractive flowering lobelia known as gagwort *(Lobelia inflata)* was once used to induce nausea. Purple locoweed *(Oxytropis lambertii)*, a prairie herb poisonous to horses, was employed by shamans in the Navajo Night Chant. Young shoots of pokeweed were relished as cooked greens by Native Americans; in the South, "poke sallet" is still a valued soul food. (According to Alchemy Works, raw pokeberries "taste terrible to humans, but birds love them, and on warm days, when the Sun turns the berries' sugar to alcohol, they will get drunk on Gaia's own pokeberry wine.")

Any self-respecting source of witching herbs is bound to offer the poisonous four, sacred to Hecate: hellebore, henbane, belladonna, and mandrake. Alchemy Works carries seed for black hellebore *(Helleborus niger)*, recommended in one old herbal "for killing wolves and foxes"; renamed Christmas rose, it is now a valued garden plant. Corsican and purple hellebore are also on the seed list, along with three toxic plants used in witches' flying ointments: deadly nightshade *(Atropa belladonna)*; black henbane *(Hyoscyamus niger)*, and black mandrake *(Mandragora officinarum* var. *autumnalis)*, whose roots were thought in Medieval times to represent a human being, screeching when uprooted.

Alchemy Works encourages customer requests for particulars needed in pagan gardens. The seed catalog is posted on the Web site, along with historical information and growing instructions. Seeds can be searched on the Web site by botanical or common name, planetary or elemental association, and traditional use. (Outdated botanical names may cause some confusion; *Papaver orientale,* for example, is referenced by a superseded name, *Papaver bracteatum.*) Most descriptions include color photographs and beautiful illustrations from old herbals. Where an image is lacking, Alchemy Works gamely offers to trade seed for digital photos. Web links provide a connection to Roth's mesmerizing planetary and elemental correspondence chart, as well as to Web sites for alchemy, natural magic, shamanism, tarot, and astrology. A Web site called Curse-B-Gone offers free hex removal.

Besides seeds, Alchemy Works sells dried bark, buds, herbs, pods, roots, petals, and fungi in resealable packets, as well as natural incense resins and scented oils. These substances are used for healing, smudging, consecration, charms, and spells. Many items have meaning in Ayurvedic, African, hoodoo, and Native American medicine. Those used in traditional Chinese medicine include corydalis root, *tabasheer* (dried bamboo sap), dragon bones and teeth (fossilized prehistoric animals), and sterile, low-THC hemp seed *(Cannabis sativa),* which is legal, it turns out. Still in demand for witchcraft, lab-grade sulphur (brimstone) is used for banishment, cleansing, and as an explosive.

Nearby attractions: Sullivan's Diner, 151 Old Ithaca Road / Route 273, Horseheads, NY (607-796-9950), is a 1940s classic with excellent omelets.

AMANDA'S GARDEN
8410 Harpers Ferry Road, Springwater, NY 14560
(585) 669-2275
E-mail *amandasgarden@bluefrog.com*
Ellen Folts

Wildflowers and native perennials*. Small specialty grower. Open mid-April through May, weekends, 9 to 5, and by appointment. Call to confirm open dates. Free catalog. Mail order. Dormant plants shipped bare root. Plant pick up by arrangement. Free delivery in Rochester area. Integrated pest management. Annual Wildflower Days, first weekend in May. Garden tours and lectures by arrangement. Display garden, peaks in May.*

Amanda's Garden is a native plant nursery in the Finger Lakes region, south of Rochester. Founded by owner Ellen Folts in 1991, this one-woman growing operation specializes in native wildflowers for woodland and meadow gardens. Amanda's Garden is home-based, with stock plants doubling as garden plants in the deciduous forest around Folts' home.

Folts is a SUNY graduate with a degree in recreational land management. In summer she works as a cemetery groundskeeper, and in winter at Harris Seeds. Amanda's Garden occupies nights and weekends. The nursery is named "Amanda" for the Folts' daughter, with nursery proceeds helping to underwrite her education. As any parent knows, this more or less qualifies the business as a nonprofit enterprise.

Folts began Amanda's Garden with 3 plants—blue-eyed grass, blue lobelia, and native columbine. She now grows more than 40 native perennial varieties, adding a few new items each year. Years of trial and error enable Folts to offer robust, healthy plants at affordable prices.

The nursery is strong in choice woodlanders: lovely native merry bells *(Uvularia sessilifolia)*, shooting star, blue cohosh, wood anemone, and blue-flowered *Hepatica americana*. Folts grows two jack-in-the-pulpits (regular and 'Green Dragon'), two Solomon's seals (true and false), and a tall-flowering black snakeroot, whose roots make a medicinal sedative. Shade ground covers include Allegheny pachysandra, crested iris, creeping phlox, wild ginger, and green-and-gold *(Chrysogonum virginianum)*.

To enliven moist areas, Folts offers white turtlehead, red cardinal flower, blue lobelia, blue flag, and pink swamp milkweed. Easy-spreading wildflowers for sunny meadows include green coneflower, blue wood aster, New England aster, and black-eyed Susan. Nectar plants for butterflies feature purple coneflower, anise hyssop, and tall meadow rue. Among the newer additions are ferns, wild leeks, Turk's-cap lilies, and palm sedge.

Amanda's Garden is impeccable in its treatment of native plants. All plants are nursery-propagated, using seeds, division, cuttings, and spores taken from plants "specifically grown as stock propagation plants." These in turn originate with reliable sources such as the New England Wildflower Society and Bowman's Hill Wildflower Preserve. A yellow lady's slipper comes from a noted tissue-culture lab.

The nursery sells mostly to garden clubs, parks, and public gardens. Its most distinguished client, New York City's Central Park, buys white trillium, mayapple, bloodroot, and downy yellow violet. The Genesee Valley Land Trust supplies its annual plant sale here.

Current inventory is listed in a small annual catalog. Most plants are winter-hardened and sold, flowering-size, in quart pots. The little woodlanders come in 4-inch pots. Customers can either pick up plants at the nursery or order them sent (bare root and dormant) by mail order. On the first weekend in May, Amanda's Garden opens for Wildflower Days, complete with garden tent, plant sales, and wildflower tours. A greenhouse built in 2003 promises to boost production and plant selection.

Her love of native perennials makes Folts an eloquent advocate for their use in garden settings. One of her goals is to educate people on the importance of incorporating wildflowers in the landscape. She offers informed advice on garden planning, gives tours of Amanda's Garden, and lectures to garden clubs by arrangement. As she states in the catalog, wildflowers "have a special beauty all their own. Using native plants in the garden not only helps to preserve the plants, but also provides food for animals such as butterflies and hummingbirds."

Directions: The nursery is located in the Finger Lakes region, one hour from Rochester. From Route 90, take Route 390 south. Take exit 9 onto Route 15 south and follow into Springwater. Just before town, atop a steep hill, turn right onto Harpers Ferry Road. The nursery is a mile on the right. From Route 86/17, turn onto Route 390 north. Take exit 3 onto Route 15 north and follow into Springwater. Turn left, staying on Route 15 north. Ascend a steep hill and turn left onto Harpers Ferry Road. The nursery is a mile on the right.

Nearby attractions: In Mumford, 20 miles southwest of Rochester, Genesee Country Village and Museum (585-538-6822; www.gcv.org) holds a plant sale every Mother's Day weekend. In Castile, Letchworth State Park (585-493-3600), the "Grand Canyon of the East," boasts magnificent scenery; the Genesee River roars through a gorge over major waterfalls between 600-foot cliffs. The park is haunted with Indian legends, such as that of Mon-a-sha-sha, a Seneca girl who perished in the falls and is said to return as a white deer. The park's restored 1920s Glen Iris Inn (585-493-2622; www.glenirisinn.com; take exit 7 off Route 390) offers overnight accommodation and meals, including picnics.

BAKERS' ACRES

1104 Auburn Road, Groton, NY 13073
(607) 533-4653; fax (607) 533-8653
www.bakersacres.net; e-mail *info@bakersacres.net*
Reenie Baker Sandsted

Perennials, annuals, and woody plants. Family-run perennial farm. Open January through March by chance or appointment; April through December, weekdays, 8 to 5:30, weekends, 9 to 5; extended hours in May and June. Closed on major holidays. No catalog or mail order. Plant lists and newsletter at front desk and on Web site. Classes. Landscape design. Garden walks. Tours, Wednesdays at 2. Country Garden Tea Room (607-533-3650). Display gardens. Visitors welcome.

If your name is Baker and you own 75 acres, it would be hard not to call it Bakers' Acres. Jackie Baker and her husband, Bob, started Bakers' Acres as a "fun" retirement project in 1980 on land north of Ithaca that they've owned for 50 years. In the manner of hobby farms, it started with annuals, hanging baskets, and pumpkins at a roadside stand.

By the mid-1990s, Bakers' Acres had become a full-fledged perennial farm, with traffic brisk enough to warrant converting an old Masonic lodge next door into a tea room, gift shop, and picnic pavilion. Staff was hired, lectures and seminars developed. A daughter, Reenie, joined the business. Small display gardens morphed into a lily pond, rock garden, rose border, and elaborate roadside perennial berm. On Sundays, Bob Baker, an emeritus professor of Poultry Science at Cornell, served barbecued chicken, using a special sauce he developed in the 1940s. Crowds came. Bakers' Acres fulfilled the dream of every farm stand, becoming a destination nursery.

Today Bakers' Acres is one of the largest perennial growers in central New York. Retirement hobbies don't last forever, but as the elder Bakers have slowed, Reenie Baker Sandsted and her staff continue the enterprise as an active perennial farm worthy of a country outing. The nursery has 10 greenhouses, 10 insulated frames, 100 sales frames, 800 apple trees, a cider press, and an acre of asparagus. The tea room is open to groups by reservation. "We still keep a few chickens to keep Dad happy," says Sandsted.

Bakers' Acres offers 1000 hardy perennials, grasses, and herbs in popular varieties, set out alphabetically on black plastic. Divided by sun and shade, plants are well labeled, well tended, and easy to find. The collection is set off from the road by handsome display beds that offer good ideas for using the nursery stock. Prices are reasonable. Checkout is in a red barn next to the Bakers' old farmhouse, attended by a helpful staff.

Flowering perennials form the heart of the collection, from acanthus to yucca. Fine groups of phlox, lily, iris, hosta, and daylily (the last from Janet Baker's special collection) are in evidence, as are Japanese tree peonies and herbaceous peonies—singles, doubles, and fernleaf forms. It's nice to see unusual drought-tolerant plants such as sea lavender and hardy cactus. The vines offer good variety—clematis, wisteria, climbing hydrangea, and American bittersweet (a seldom-seen native plant, as opposed to Oriental bittersweet, a nasty invasive).

In the shade perennial collection, the spring woodlanders are particularly delightful—white trillium, pink shooting star, and various hellebores and primroses. European ginger, pink lily-of-the-valley, crested iris, and the better-behaved spotted dead nettles make valuable ground covers. Pond plants feature hardy water lilies, variegated petasites, sweet flags, shallow water grasses, and several ligularias.

Each spring, Bakers' Acres offers more pansies and petunias than one could possibly want, along with container plants, cutting-garden annuals, and vegetable flats. In recent years a modest tree and shrub collection has become unexpectedly rich in roses, fruit trees and bushes, and unusual woody ornamentals. A few conifers and broadleaf evergreens round out the group. Unlike the perennials and annuals, these are clearly bought in, but the stock is good.

Perhaps the farm's nicest amenities are its simplest. Copies of Bob Baker's "Cornell Chicken Barbecue" recipe are on hand in the checkout barn. So are packets of breadseed poppies *(Papaver somniferum)* of the kind that made Dorothy doze on her way to Oz. Divided by "pink" and "red," seeds are harvested from double poppies grown on the farm. Like spring asparagus, autumn apples, and pressed cider, such touches are like magic notes from the area's farming past.

Directions: From Ithaca, take Route 13 to the Triphammer exit and turn left on Triphammer Road. Go 4 miles to the end and turn right at the stop sign on to Route 34 north. The farm is 5 miles on the left. From Cortland, take Route 222 to Groton, turn onto Route 38 south, and turn right onto Route 34B. In Lansing, turn right at the stop light and then right at the stop sign onto Route 34 north. The farm is 5 miles on the left.

Nearby attractions: For Emeritus Professor Robert C. Baker's instructions for large-group barbecues, write for Bulletin No. 862 ($2) from Cornell Cooperative Extension, Research Park, Ithaca, NY 14850.

BEAVER MEADOWLANDS
1506 Beaver Meadow Road, Java Center, NY 14082
(585) 457-3584 phone and fax
Patricia Denis

Ornamental trees, shrubs, and perennials. *Solo nursery. Open May 1 to October 31, daily, 8 to 6; closed Wednesdays. Other times by appointment. No catalog. Limited mail order. Spring container planting service. Garden planning. Special orders. Display garden. Peak bloom in July. Visitors welcome.*

A distinctive nursery run by a single person is almost always the product of devotion. As any artist will confirm, only love can make a decade of hard work seem enjoyable.

Beaver Meadowlands, a solo nursery in western New York, has thrived through the industry of its owner, Pat Denis. Growing up in a household of girls, she always volunteered for yard work. "I'd say, 'Mom, I'll do the garden if I don't have to clean house,'" she recalls. "I've had my nose in a plant book since I was thirteen." When she retired from work as an obstetrical nurse, with grown children and a busy-schoolteacher husband, Denis resolved to pursue her love of gardening by starting a nursery.

Founded in 1993 on home acreage, Beaver Meadowlands strives for performance ornamentals suitable for western New York. "I look for plants of distinction," says Denis. "In our climate we have to be careful about root-zone hardiness." The nursery carries flowering trees, shrubs, perennials, and enough colorful annuals to fill custom containers in the spring. Most stock is grown from seed, plug, and bare-root seedling in the nursery's three greenhouses. "I do it all myself," says Denis. "Choosing the right plants takes a lot of research."

One of the nursery's strong suits is decorative trees and shrubs for small gardens. These include Carolina silver-bell, weeping mulberry, standards of

'Peegee' hydrangea, colorful smoketree hybrids, and a graceful dwarf crab, *Malus* 'Tina'. Popular flowering shrubs include weeping Siberian pea shrub, shrubby St.-John's-wort, and a bushlike form of kousa dogwood. The nursery offers old English roses and David Austin hybrids screened for hardiness. Its lilacs are right for small gardens: compact 'Palabin', Japanese tree-lilac standards, and miniatures such as pink 'Tinkerbelle'. "I also find 'Miss Canada' to be a wonderful lilac, with pink blossoms and red leaves in autumn," says Denis. "Sometimes one big plant does wonders for a small yard."

Stock choices betray Denis' love of baroque garden lilies: fragrant Asiatic, aurelian, and trumpet lilies illuminate the display gardens in July. Peonies are another passion. Japanese-style herbaceous peonies such as 'Krinkled White' and 'Bowl of Beauty' make great garden subjects—provided the owner can resist cutting them for the house. Denis also sells Japanese tree peonies, which she began growing fifteen years ago. "They're glorious. We're lucky they like the cold! Gardeners can't even touch them down South," Denis says. "I have all my Mom's old herbaceous peonies, too."

Beaver Meadowlands prides itself on its customer service. Denis plants spring containers, takes special orders, gives lectures and garden tours, and even does a bit of mail order. Gardeners can bring in pictures of problem areas, and on her day off, Denis sometimes makes site visits. "Consultations are on the honor system. There's no charge, but I do ask that they buy the plants from me, and people respect that," she says.

The nursery's eight acres are ribboned with display gardens in woodland, semi-shade, and full sun. Denis has lived in the area all her life and is well-known to gardeners in greater Buffalo. Because it's impossible to groom a garden and run a nursery by oneself, Denis invites friends and customers to help with gardening tasks in exchange for selected plants. "It keeps the garden looking nice. They work for a day and learn how to edge, fertilize, transfer, and divide. They take home plants and they're thrilled."

Gardening binds us to the cycle of seasons, never more so than in spring. "People come here just itching to get started," says Denis. "They always ask, 'What do you have that's new?'"

Directions: The nursery is west of the Finger Lakes. From the east on Route I-90, take exit 48A and turn onto Route 77 south. In 31 miles, in Java Center, turn left onto Beaver Meadow Road; the nursery is at #1506. From Buffalo, take Route I-90 south to exit 54 and turn onto Route 16 south. In 13 miles, turn left onto Route 20A east; in 12 miles, turn right onto Route 77 south and follow directions above. From

Rochester, take Route 390 south to exit 10 and turn onto Route 20 west. In 35 miles, in Darien Center, turn left onto Route 77 south; follow directions above.

Nearby attractions: The Village Pub Restaurant, 3974 Main Street, Strykersville, NY 14145 (585-457-9545; www.villagepubrt78.com), is the only place to eat in striking distance. North of Java off Route 20, Country Cottage Gifts & Gardens, 10448 Harper Road, Darien, NY 14040 (585-547-9591), sells country wares surrounded by country gardens.

BEDLAM GARDENS
1893 Route 34B, King Ferry, NY 13081
(315) 364-8725
Debi Lampman

Perennials. Hardy semi-tropicals. Small fruits. *Solo nursery. Open May through September, Wednesday through Saturday, 9 to 6, and Tuesday at the Auburn Farmer's Market. No catalog or mail order. Display gardens. Cut flowers and wedding bouquets. Visitors welcome.*

Bedlam Gardens near Ithaca grows a delightfully chaotic mix of flowering perennials, semi-tropicals, and ornamental shrubs. Its proprietor, Debi Lampman, founded the nursery in her front yard in 1996. Today the nursery (still in the front yard) has two greenhouses and a retail barn.

A Master Gardener and enthusiastic plant lover raised on an upstate dairy farm, Lampman learned to love plants in infancy. "When I was young, my mother taught me how to read a seed catalog," Lampman recalls. "By the time I was 15, I was growing perennials and building stone walls." She got a degree in nursery management and design from SUNY Cobleskill. She is president of the Cornell chapter of the Garden Club of America (originally known as "The Men's Garden Club"), former president of the Bearded Iris Society, and active in the North American Rock Garden Society. Her favorite nursery is Heronswood, the West Coast mecca for serious plant collectors.

For a small operation, Bedlam Gardens sells plants of surprising variety, collected from sources high and low. "I tend to be eclectic. If I see something at the wholesale market that's odd or unusual, I buy it. I got 'Dancing Butterflies' peony from Wal-Mart. I order every year from Heronswood. I get things from plant exchanges and raffles. I love pass-along plants. That date palm was from my grandmother," says Lampman. "That's why it's called Bedlam Gardens."

An eclectic repertoire defies easy summary. One notices perennials used for cut flowers and everlastings; lime, purple, and variegated foliage; and lots of ornamental grasses. Fall-bloomers and self-sowers keep the garden lively well into autumn. Native plants include a wild orchid called swamp ladies'-tresses (*Spiranthes cernua* var. *odorata*) and *Spigelia marilandica*, once considered tender above Zone 8. An interest in clematis is apparent in the stock of orange-peel clematis *(C. tangutica)* and two shrubby, non-vining forms *(C. integrefolia; C. heracleifolia)*. Bedlam Gardens offers up-to-date choices of careopteris, butterfly bush, and smoke bush (especially color-splashed novelties such as 'Pink Champagne' and 'Nordine Red'). Choice small trees, such as Shantung maple *(Acer truncatum),* occasionally show up in the sales yard.

One of Lampman's out-of-the-way specialties is hardy fuchsia. Semi-tropicals valued for their dangling multicolored flowers, fuchsias are not supposed to survive beyond Zone 6. Lampman secured her first hardy fuchsia from a gardener in Zone 4 and has since developed a healthy disrespect for hardiness zone ratings. Her favorite is the red-and-violet Magellan fuchsia (*Fuchsia magellanica licartonii*), which is naturalized along southern Ireland's roadsides. In Bedlam's Zone 5 garden, hardy fuchsias can reach three feet and produce hundreds of blooms per stem. (The trick to survival, Lampman says, is to plant deep and add manure.)

Perhaps it was the fuchsias that inspired Lampman's ardor for plants with a steamy, tropical look. "I love big, lush, in-your-face plants," she says. "Just because we live in a cold climate doesn't mean we can't *look* warm." Lampman grows a dozen hardy hibiscus for their Frisbee-size blossoms in juicy-fruit colors. She grows princess tree *(Paulownia tomentosa),* which refuses to bloom this far north, just for its sultry 3-foot leaves. Her tender amaryllis lilies grow like weeds in the window boxes. "I've kept some amaryllis going for 15 years," she says. "I got one from a gardener who had it 50 years."

Lampman cannot resist growing unusual small fruits such as gooseberry and currant. "They're easy and there aren't many people growing them," says Lampman. "We sell them at the farmers' markets in Auburn and Skaneateles." It's all part of the bedlam.

The 6-acre nursery is located on a limestone shelf, two miles from Cornell's field-crop testing garden. Former hay fields have been converted to display gardens for stock plants. These include a "cathedral" trellis of Eastern cedar, a "bone yard" for rock garden plants, and a red-and-yellow "hot" garden on the sunny side of the house.

As with everything at Bedlam Gardens, there is constant spillover between garden and nursery. Lampman propagates half her stock from seed and divisions. The rest is grown from plugs and small plants. If it passes muster, a plant eventually ends up in the retail shed. "Whenever I buy new stock, I plant a good chunk in the garden for testing and send it to friends for feedback," says Lampman. "I like to push the envelope."

Directions: From Route I-90, take exit 40 and turn right off the ramp onto Route 34 south. In 15 miles, in Fleming, turn right onto Route 34B. The nursery is in 13 miles at #1893. From Ithaca, take Route 34B north to King Ferry and look for the nursery at #1893.

Nearby attractions: King Ferry Winery, 658 Lake Road, King Ferry, NY 13081 (315-364-5100; treleavenwines.com; open daily), produces award-winning Treleaven Wines. In the lovely heritage town of Aurora, the refurbished Aurora Inn, 391 Main Street, Aurora, NY 13026 (toll-free 866-364-8808; 315-364-8888; www.aurora-inn.com), has a delightful restaurant and rooms overlooking Cayuga Lake.

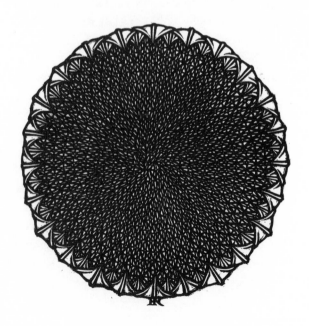

BORGLUM'S IRIS GARDENS

2202 Austin Road, Geneva, NY 14456-9118

(585) 526-6729

www.borglumsirisgardens.com; e-mail *sylborg@aol.com*

Dana and Sylvia Borglum

Siberian and tall bearded iris. Small specialty nursery. Open in bloom season (approximately May 15 to June 25), Sunday through Friday, 8 to 8, and by appointment. Call for exact dates. Plant list. Catalog on Web site. Mail order. Dig-your-own plants. Photos and newsletter on Web site. Gift certificates. Display garden. Visitors welcome.

Dana Borglum is an amateur iris hybridizer with a four-acre garden near Geneva, which he works with his wife, Sylvia. In 2002, Borglum's 'Lake Keuka', a stunning violet-blue Siberian iris hybrid with aqua styles, won the American Iris Society's Morgan Wood Medal, the highest award given to a Siberian iris. A hobbyist at heart, Borglum sells Siberian and tall bearded iris directly from his home garden during bloom season.

Borglum's trajectory is typical of the ardent home hybridizer. According to Borglum, he "started pollen dabbing in the mid-80s, after a kindly, helpful iris hybridizer showed me where the pollen goes." In no time he had produced 8000 seedlings. Seeking a home for overstock, Borglum placed ads in the weekly Penny Saver and sold bargain-priced iris in paper bags. Ten years later, the garden was so overrun with customers that the Borglums could hardly keep up with demand. To save labor, they began handing out spades and asking visitors to help with digging. In 2002, the same year 'Lake Keuka' won the AIS award, Borglum began selling dig-your-own named iris from the garden. Today, the garden attracts 1000 customers from 16 states and Canada. "A hobby got out of hand," says Borglum, "and turned into a living IRA."

Borglum's own Siberian iris hybrids are the garden's true riches, comprising some 20 named varieties. The best come in lovely tones reflecting the cool blues of the nearby Finger Lakes: marine 'Canandaigua Lady', sapphire 'Lake Seneca', and blue-argent 'Seneca Silvery Skies'. Recent introductions are 'Seneca Wine Trail', a grape-purple Siberian honoring local vineyards, and 'Seneca Kaleidoscope', a pale amethyst Siberian of "parentage unknown." The nursery also offers elegant Siberian iris from award-winning breeders such as the Schafer-Sacks team and the late Dr. Currier McEwen.

Besides Siberians, Borglum Iris Gardens offers tall bearded iris hybrids bred at the nursery, most resembling sweet confections. 'Seneca Creamsicle' is cream-tangerine, and 'Silly Girl' is frilly, perfumed, and pink-orange. One of the most unusual iris in the garden, 'Alley Oops', is a "chance cross" between a Siberian iris and a yellow swamp iris *(I. pseudacorus)*. Its intriguing flower is a swirl of pale blue and yellow, with blue netting.

Borglum's Iris Gardens opens to visitors during bloom season, from mid-May to late July. The nursery is set among corn fields in an open landscape. Signs point the way to the iris beds bordering the road, backed by attractive gardens graced with ornamental trees. The nursery's dig-your-own policy extends to iris and daylilies. All plants are meticulously labeled. Potted peonies, poppies, and hostas are also for sale. For non-diggers, Borglum's iris hybrids can be ordered through its catalog or Web site. New Siberian iris hybrids generally run $20 or $25, while 'Lake Keuka' sells for $10 and older named varieties for less.

The amateur hybridizer's biggest challenge is knowing what to throw out. "So many new seedlings are so interesting," says Borglum. In autumn, when the garden grows quiet, he says, "We look forward to a winter's rest, like the woodchucks."

Directions: From Rochester, take Route I-90 east to the Canandaigua exit, turn onto Route 332 south, and in Canandaigua, turn left onto Routes 5 & 20 east. In several miles, turn south on Route 5; in Hall, turn right at the 4-way stop sign, and take the second right onto Austin Road. The farm is 1 mile on the right. From Syracuse, take Route I-90 west to the Geneva exit, turn right onto Route 14 south, and in Geneva, turn right onto Routes 5 & 20 west. Turn left onto Route 14A south; in Hall, go straight at the 4-way stop sign, and follow directions above. From Route I-86/17, take the western Bath exit onto Route 54 north; in Penn Yan, turn onto Route 14A north; in Hall, turn left at the 4-way stop sign, and follow directions above.

Nearby attractions: Keuka Flower Farm, 3597 Skyline Drive, Penn Yan, NY 14527 (315-536-2736; www.driedflowersdirect.com), is a family-run mail-order flower farm specializing in dried flowers or everlastings; open house, last weekend in August.

THE CATHOLIC HOMESTEADING MOVEMENT

21 Delaware Square, Norwich, NY 13815
Richard and Anna Marie Fahey and family

Fruit trees. Apple scion wood. Vegetable seeds. Medicinals. Family-run horticultural farm. Open by appointment. Mail order only. Send two stamps each for seed flyer, apple scion list, or herb catalog. Organic. Dried herbs, salves, and tinctures. Subscription to The Homesteader *20 stamps or $8 per year. Courses on premises; write for schedule.*

At the heart of modern ecology is an age-old golden rule: as we treat the earth, so we treat ourselves. For those seeking accord with this tradition, the call to live harmoniously with nature may be heard as a vocation—as a call to live simply and thoughtfully, and to treat the earth lovingly, as a gift from God.

The Catholic Homesteading Movement (CHM) is a homestead farm run by Richard and Anna Marie Fahey and their children on a farm in Oxford, New York, between Ithaca and Cooperstown. The Faheys began homesteading in 1961 and are among the region's most experienced experts. They live and work on a self-sustaining 90-acre hill farm surrounded by woods and meadows. Wild foods such as woodchuck and dandelion combine with homegrown food to sustain this natural way of life.

Growing your own food and medicine is one of the principal tenets of self-reliance farming. According to Richard Fahey, "We have chickens, ducks, goats, cats, cows, bees, and workhorses. Buildings are small and made of logs. Visitors are sometimes surprised by the primitiveness of our life. We are living from the land as much as we are teaching other people to do so. The serenity and beauty of our natural surroundings is our greatest asset."

Through the CHM, family members offer several organic farm products of importance to gardeners and homesteaders. Foremost of these are grafted apple and fruit trees. The apple trees are 'Billy Bound', a blocky yellow heirloom dating to George Washington's day; 'Gilliflower', a once-popular drying and baking apple; and 'Crown Jewel', a unique porcelain-yellow fruit with a golden russet topping, which the Faheys call "the most breathtaking apple in our collection." All three are vigorous and productive, especially 'Billy Bound', favored by the Faheys for fresh eating in winter.

CHM's two unique fruit discoveries are 'David Smith', a hardy everbearing mulberry tree; and 'Heart's Desire', a cherry hawthorn whose fruit resembles a cherry in size and taste. Neither of these plants is in commercial production, making CHM virtually the sole source.

CHM also sells scion wood from its fruit orchards for use in grafting onto hardy rootstock to create new fruit trees. CHM's list of cultivated apple varieties is a near-complete compendium of heirloom and modern apples known and grown in New York State—some 350 named varieties, including many first-rate "keepers" whose flavor and quality are enhanced by winter storage. Scion wood is also sold for 16 kinds of pear, 14 sweet and tart cherries, 29 plums, 5 medlars, 6 edible hawthorns, and one each of mulberry, peach, hardy apricot, and hardy almond. Scion wood costs $2 per scion, about what a nonprofit arboretum would charge.

Organic garden seed raised on the farm is sold through CHM Seeds. This enterprise began in 1986 with nutritious vegetables developed on the Fahey homestead, gathered into a generous seed package called "Winter Storage Garden: Seeds for Self-Sufficiency." This modestly priced package contains 5 salad and cooking greens; 5 pumpkins, squashes, and cucumbers; 5 drying beans, peas and corn; and 11 edible roots. Seeds are selected for storage capability, short maturity, best flavor, and open-pollination (enabling seed saving). Some of the farm's organically grown onion bulbs, such as woodland leeks, are hard to find in commerce.

Homestead Herbs, a companion effort, is a mail-order catalog of medicinal tinctures crafted from organic herbs grown on the farm. Plantain tincture is recommended for insect bites; boneset for flu; crampbark for cramps, and shepherd's purse *(Capsella bursa-pastoris)* to staunch bleeding. While not officially guaranteed, tincture descriptions reflect fairly solid modern understandings about the medicinal value of herbs. (A naive hand-drawing in the catalog shows Anna Marie Fahey seated in the garden, doing herb research.) Comforting salves are crafted from calendula, comfrey, and lavender, mixed with fresh beeswax from family hives. A species of hen-and-chickens known as "roof leek" *(Sempervivum tectorum)*—used for burns and rashes—is the only medicinal sold in plant form.

The Faheys publish a bimonthly newsletter, *The Homesteader*, containing advice on homesteading. One newsletter recounts the virtues of 'Red Top' turnips, along with storage and cooking tips. (Open-pollinated 'Red Top' turnip seed may be purchased for a nominal sum.) The newsletter is by subscription, with publication occurring "when the other chores are done."

The Faheys open their homestead in summer to people who want to learn about homesteading and simple living. For a modest fee, courses are offered on basic homesteading, organic gardening, fruit tree grafting, medicinal herbs, home birthing, and others. Attendees bring tents and sleeping bags. While CHM's purpose is to help people homestead in accord with Christian principles, programs are open to all, without regard to race or creed. Most are family oriented and children are welcome. Enthusiastic accolades pour in from CHM graduates. As one exhausted attendant from California wrote, "I never learned so much in a week in my life!"

Related source: Seeds for Survival, P.O. Box 111, Waterport, NY 14571 (888-686-0056; www.seedsforsurvival.com), is a small, family-run seed company offering open-pollinated vegetable seed, including an "Ultimate Survival Garden" package and many older varieties that are being lost to commerce.

COTTAGE GARDENS
4540 East Shelby Road, Medina, NY 14103
(585) 798-5441
www.daylily.net/gardens/cottagegardens; e-mail *cglilies@eznet.net*
Brent and Deborah Ross

Daylily hybrids. Small hybridizer's nursery. Open mid-July through August, Wednesday through Saturday, 10 to 5; Sundays, 11 to 4, and other times by arrangement. Mail order. American Hemerocallis Society Display Garden. Peak bloom mid to late July. Visitors welcome. Call ahead if coming from a distance.

Established in 1995, Cottage Gardens is a small nursery in Medina, midway between Buffalo and Rochester, specializing in daylily hybrids. Owners Brent and Deborah Ross grow some 1700 registered daylilies in their display garden, including several Brent Ross introductions. The collection includes fine older varieties, award winners, and newer introductions from noted hybridizers. These are not only vibrant performers in northern gardens but also provide good breeding stock for daylily hybridizers and enthusiasts.

Because of their ease of growth and reproduction, daylilies attract more backyard breeders than any other perennial. Savvy amateurs can produce dramatic results, especially if good breeding stock and clear goals form the basis of a disciplined breeding program. Cottage Gardens specializes in seedlings of local Daylily Society breeders—original hybrids well suited to the conditions of western New York. An exceptional example is 'Granny Smith Surprise', a ruffled yellow-and-white sophisticate introduced by Brent Ross in 2004 ($150).

The nursery also samples the work of daylily breeders on the national scene, such as Patrick Stamile, Dan Trimmer, Darrel Apps, Jeff Salter, Ray Moldovan, and David Kirchhoff. Notable up-and-comers are ruffled, sunset-colored 'Spacecoast' hybrids of Florida breeder John Kinnebrew, and award-winning "spider" daylilies of Pennsylvania breeder Clayton Burkey.

Cottage Gardens is an official American Hemerocallis Society Display Garden, one of fifty-eight in the northeastern United States. The name derives from the cottage-garden style of its displays, where perennials and daylilies mingle together in colorful harmonies. A small water garden with water lilies and goldfish provides a relaxing point from which to view the beds and borders. The "candy bed" is particularly fun, so named because it contains Patrick Stamile's famous 'Candy' series: 'Strawberry Candy', 'Raspberry Candy', 'Blackberry Candy', 'Blueberry Candy', and 'Custard Candy', which won the AHS Stout Silver Medal in 1999.

Cottage Gardens is open during bloom season, from mid-July through August; a Daylily Event is held in late July. This is the best time to choose daylilies, one of the few perennials that endure being transplanted while in bloom. Prices range from $5 to $200, with most at the affordable end. Double-fan plants are dug at the garden, on request, or shipped by USPS Priority Mail. Bonus plants go with each shipment.

Directions: From Route I-90, take the Pembroke exit, turn onto Route 77 north and then Route 63 north. In Medina, turn right at the first light onto Route 31A. In Millville, take the first right turn onto East Shelby Road. The nursery is an old cobblestone house (#4540).

Nearby attractions: Medina is an old quarry town; its sandstone was used to construct Buckingham Palace. The Culvert, listed in Ripley's Believe It or Not, is the only tunnel under the Erie Canal. Medina Stone Farm, P.O. Box 13, 255 North Gravel Road, Medina, NY 14103 (585-798-9238; www.medinastonefarm.com), offers accommodations, a corn maze, and American music shows put on by the owners, a professional duo named Ron and Nancy OneSong.

CROSMAN'S SEEDS

P.O. Box 110, 511 West Commercial Street, East Rochester, NY 14445
(800) 446-SEED; (585) 586-1928; fax (585) 586-6093
www.crosmanseed.com; e-mail *crosman@mindspring.com*
William Mapstone family

Vegetable, flower, and lawn seed. Family-owned seed house. Business office open year-round, Monday through Friday, 8 to 5; and Saturdays, 9 to 11, mid-April to early October. Catalog on Web site. Mail order only. Promotional seed packets for organizations.

In 1838, just 13 years after the opening of the Erie Canal brought prosperity to every farm in the region, Charles Crosman founded a seed house in Rochester to serve the area's booming farm population. Most of Genesee County land was devoted to agriculture, and new settlers made constant demand for seed. Trial beds at the Crosman's Seeds were used to develop improved varieties, which were distributed to cash-poor farmers in exchange for a percentage of the crop.

Crosman's Seeds prospered, absorbing small seed houses and expanding its real estate. In 1924, the enterprise moved into large factory buildings once used to manufacture trailer cars. In 1928, management passed to Herbert W. Mapstone, a former sales manager who introduced wholesale packet production and remained president until 1979. The Smithsonian Institution has documented Crosman's Seeds in recognition of its importance in the history of agricultural entrepreneurship in New York State. The Mapstone family continues its ownership to the present day.

Although customers are no longer compelled to cede part of their crops, Crosman's Seeds is still in the business of selling improved vegetable seed to growers and gardeners. The business is strictly mail order. To conserve costs, Crosman's seed list is published only on the Internet. The company boasts of excellent prices for top-rated seed varieties in large or small quantities. Most vegetable and flower seed packets cost 59 cents. Beans, peas, and sweet corn in two-ounce packets cost 89 cents. That, plus shipping, is the price of a garden.

Among Crosman's 200-odd vegetable varieties, some stand out as mid-20th century classics: 'Iceberg' lettuce, 'Silver Queen' corn, 'Kentucky Wonder' green bean, and 'Red Cherry' tomato. The seed list features beets, broccoli, cabbages, cukes, eggplant, endive, kohlrabi, lettuce, onions,

parsnips, peppers, rhubarb, squash, tomatoes, and
turnip greens. Gourmets value Nantes scarlet
carrots, Italian cardoons, Chinese cabbage,
Hungarian yellow wax pepper, and early
sugar pumpkins. Short-season varieties are
best suited to northern gardens, while 'Hales
Best Jumbo' muskmelon and okra are for
the South. 'Kingshorn Wax Round Pod
Bush' and 'Cherokee Wax'—the names alone
make you want to grow yellow beans.

Crosman's flower seed packets offer 130
flowering plants. Old-timers will surely snap up the
double hollyhocks, China asters, dwarf snapdragons,
Texas bluebonnets, long-spurred columbines, and morning-glories. For the
rock garden there are poppy, rock cress, armeria (sea pink), and even cactus
seeds. Ornamental herbs feature red amaranth, dark opal basil, and calendula.
Crosman's sells seeds for pompom-, cactus-, and dahlia-flowered zinnia
(including green 'Envy') and a dozen marigolds, including 'Dainty Marietta',
a single dwarf yellow with a mahogany daub on each petal.

Another Crosman seed product is turf grass suited to cool climates.
Special lawn mixes address turf grass needs in shade, sandy soil, heavy clay,
and high-traffic areas; and for disease resistance and erosion control. Grass
seed is also sold by species, such as perennial ryegrass and creeping red
fescue. According to Crosman's, "Our niche in the market is to supply the
customer with a quality of turf grass usually not available at home and
garden stores."

Promotional seed packets are Crosman's latest innovation. A good part of
its trade is selling custom-printed seed packets to businesses, charities, and
governmental organizations for use in sales, promotions, and fundraisers.
Politicians have been known to distribute "Forget-Me-Not" packets to
voters before elections.

Like everything else at Crosman's Seeds, after 160 years such hucksterism
is endearing. "If it grows, we can probably get it," asserts the company on
special seed requests. "We have suppliers all over the world. You are not
limited to the varieties that we use in our seed packet line. We can even
supply you with organic seed."

CUMMINS NURSERY

4233 Glass Factory Bay Road, Geneva, NY 14456
(315) 789-7083
www.cumminsnursery.com; e-mail *jnc1@localnet.com*
The Cummins family

Custom-propagated apple trees and fruit trees. Apple rootstock. Small fruits. *Small specialty nursery. Open by appointment. Free catalog. Mail order only. Minimum order 3 trees. Minimum shipping charge $15. Custom grafting. Apple rootstocks from Cornell breeding program. Indian Creek Farm in Ithaca open for tree pick up and visitors (see directions). Geneva production nursery closed to visitors.*

Cummins Nursery is operated by the Cummins family on two orchards in western New York. Its expertise is growing hardy apple trees, fruit trees, and improved apple rootstock developed at Cornell's fruit research station. Founder Jim Cummins is emeritus professor of Pomology at Cornell, where he worked on breeding apple rootstock. After retiring in 1993, Cummins continued growing fruit trees and rootstocks on farmland in Geneva. In 1994, when the New York State Fruit Testing Station closed its nursery, he saw an opportunity to fill the gap.

Cummins Nursery specializes in custom-grafted fruit tree production. This is an ideal way to secure uncommon trees from the nursery's orchards or to perpetuate a beloved old fruit tree from family property—what Jim Cummins calls "a genuine Grampa tree." The catalog lists many wonderful apple varieties, as well as hardy pears, stone fruits, soft fruits, and a dozen grape cultivars from university breeding programs.

The nursery's main focus is apples—160 varieties of disease-resistant commercial, heirloom, and cider apple trees. Among them are updated strains of well-known modern apples, such as 'Fuji', 'Liberty', and 'Freedom' (great for organic orchards), as well as new storage apples from Cornell. The nursery grows the original crisp 'Hawkeye' apple, first marketed as 'Delicious' in 1876. Its strain of 'Jonathan' retains the old snappy sweetness Jim Cummins recalls from boyhood. Cummins especially recommends 'Wolf River', a hardy cooking apple that is "immune to everything under the sun," and 'Dolgo' crab, "a gorgeous thing to eat out of hand—it cleans the teeth."

Cider apples are an important subspecialty. "Our cider apple orders have gone through the roof," Cummins says. "We now do a lot of custom propagation for commercial cider makers in Vermont and New Hampshire."

Some years ago, Frank Bowen, author of *Apples*, asked the Cummins to graft hundreds of experimental cider-variety trees for his family's Kentucky orchard—a job that increased their vintage-quality cider apples to 26 varieties. They also grow 15 cider pears, used to make "perry" (pear cider).

The nursery grows Asian pears ("nashi"), European pears, hardy apricots, sweet and tart cherries, peaches, nectarines, and European and Japanese plums. Some are worth putting in the orchard even if fruit is lost in cold years. "People go crazy for hardy apricots, even when they're small and don't fruit every year," Jim Cummins says. "Some of the cherries are so good they're dangerous."

As founding nurseryman, Jim Cummins collaborates with his wife, Cindy, and son, Stephen, in what is essentially a family enterprise. Jim Cummins oversees the production orchard in Geneva, while Steve Cummins runs Indian Creek Farm in Ithaca. "We grow our trees in Geneva, store and ship our trees in Ithaca, and our office is wherever Mom and Dad happen to be at the moment," says Steve Cummins, Captivating family stories, posted on the Web site, include a delightful word-song by Jim Cummins about his boyhood in Southern Illinois, called "Kicking Leaves in Mr. Gage's Orchard."

The nursery produces about 25,000 fruit trees a year— a small output by commercial standards, but the Cummins want their nursery to stay small. While not quite organic, they spray sparingly, for specific problems. As the catalog states, "We do not subscribe to the prevalent nursery philosophy of 'Who cares, nobody eats a tree.' We try to be good stewards of land and water and the air we breathe."

Directions: The production fields in Geneva are not open to the public. Fruit tree orders can be picked up at Indian Creek Farm, 1408 Trumansburg Road, Ithaca, NY 14850 (607-273-9544). From Ithaca, take Route 96 north; the farm is 2.5 miles up the road, just after Hayts Corners; open May through October, daily, 8 to 6, for fruit trees, seasonal vegetables, pumpkins, melons, bedding plants, and baskets.

Nearby attractions: At its annual Field Day, Cornell's Agricultural Experiment Station in Geneva (www.cornell.edu) opens its experimental orchards; the Station's land was once "Kanadesega," capital of the Seneca Tribe. Patti's Lakeview Diner, 43 Lake Street, Geneva (315-789-6433), is a 1950s throwback with cozy booths and good food.

Related sources: North of the Border, 2969 North Genesee Street, Geneva, NY 14456 (315-789-3832 evenings; 315-521-4255 days; www.cumminsnursery.com/wine.htm; Tony Bruno), is a Cummins Nursery employee who sells 2-year-old grafted wine and table grape vines. Foster Nurseries, 10175 Mile Block Road, North Collins, NY 14111 (800-223-2211; www.concordnurseries.com), sells bare-root grape vines by mail order; $100 minimum. Amberg's Nursery, 3164 Whitney Road, Stanley, NY 14561 (585-526-5405), distributes professional-quality orchard supplies and pruning tools.

DER ROSENMEISTER
190 Seven Mile Drive, Ithaca, NY 14850
(607) 273-8610
www.rosenmeister.com; e-mail *slvrbckg@yahoo.com*
Leon Ginenthal

Heirloom and modern roses. *Small specialty nursery. Open May through Labor Day, weekends, 10 to 5; other hours by appointment. Plant list. Catalog on Web site. No mail order. Display garden. Peak bloom in June. Visitors welcome.*

Der Rosenmeister, German for "The Rosemaster," is a small nursery in the Finger Lakes region with a good selection of heirloom and modern roses. Lee Ginenthal started selling roses from home acreage in 2003, he says, "as a segue into a retirement business." An energetic gardener for more than 30 years, Ginenthal has long been fascinated with roses. "The first rose I grew was from a cutting I took from a rambler my grandmother grew—Dr. Van Fleet," he recalls. "I still have that rose—it's what got me interested in old roses."

Ginenthal's credentials go well beyond roses. As a special education teacher in Ithaca's public schools, he directed the city's award-winning Youth Horticultural Apprentice Program for at-risk teenagers and created the city's Youth Urban Forestry Initiative. On a Fulbright grant in Japan in 2002, he developed a curriculum unit on bonsai for youth. Ginenthal was the responsible adult behind the design, planting, and maintenance of Ithaca Commons, the city's downtown pedestrian mall.

Der Rosenmeister's plant list opens what Graham Stuart Thomas calls the "storehouse of loveliness" represented by the world's leading heirloom roses. One glowing example is 'Madame Hardy', a French damask rose from Empress Josephine's 19th-century garden at Malmaison, considered by some to be the most beautiful white rose. 'Quatre Saisons', an antique pink autumn damask, is famous for its repeat bloom and powerful fragrance. 'Stanwell Perpetual', a double-white burnet, inspired English rose historian Edward Bunyard to remark, "Stanwell should be in every garden, as from May to December it will rarely be without flowers, and these are deliciously scented, and it makes an admirable hedge of four or five feet or so."

Ginenthal is proud of the 50 varieties offered in the nursery's opening year, each chosen for beauty, hardiness, and disease resistance. A diverse stock includes a pink shade-tolerant scrambler called 'Evangeline', a century-old "blue" multiflora rambler called 'Bleu Magenta', and a rarely offered climber named 'White Cap', admired by rose expert Stephen Scanniello in his book, *Climbing Roses*. For gallica roses there's the famous black-red 'Tuscany Superb', the purple-crimson 'Cardinal de Richelieu', and the ancient apothecary's rose. Ginenthal's love of roses is further evident is his highly rated shrub roses, unusual rugosas, antique albas, and excellent modern Canadian hybrids.

"Many of the roses we carry are from Germany," says Ginenthal. "The Germans are keen on using roses in the landscape rather than in formal beds." The most celebrated German roses were bred by Wilhelm Kordes for use in German parklands, where plants had to be hardy, carefree, floriferous, and large enough to be seen from a distance. One example grown here is Kordes' 'Lichtkonigin Lucia', which has been called "the most underrated yellow shrub that has ever been raised." Even the nursery name originates in Germany. "My wife is from a little town in Pfalz," says Ginenthal. "When we visited there seven years ago, her relatives called me '*Der Rosenmeister!*'"

Der Rosenmeister is located on a rather bare new house lot, recently planted out with a 100-foot bed of *Rosa rugosa* hybrids and a small *roseraie*, or rose circle, surrounding a stone patio. Its sources include "rustled" roses and roses from specialty sources in America and Canada. A current list appears on the Web site. Mature roses in 3-gallon pots are offered for $25 per plant. Current stock is a 50-50 mix of own-root and grafted roses, which promises to shift toward more own-root plants as nursery momentum increases. Ginenthal propagates his own-root roses organically in a 50-foot hoop house, preferring them over grafted stock because of their longevity and unchanging authenticity to type.

Directions: From Ithaca, take Route 13 south, turn right at the light onto Route 13A, and in 0.5 mile, turn left onto Bostwick Road. In 0.5 mile, turn left onto Seven Mile Drive; the nursery is the first driveway on the right.

Nearby attractions: Veronica's Garden, 1748 Trumansburg Road/Route 96, Trumansburg, NY 14886 (607-387-3365; http://jdvservices.com/Vgarden; open May through October; Veronica DeVivo), is an organic nursery with 600 varieties of perennials.

ENGLISH BASKETRY WILLOWS
412 County Road #31, Norwich, NY 13815-3149
(607) 336-9031 phone and fax
www.msu.edu/user/shermanh/galeb/index.htm; e-mail *bonwillow@ascent.net*
Bonnie Gale

Dormant willow cuttings. *Small specialty nursery. Mail order only. Catalog on Web site. Orders due by May 31. Minimum order 2 cuttings per variety. Handcrafted baskets and custom willow work. Basketry tools, books, patterns, and kits. Dried willows and bulrushes. Classes. Membership forum, willow exchange, and newsletter. Visitors by appointment only.*

To horticulturists, willows are a genetic muddle, fraught with pests. To gardeners, they are restless swishing landscape presences whose early catkins, or "pussy willows," are a joyful sign of spring. Long valued as the most graceful of garden shrubs, willows have a rich history of use since prehistoric times for bank stabilization, fuel, windbreak, fishing weir, wicker furniture, and woven basketry.

English Basketry Willows is a small specialty supplier of dried basketry willows and bulrushes imported from England, with an intriguing side list of live willow whips for those wishing to grow their own supplies. Since its founding in the early 1980s, English Basketry Willows has expanded to incorporate a complete line of basketry books and tools, a newsletter, and willow baskets handcrafted by its owner, basket-maker Bonnie Gale.

English-born Gale is an award-winning artisan who apprenticed in Europe, teaches traditional willow basketry, and writes widely for basketry publications. Classes are held at her home in Norwich, New York, every summer. Willow basketry and wickerwork are living legacies of an ancient weaving craft. Gale's work aims to keep alive English basketry skills and the vanishing American traditions brought here by immigrants in the 19th century.

Gale's interests as a master basket maker extend to the cultivation of willow plants for basketry and wattle craft. Although basketry willows have been purpose-bred for centuries, until recently, specialized willows have been rare in American nurseries. In 1988, Gale founded the American Willow Growers Network to promote the cultivation and use of willow plants in North America.

Like most willow nurseries in England, Gale sells dormant, hardwood willow cuttings by mail order every spring. Willow whips cost from 50 cents to $3 each, depending on the variety. Simple planting instructions accompany each order. Because willows root easily (they are the source for root hormone powder), planting willow whips mainly consists of pushing the cuttings straight into the ground.

The willow most frequently used for basketry is the purple osier willow *(Salix purpurea)*, an unbranched 9-foot shrub, at once stocky and vigorous. In moist soil, the wild purple osier forms an impenetrable twiggy mass that more or less disqualifies it as a garden plant. Gale sells six kinds of purple osier domesticated for basketry use that are also attractive in gardens. Included are 'Green Dicks', a slender, light green osier, and 'Eugene', a long, flexible osier with green withes and colorful catkins. A hybrid purple osier *(S. purpurea × daphnoides)* produces slender withes in smoky purple-plum tones. All can be coppiced regularly for increased basketry supplies or aesthetics.

Gale's most decorative willows are a black-stemmed British basketry willow (*S. triandra* 'Black Maul'); a vermillion crack willow from the Low Countries (*S. fragilis* 'Belgium Red'); and a vigorous hedge willow (*S. alba* 'Vitellina') that, when coppiced, produces slender red-tipped golden rods. The most colorful willow, *Salix × rigida* 'American McKay', produces purple-red stems with golden pussies in spring. Willows grown purely for ornament are the curly corkscrew willow (*S. matsudana* 'Tortuosa') and Japanese fan-tail willow (*S. sachalinensis* 'Sekko'), valued in flower arrangements.

Gale also sells whips for a stocky, tough class of willows used for making furniture, trellises, fencing, and hurdles. All are eastern North America natives (*Salix × dasyclados, Salix × hagensus,* and *Salix americana).* She also offers 'Streamco', a suckering, self-layering purple osier developed by the USDA for bank stabilization.

As an artisan, Gale creates sturdy willow baskets, such as laundry baskets, bassinettes, and 19th-century Liverpool baskets. She is known for her beautiful handwoven harnesses, backpacks, willow-and-leather fishing creels, and custom drawers for designer kitchens. Using the living willow, Gale's work reflects what Willa Cather once called "that irregular and intimate quality of things made entirely by the human hand."

Related source: Forest Farm (541-846-7269; www.forestfarm.com) is a distinguished mail-order nursery in Oregon with a good list of unusual willows.

GRACE GARDENS
1064 Angus Road, Penn Yan, NY 14527-9606
(315) 536-2556 phone and fax
www.gracegardens.com; e-mail *tkrood@linkny.com* (mark subject "private")
Tom and Kathy Rood

Daylilies. *Small hybridizer's nursery. Open late June through early August, Wednesday through Friday, 10 to 6; Saturday, 10 to 4; Sunday, noon to 4. Catalog $2, refundable with order. Catalog on Web site. Mail order. AHS Display Garden. Peak bloom mid- to late July. Picnic tables. Visitors and children welcome. Call ahead if traveling a distance.*

Situated in the Finger Lakes region, Grace Gardens is a hybridizer's nursery specializing in distinctive cold-hardy daylilies. Tom and Kathy Rood are Master Gardeners and well-known daylily breeders and judges; their 4-acre garden is appended to their home in Penn Yan, overlooking Seneca Lake. The garden is named for Tom Rood's mother, Grace, who began breeding daylilies in the late 1950s. Her collection of 400 daylilies was transplanted to the Rood home in 1972. Upon Tom Rood's retirement in 1994, the Roods requisitioned part of a vineyard to accommodate 1300 new daylilies and a revived breeding program.

Today, Grace Gardens is a nationally recognized American Hemerocallis Society Display Garden containing more than 1800 registered daylily varieties—one of the largest collections in upstate New York. The display occupies 30 daylily beds laid out in an attractive grid, with glimpses over Seneca Lake. Another 40,000 Rood crosses are set out in breeding beds at the bottom of the garden, near a miniature garden shed. A *tuteur* here and a rose bed there give the garden a pleasing semi-formality that accords well with the relaxed beauty of the daylilies.

The Rood's inventory includes daylily classics and introductions from leading hybridizers, many of which have won international awards. The Roods grow more than 200 'Siloam' hybrids of the late Pauline Henry, the little old lady from Siloam Springs, Arkansas, whose daylily miniatures with contrasting eyes and haloes came to dominate trade and popularity lists. Her most illustrious hybrid, 'Siloam Double Classic' (double rose), won the Stout Medal in 1993. Another group contains more than 100 daylilies bred by William Munson Jr., who was known for large, patterned varieties such as 'Mountain Velvet' (purple with a violet band) and 'Persian Market' (cherry with a rose-red eye). In honor of Munson's work, the American Hemerocallis Society presents the R. W. Munson Award each year to the most outstanding distinctly patterned daylily.

Not to be missed are the Roods' own registered daylily hybrids—choice picks from a breeding program that has produced 50,000 seedlings over 10 years. Tom Rood's 'Seneca Jewel' is ruffled rose with a yellow halo, 'Seneca Coral Song' a warm-coral evening bloomer. Kathy Rood's 'Seneca Princess' is a peach miniature with a burgundy eye (much resembling a 'Siloam'), while 'Belle of Amherst' is pale cream with cascading petals. Several other charmers—'Grace's Little Lady', 'Grace's Elegance', and 'Little Red Spring Song'—were discovered growing in Grace Rood's old seedling bed.

Grace Gardens is also careful to grow older daylilies, many costing just $5. All daylilies are field-grown in natural clay soil. Plants are shipped as double fans, guaranteed to arrive in good condition. For aspiring collectors, classes in daylily cultivation and hybridization are held on weekends in July and August. The Web site offers good growing advice.

Besides daylily breeding, Tom Rood writes a weekly gardening column for the Master Gardener's program and tries his hand at young-adult fiction. Kathy Rood is a basket maker and watercolor artist whose original daylily note cards are sold at the nursery.

Grace Gardens provides a good excuse to visit the warm microclimate of the Finger Lakes, known for its rolling terrain and award-winning vineyards. It's sited on a gentle slope overlooking the widest and warmest part of

Seneca Lake—one of five sacred lakes that, according to Indian legend, were made by the imprinted "fingers" of the Great Spirit's hand.

Directions: From I-90, take exit 42 and turn onto Route 14 south. In Geneva, turn left onto Route 14 south Truck Route. After the railroad tracks (admire the view of Seneca Lake), turn right onto Routes 5 & 20, pass under a bridge, and turn right onto Route 14 south; in 9 miles, turn right on Angus Road. The garden is 1000 feet on the right. From Ithaca, take Route 79 west into Watkins Glen, turn right onto Route 14 north; in 25 miles, just past Fox Run Winery, turn left onto Angus Road; the garden is 1000 feet on the right. From Route I-86/17 in Corning, take Route 414 north to Watkins Glen, turn left onto Route 14 north, and follow directions above.

Nearby attractions: Local wine trails, parks, pubs, and inns are listed on the nursery's Web site. Cross Roads Ice Cream is an old-fashioned ice cream parlor in Dresden, at the junction of Route 14 south and Route 54. Fox Run Vineyards, 670 Route 14, Penn Yan, NY 14527 (800-636-9786; www.foxrunvineyards.com), is an award-winning winery with wine tastings and vineyard tours. 10,000 Delights B&B, Route 54A south of Penn Yan (607-868-3731), overlooks Keuka Lake; nearby, a glass-floored Japanese tea house is suspended over a 60-foot waterfall.

GRACEFUL GARDENS
P.O. Box 100, Mecklenburg, NY 14863
(607) 387-5529 phone and fax
www.gracefulgardens.com; e-mail *grace@clarityconnect.com*
Mark and Amanda Shenstone

Cottage-garden annuals and perennials. *Books and supplies. Small specialty greenhouses. Mail order only. Open year-round. Free catalog. Catalog and plant photos on Web site. Shipping season mid-April through early summer. Minimum order one flat (eight 4-packs). Integrated pest management. Not open to visitors.*

Every spring, from its greenhouses in upstate New York, Graceful Gardens produces a riot of bright cottage-garden plants in affordable flats. This home-based nursery is strictly mail order. Gardeners place their orders for flats of freshly grown seedlings, which are sent out in spring just in time to repopulate the flower garden.

The owners of Graceful Gardens, Mark and Amanda Shenstone, are former organic vegetable farmers who switched over to growing cottage-garden plants in 1997. "Field labor is rough on your body, so we were looking for ways to do more in the greenhouses," Amanda Shenstone recalls. "Gardening helps you slow down and see the important things."

English gardener Gertrude Jekyll valued cottage gardens for their "flower borders filled to overflowing with simple, old-fashioned flowers." These romantic, free-blooming gardens naturally develop their own complexity, with abundance to spare for cut flowers, bees, butterflies, and daisy chains. "I like to cram in all the flowers I can," says Shenstone. "I see arboretum plants set three feet apart and think, 'Wow, how can they restrain themselves?'"

Graceful Gardens offers 150 hardy perennials and self-seeding annuals that are perfect for informal cottage gardens—colorful, fragrant, and easy to grow. Essential to the soul of such gardens, of course, are majestic delphiniums, the elegant floral spires that Graceful Gardens grows in profusion. Delphiniums come short and tall, in rich blues, violets, pinks, lilacs, and whites, some adorned with central blotches or "bees." Well-known series hybrids include 'Belladonna', 'Clear Spring', 'Magic Fountain', and 'Pacific Giant', as well as the amazing 'New Millennium' hybrids from New Zealand.

The rest of the plant list includes bellflowers, balloon flowers, larkspurs, lupines, salvias, and snapdragons. Among the old-fashioned favorites are hollyhocks, columbines, cottage pinks, wallflowers, and mallows. Popular varieties span the growing season—spring primroses, autumn rudbeckias, and coneflowers whose seed heads feed winter birds. "Vespertine" or moonflowers, such as angel's-trumpets and flowering tobacco, pleasantly scent the evening air. Self-seeders give the flower garden an air of abandon: poppy, purple mullein, golden marguerite, love-in-a-mist, and forget-me-not.

The Shenstones operate two big greenhouses brimming with seedlings each spring. Plants are grown in cell-packs containing four of the same variety; the minimum order is one full tray, or eight 4-packs. It is okay to mix and match 4-packs, as long as the total fills a complete tray. Trays are shipped, each in its own box, from mid-April and early summer.

Because plants are greenhouse grown, they may need hardening off in cold locations. To assist the buyer's choice, photographs of most plants appear on the nursery's Web site. Gardeners frozen by indecision can order sampler trays of cottage-garden, cutting-garden, hummingbird-and-butterfly-lure, and shade-garden plants.

For the growers, getting everything to mature at once is a challenge, so the Shenstones keep meticulous notes on start dates to ensure trays that are even in growth. Chemicals and pesticides are kept to an absolute minimum. Extras are sold on Saturdays at the Ithaca Farmer's Market, where the couple has run a popular stand since 1986. There they also offer vines, such as *Cobea scandens*, that are too fragile for mail order. The couple's daughter, Esperanza, grows nasturtiums, petunias, and sunflowers to earn her allowance.

One of the delights of Graceful Gardens is its use of text and images from antique garden catalogs. Amanda Shenstone, who attended Cornell's College of Agriculture, discovered a treasury of 19th-century nursery catalogs at the Bailey Hortorium Library while preparing her own. She quotes Dreer's 1888 catalog for its enduring view of hollyhocks: "It is not surprising that this old-fashioned favorite should again become popular. They are a marvel of beauty and elegance." She quotes Miss Lippincott's 1896 garden catalog even more meaningfully: "Let us have all the flowers we can afford; they are the veritable smiles of nature."

Nearby attractions: The Bailey Hortorium Library, 228 Plant Science Building, Cornell University, Ithaca, NY 14853 (607-256-5343; www.plantbio.cornell.edu/hort.php), is a world-class collection of botanical books and journals; the 134,000-piece collection of nursery and seed catalogues is one of the largest in the world. It's housed in temporary quarters during building renovations; call for directions.

HARRIS SEEDS

P.O. Box 24966, 355 Paul Road, Rochester, NY 14624
(800) 514-4441; fax (877) 892-9197
www.harrisseeds.com; e-mail *gardeners@harrisseeds.com*
Dick Chamberlain, President

Vegetable and flower seed. Plants, bulbs, and garden supplies. *Commercial seed house. Office open October through June, Monday through Friday, 8 to 6; July through September, Monday through Friday, 8 to 4:30; and Saturdays, December through May, 8 to 2. Free catalog. Mail order. Catalog on Web site. Some organic seed. Seed-starting supplies, greenhouses, cold frames. Seasonal specials. Gift certificates. AAS Trial Grounds open by appointment.*

A seed packet contains what writer Peter Loewer, in *Seeds*, calls "earthbound starships that fly or fall through the air, never leaving our planet." These starships provide three-quarters of the human diet throughout the world.

Harris Seeds is a Rochester-based seed supplier long known for its exceptional vegetable hybrids. The seed house was founded in 1879 by Joseph Harris, an English immigrant who settled in New York's Genesee Valley and developed superior strains of vegetables and grains for area farmers. Harris Seeds succeeded by offering what Harris called "a quality product at a fair price."

During 100 years of family management, Harris Seeds introduced many new vegetable hybrids that became leading cultivars. After the last Harris family member sold to an agribusiness in 1979, some former employees repurchased the company in 1987. According to current management, "Our agenda for our customers remains much as it was in 1879, to provide the finest products available and at a fair price, coupled with friendly and courteous service."

Harris Seeds retains a loyal following by offering variety, selection, and professional handling of seeds, transplants, and growing supplies sold to growers and homeowners around the country. Seed is stored and packed in modern climate-controlled conditions. An in-house shop prints the seed packets. An on-site germination lab monitors seed-stock quality. Untreated and pelleted seeds are available in some varieties. The company achieves good corporate citizenship by supporting horticultural education at local schools.

Each year Harris Seeds scours the United States and Europe for worthy new vegetable and flower varieties and supports a number of small, independent seed-research efforts. All seed is developed through traditional breeding methods (no genetic modification). An All-America Selections Trial Ground, testing some 300 new hybrids at the Rochester facility, is open by appointment. A wealth of information appears on the company's Web site.

Some of the new introductions are captivating. Yellow icebox watermelon, grape cluster tomatoes, white eggplant, sweet slicing cucumbers, storage and bunching onions, and improved green beans—all are Harris Seeds strains marking palpable improvements over older varieties. New bicolor sweet corn hybrids (descendants of 'Butter and Sugar') include 'Sweet Symphony', which stands up to Northeastern weather, and 'Delectable', perfected for corn roasts and clam bakes. Children love

'Munchkin', a new mini-pumpkin. A novelty popcorn called 'Strawberry Corn' produces tiny ruby ears. 'Little Guys', a mini-squash mix, makes a great fall centerpiece.

In recent years, Harris Seeds has developed a line of seeds devoted to the organic grower. The list offers more than 40 kinds of organic vegetable seed; organic cut-flower seed, and untreated seed for popular vegetables. "In 2004, we had 8 of our most popular varieties produced organically," says Vegetable Seed Manager Mark Willis. "We are the first seed company to offer this many hybrids as organic seed."

As Harris searches for new varieties, classic vegetables remain its backbone. Tomatoes like 'Jet Star' and 'Supersonic' have real tomato flavor. 'Lady Bell' green pepper and 'Superstar' cantaloupe are popular at farm stands. 'Blue Hubbard' squash and 'Magic Lantern' pumpkins make colorful autumnal piles. For retro chic, Harris continues such pre-World War II classics as 'Scarlet Nantes' carrot, 'Slobolt' lettuce, 'Jubilee' tomato, and 'Alderman' tall pea. A dwarf lima bean called 'Fordhook 242', still popular, was recommended in Harris' 1940 catalog.

Harris Seeds publishes different seed catalogs for professional growers, organic growers, and home gardeners. All express a progressive attitude toward vegetable development, echoing an eternally appealing, uniquely American conviction that life can be bettered and nature improved. For value, Harris Seeds is right—it's hard to beat a good packet of seeds.

Related source: Founded in 1878, Stokes Seeds, P.O. Box 548, Buffalo, NY 14240-0548 (800-263-7233; www.stokeseeds.com), was the first American seed house to import broccoli seed from Italy; today it offers 3000 kinds of vegetable and flower seeds, focusing on short-season, disease-resistant, and cream-of-the-crop hybrids.

HOLMES HOLLOW FARM

2334 Turk Hill Road, Victor, NY 14564
(585) 223-0959
E-mail *Tree4u@frontiernet.net*
Andrew Fowler and Barbara Holmes

Native and ornamental trees and shrubs. Grasses and perennials. Christmas trees. *Small specialty nursery. Open by appointment or chance. Plant list. No catalog or mail order. Delivery in Rochester area. Visitors welcome. Call ahead. Choose-and-cut Christmas tree farm open from the Friday after Thanksgiving through Christmas, weekdays, 12 to 5, weekends, 9 to 5.*

Andrew Fowler, a British-born archaeologist, is an adventurous plantsman with a tendency to delve deep into things. His wife, Barbara Holmes, is a cultural anthropologist from New York State. For many years, the couple worked together on a Zuni Indian reservation in the Southwest. In a land littered with earthworks and ruins, they surveyed old sites—including local flora—and evaluated the impact of land development on Indian culture and archaeology. In 1989, they moved with their daughter to Holmes Hollow Farm, where Barbara Holmes grew up, to assume management of a 62-acre Christmas tree plantation her father started in 1959.

In 1991 Fowler opened a small experimental nursery on the farm to grow flowering trees and shrubs. "I wanted to grow species not commonly found in the area garden centers," he recalls. He began collecting seed and testing uncommon trees and shrubs from indigenous groves and exotic sources. "In a way, I'm on the fringe of the business," says Fowler. "My inventory changes frequently as I continue trying different species to see what will and will not grow here."

Today, Holmes Hollow Farm carries a small but intriguing inventory. Many woody plants are seedlings and therefore variable in shape and appearance—a quality evincing genetic diversity that many sophisticated gardeners enjoy seeing in plants. As with any small nursery, some holdings are represented by just a few plants in varying stages of growth. Prices are modest. A gallon-size red horse chestnut *(Aesculus × carnea)*, for example, costs about $10. Other plants come in 2- and 3-gallon sizes. According to Fowler, "All trees are grown in root-control bags to ensure a more compact fibrous root system, less root loss in digging, and rapid establishment in the landscape." This was our experience, too—the trees went right into the ground without a hitch.

The nursery's plant list is strong in woody plants deserving a greater place in gardens. Many are attractive native trees that make a superb effect in woodland borders: yellowwood, black gum, Kentucky coffee tree, sweet bay magnolia, and red and yellow buckeye. Underappreciated Asian trees include Japanese hornbeam; three-flowered maple, hardy rubber tree, Japanese photinia, and *Amur maakia*.

Fowler also grows beautiful flowering understory trees: Carolina silver-bell, Japanese snowbell, Japanese stewartia, Chinese redbud, Cornelian cherry, American and Chinese forms of fringe tree, and *Amelanchier grandi-flora* 'Forest Prince'. Efforts to grow the enchanting dove tree *(Davidia involucrata)* have met with mixed results, but Fowler still hopes for success. "I just love the diversity of these plants," Fowler says. "The American styrax—nobody seems to have it. Native stewartias—are the mountain forms hardy? I'm always looking for something else to try."

The deciduous tree list is salted with curiosities such as *Betula* × *potaninii*, a shrubby, often prostrate Tibetan birch, and *Acer distylum*, a small maple with simple, un-maple-like leaves. Both can be used to stump horticultural know-it-alls. A rarely offered Oriental striped-bark maple *(Acer tegmentosum)* unfurls bright-red new foliage. Ocean-spray *(Holodiscus discolor)* is a Western native shrub with cream flowers, unusual in commerce. Among the fruit seedlings are native pawpaw, golden currant, and Japanese apricot.

The nursery's conifer holdings concede the superior ornamentality of pines: Himalayan, Korean, lace-bark, loblolly, Japanese white, and Japanese umbrella pine. There is also golden larch, corkbark fir, native tamarack, and dawn redwood. Shrubs include Chinese seven-son flower, native viburnums, and sweet fern. A native bearberry comes from seed collected on Cape Cod, and a Chinese false spiraea *(Sorbaria arborea)* from seed at a Rochester arboretum.

Holmes Hollow Farm is located near the Eastside Mall in Victor, just ten miles southeast of Rochester, yet its hidden valley seems like another world. While officially sited in Zone 6, according to Fowler, the cold valley micro-climate "strongly favors Zone 5." Stock is grown in the ground, on the premises, and is therefore fully acclimatized. The nursery practices integrated pest management, using few fertilizers or pesticides. Like all gardeners, though, the owners struggle with predators. An 8-foot deer fence surrounds the growing yard. "Deer will eat anything," sighs Fowler, "especially if it's expensive."

Directions: From Route I-90, take exit 45, turn onto Route 96 north, and at the fourth light, opposite the Eastview Mall, turn right (east) onto Turk Hill Road. In about 1 mile, turn right at a mailbox (#2334) onto a gravel driveway, pass the greenhouse, and proceed downhill for 0.3 mile to a white farmhouse on the right. From Route I-490, take exit 28, turning off the ramp onto Route 96 south, and follow directions above. Visitors welcome; call ahead.

Nearby attractions: Ganondagan State Historic Site, 1488 Victor-Bloomfield Road, Victor, NY 14564 (585-924-5848; open mid-May through October), a destroyed 17th-century Seneca Indian village, is managed by Peter Jemison, a Seneca descendant of Mary Jemison, a captive adopted by the tribe. Highlights include a Seneca longhouse, small museum, interpreted hiking trails, and a garden of traditional Indian crops. Rochester's Highland Park (585-256-4950; www.monroecounty.gov) is an Olmsted-designed arboretum with notable Japanese maple and magnolia collections; famous for its 1200 lilacs, the park's Lilac Festival (www.lilacfestival.com) attracts thousands in May. Durand-Eastman Park, Lakeshore Boulevard, Rochester (585-256-4950; www.monroecounty.gov), is an equally distinguished 965-acre arboretum.

INTERNATIONAL BONSAI

P.O. Box 23894, Rochester, NY 14692-3894
(585) 334-2595; fax (585) 334-6239
www.internationalbonsai.com; e-mail *wnv@internationalbonsai.com*
William N. Valavanis

Bonsai specimens and starter plants. Bonsai tools and containers. *Small specialty nursery. Open by appointment. Catalog on Web site. Mail order of starter plants. Mature specimens may be picked up at nursery or delivered to bonsai conventions. Display arboretum open for spring and fall Open House.* International Bonsai *magazine. Classes and symposia.*

Bonsai, which means "potted plant" in Japanese, is the Asian art of growing miniature trees and landscapes. The practice began in ancient China, where naturally dwarf trees were collected in the mountains and planted in decorative pots for the aristocracy. Sent to Japan as diplomatic gifts, these miniature trees acquired spiritual significance beginning in the eighth century, when Zen Buddhist monks used them as teaching tools for philosophical values on the harmony of nature and man's relation to heaven and earth. Over centuries in Japan, bonsai became the refined horticultural art we know today.

William Valavanis is a world-famous bonsai artist and educator, whose nursery and teaching center, the International Bonsai Arboretum, is based in Rochester. He began practicing the gentle art of bonsai at age eleven, when his mother dragged him to a bonsai demonstration at a local nursery in Illinois. Each guest received a free Japanese yew for beginner practice. In no time, Valavanis was scouring the woods for specimens. By age 16, he was lecturing to garden clubs and had opened his own nursery. His life has been consumed by bonsai ever since.

Valavanis studied bonsai intensively during a year-long apprenticeship in Japan and holds degrees in ornamental horticulture from SUNY Long Island and Cornell University. Since 1979 he has published *International Bonsai*, a journal for English-speaking bonsai fanciers, distributed in 52 countries. He is a director of the National Bonsai Foundation and American Bonsai Society. He has won countless bonsai awards and holds a Lifetime Achievement Award from the Bonsai Society of Upstate New York. He has traveled to Japan more than 40 times on study and lecture tours; his current teaching obligations take him all over the world. Valavanis is on the steering committee of Rochester's GardenScape, which mounts the city's annual flower show where his bonsai displays routinely win top awards.

International Bonsai houses Valavanis' masterpieces, an exemplary collection of classical bonsai, created through decades of painstaking practice on rare and dwarf plants. Valavanis' mature bonsai specimens succeed admirably in simulating antiquity, so that a contorted foot-high specimen resembles an ancient tree in nature. A walled Asian-style courtyard provides a picturesque backdrop for hardy bonsai specimens, set outdoors on bonsai benches. The dignity and beauty of twisted dwarf trees displayed in a whitewashed cloister is breathtaking.

International Bonsai houses 300 mature specimens and 1000 bonsai for sale. The collection is strong in pine and maple bonsai, for which Valavanis is best known. While mature bonsai give the impression of being priceless, plants are available in a range of prices. Mature award winners in perfect condition may be valued at thousands of dollars, but many remarkable specimens are far more affordable. The sales benches contain Valavanis' original bonsai and works created by other masters and former students. Cold greenhouses are used to foster starter plants and winter-over dormant bonsai. Plant-sitting services are available for owners on vacation. A warm greenhouse contains a group of tropical bonsai and tender starter plants.

One of Valavanis' most endearing habits is taking "baby pictures" of his bonsai, a reminder that even his most august creations began as mere seedlings. Beginners can purchase starter plants in suitable species such as trident maple, Japanese snowbell, European beech, Korean hornbeam, spike winter hazel, and Japanese wisteria. One particular treasure is a dwarf white cedar (*Chamaecyparis thyoides* 'Valavanis') discovered by Valavanis and named for him.

Bonsai are developed artistically over many years, through thoughtful evolution that sometimes involves more than one artist. One of Valavanis' most distinguished specimens is a beautiful full-moon maple acquired as a seedling in 1975 from his teacher, Yuji Yoshimura. Planted in turquoise Tokoname-ware from Japan's Heikisui Kiln, this 30-year-old upright-form maple was judged among the top 100 exhibited photographs in the 1999 JAL World Bonsai Contest in Kyoto, Japan. Another award winner is 'Mrs. Pine', a dwarf Austrian pine (*Pinus nigra* 'Hornibrook') that Valavanis began in 1969 from a witches' broom; the original plant came from Rochester's Seneca Park in 1932. After 35 years of trimming, wiring, needle-plucking, and bud pruning, 'Mrs. Pine' was transformed into a spectacular upright bonsai valued at $25,000.

Sophisticated horticultural techniques such as air-layering and thread-grafting generate some of Valavanis' most artistic bonsai. A noted trident maple bonsai *(Acer buergeranum)*, for example, was created by "drastic pruning"—a professional trick that employs mature plants to hasten the illusion of age. Valavanis began in the 1970s with a field-grown tree, 10 feet tall, slashed down to 12 inches. By slow shaping and root restriction, the tree was transformed, over 30 years, into a photogenic bonsai classic with stunning fall foliage.

Arboretum visitors may be amused to compare Valavanis' mature bonsai to full-grown seedlings of the same specimen. Because a plant, however closely pruned, cannot reduce the size of its leaves or fruit, the offspring of fertile bonsai grow to full stature. Valavanis has fun with this concept by planting full-size Japanese maples, Chinese elms, and quince trees at the edge of the bonsai courtyard. There sharp-eyed visitors may observe strapping 15-foot trees in the presence of their diminutive mothers.

Inside International Bonsai Arboretum, a beautiful Japanese-style room is equipped for frequent bonsai classes, lectures, and photo shoots. Here a yearly symposium with famous bonsai artists is held for several hundred participants. Because International Bonsai functions as a teaching space as well as a nursery, students often acquire small cuttings and seedlings as part of their education. An authentic *Tokonoma* alcove, complete with wall scroll, low table, water basin, and viewing stone, is used for special bonsai displays and photo shoots. Valavanis' collection of masterpiece viewing stones includes a fascinating "thatched hut" stone he found in Puerto Rico.

Besides bonsai, the nursery is a source for bonsai tools, containers, reference books, calendars, viewing stones, and Japanese lapel pins. The use of stone in bonsai is an art in itself, for great age can be simulated by placing contorted rocks just so. Miniature mosses, dwarf hosta, and tiny Corsican mint provide scale to bonsai landscapes. Even shoe polish has its place. "We polish the bark in winter," says Valavanis. "In Italy they use olive oil."

Directions: Call or write for an appointment.

Nearby attractions: Tokyo Japanese Restaurant, 2930 West Henrietta Road, Rochester (585-424-4166; www.restaurantpix.com), prepares traditional Japanese cuisine and sushi.

Related source: PFM Bonsai Studio, 7 Western Avenue, West Charlton, NY 02010 (518-882-1039; www.pfmbonsai.com), is a small bonsai nursery and teaching studio operated by Pauline Muth, just north of Schenectady (starter materials, finished bonsai, display gardens).

JANE'S HERB FARM

1042 State Road, Webster, NY 14580

(585) 872-3720

E-mail *kuitems@netacc.net*

Jane Kuitems

Herbs and perennials. Small specialty nursery. Open from late April through late June, Wednesday and Thursday, noon to 5; Friday, noon to 6; Saturday, 10 to 5; and Sunday, noon to 4. Call for exact dates. Open in July, Saturdays, 10 to 5; and by chance or appointment. No catalog or mail order. Free brochure. Calls returned in evening. Classes and lectures. Display garden. Garden tours on weekends and by appointment. Visitors welcome.

Founded in 1978, Jane's Herb Farm is a small nursery in Webster, west of Rochester, specializing in unusual herbs, everlastings, and like-minded cottage-garden perennials. Jane Kuitems is a 4th-generation gardener who grew up on a dairy farm near the St. Lawrence River. Her mother and both grandmothers were avid gardeners. The passion appears to be genetic. "After I was born," she says, "the first thing my mother did was to go out and weed the garden."

After earning a degree in culinary science at Rochester Institute of Technology, Kuitems began growing kitchen herbs. Farm heritage drew her toward fragrant flowers, medicinal herbs, and everlastings (used in dried arrangements). "I have a 'Flowers for Sale' sign that belonged to my great-grandmother. As a farm wife in upstate New York, she sold flowers from her garden," says Kuitems. "She also worked with a Native American healer and made home remedies." Kuitems was the source for Old House Gardens' revival of an heirloom white daffodil, 'Mme. De Graaff', which her mother rescued from a discarded Easter pot.

While Jane's Herb Farm has purposely stayed small, its stock contains much that is uncommon and beautiful. The repertoire boasts 1000 varieties of herbs and perennials in beautiful display beds, which also function as trial and stock beds. Kuitems describes her garden as a "stuff-and-cram cottage garden," with something in bloom from snow melt to frost. The gardens attract such popular interest that Kuitems gives complimentary public tours on weekends.

"Over the years I have grown incredible numbers of plants," says Kuitems. "I have tended to concentrate on specific families and then move on to others." Kuitems has had love affairs with salvia, digitalis, campanula, nepeta, agastache, verbascum, dianthus, cranesbill geranium, oregano, and lavender. When passion abates, she selects and grows the varieties she most admires. The campanulas have been honed down to eight great performers. The cranesbills have settled down to a dozen ground covers which, as perennial guru Allen Armitage says, "can be collected like fine silver." A whittled-down list of bee-loved foxgloves (*Digitalis* spp.) come in yellow, white, apricot, and rose. The better violets and primroses are in good supply. Among the sea hollies is 'Miss Willmott's Ghost', a bluish form named after an English designer who surreptitiously trailed its seed through other people's gardens. Even in edited form, Jane's perennial list is remarkable.

Fragrant and culinary herbs are the heart of the farm. Kuitems sells some 18 potted basils, numerous thymes, and a dozen each of lavender, rosemary, and oregano. Tasty condiments such as lemongrass, bronze fennel, and chocolate mint can be sourced here. The nursery also grows everlastings and aromatics used for dried flower wreaths and potpourri. Kuitems offers two easy heirlooms (feverfew and lily-of-the-valley) inherited from her grandmother.

"If it's growable, I've probably grown it," Kuitems says. "I've even grown Ayurvedic herbs such as Asafetida *[Ferula assa-foetida]* and Ashwagandha *[Withania somnifera]*—beautiful plants, but nobody knew what they were." As a testament to the enduring power of herbal remedies, Kuitems drinks rosemary tea every morning and hardly ever gets sick.

In recent years, Kuitems' interest has migrated toward hardy cyclamen and hellebore. She grows speckled and double hellebores from seed culled in Tasmania, where the climate is similar to Rochester's (Zone 6). Tasmanian plants produce ripe seed in spring (our autumn), just in time to be planted in upstate New York. "Ten years ago I couldn't sell a hellebore, but now people know what great plants they are," Kuitems says. Hardy cyclamen seed comes from the Cyclamen Society of Britain, where these small-flowered primrose relatives grow under trees, the very delight of dry shade. Kuitems grows fall-blooming Neapolitan cyclamen *(Cyclamen hederifolium)* and spring-blooming Atkin's cyclamen *(C. coum),* both hardy to Zone 6. "What I like best is *Cyclamen hederifolium* coming along in September and October, when we don't have much in bloom," she says. "Suddenly, you have dainty flowers, mottled silver foliage, and fragrance."

Jane's Herb Farm produces some 20,000 herb and perennial plants each year—a fairly small production by commercial standards, but enough to retain interest and variety. Nursery stock changes constantly to reflect new interests and better plants. Kuitems propagates most plants from seed and cuttings in two greenhouses. Finished plants are sold in 4- and 6-inch squares. Some plants and the odd garden division come in larger sizes.

Considering the stock's quality and variety, prices are reasonable, especially compared to what is sold in nearby Big Box stores.

Besides a propagator and gardener, Kuitems is a gifted educator who has lectured widely about herbs and perennials since 1981. She holds classes at the farm and is revered for her ability to teach gardening as a practical art. A large slide library supports lectures on diverse topics: English and French herb gardens, 19th-century gardens, medicine-chest gardens, cooking with herbs, and putting the garden to sleep. Workshops address garden cosmetics and potpourri. A slide show Kuitems presented at the Rochester Flower and Garden show, "Tried and True Perennials for Clay and Sandy Soil," suggests edifying plant choices for difficult soils.

Kuitems' profound knowledge of garden plants enables her to perceive her own role in nature's continuum. "Plants have been an integral part of mankind's life even before the age of the 'iceman,'" she says. "As a gardener, I am steward not only of the earth but of this heritage."

Directions: Webster is 10 miles west of Rochester. From Route I-90, take exit 45 onto Route I-490 north. At exit 21, turn onto Route 590 north. At exit 8, turn right (toward Webster) onto Route 404/Empire Boulevard. In 2 miles, turn right onto Plank Road and in 2 miles, bear left onto State Road. The nursery is 1 mile on the right.

Related source: Jane's mother's heirloom white daffodil, 'Mme. de Graaff', is available from Old House Gardens, 536 Third Street, Ann Arbor, MI 48103 (734-995-1486; www.oldhousegardens.com), a preeminent source for antique flower bulbs.

JOHN GORDON NURSERY

1385 Campbell Boulevard, Amherst, NY 14228-1403
(716) 691-9371; (801) 881-8842
www.geocities.com/nuttreegordon; e-mail *nuttreegordon@att.net;*
nuttreegordon@hotmail.com
John H. Gordon Jr.

Nut trees. Pawpaw and persimmon trees. Hybridizer's nursery. Trees, scions, and tree nuts and seeds by mail order. Larger stock at nursery. Catalog on Web site; click "OKgordon" and "OKitems" for catalog and tree list. No credit cards. Messages, lectures, and nut photos posted on Web site. Open by appointment only. Call ahead.

John Gordon Nursery is a mail-order tree farm specializing in nut trees, many of which are native forest trees. The nursery is famous for its uncommon hardy nut trees—hybrid chestnut, shagbark and shellbark hickory, northern pecan, walnut, heart nut, hican, filbert, and almond—as well as native pawpaw and persimmon trees. The nursery occupies a 50-acre nut tree plantation 15 miles east of Buffalo (Zone 5). Nursery ground consists of eight inches of garden soil over nine feet of sand and clam shells—the prehistoric bed of Lake Tonawanda. Gordon sends trees and nuts to customers all over the world.

Nursery proprietor John Gordon, who lives on the plantation and operates largely without help, has been a nut enthusiast, or nut nut, for 40 years. An engineer and land surveyor turned nut-tree explorer, Gordon is the first to admit how things got out of hand. What started as an experimental planting of Chinese chestnuts in 1962 has since evolved into a "research station" with 10,000 nut trees, extending as far as the eye can see.

Gordon belongs to a small fraternity of nut buffs committed to improving nut trees for northern climates. The work is experimental, closely akin to that of a hybridizer—selecting and growing promising strains of nut trees over many generations. Since 1965, Gordon has been active in the New York Nut Growers Association, a professional group dedicated to promoting nut trees as a source of food, timber, and enjoyment. He does field testing in cooperation with the Northern Nut Growers Association, the North American Fruit Explorers, and the Pawpaw Foundation. His closest allies are in the Society of Ontario Nut Growers, with whom he exchanges tree scions for nursery and breeding stock.

Chestnuts were the first to ignite Gordon's passion, and his nursery remains a respected source of these hybrids. According to Gordon, "Hybrid chestnuts are like dogs, mutts, mongrels. They are not like our cats. Cats look like each other. Dogs are weird. Chestnuts are weird."

Gordon's hardy 'Hemming strain' of Chinese chestnut *(Castanea mollissima)* came from a bushel of seed collected in Maryland, back when scouring backyards for nut trees was merely a hobby. Considered tender north of Maryland, Gordon's first 'Hemming' chestnut seedlings not only survived but took up New York citizenship and have since spread enthusiastically upstate. Success with Chinese chestnuts catapulted Gordon into full-time nut exploration.

The pecan forms another key category of native nut trees at the nursery. The shagbark hickory *(Carya ovata)*, for example, is a handsome forest giant known for its bushy gray bark, gold fall foliage, and elegant hard nuts. Shagbarks are so difficult to transplant that few nurseries bother. Gordon grows several productive, cold-hardy strains characterized by easy kernel removal ('Weschcke', 'Porter', and 'Yoder #1'). He also grows hardy strains of Southern shellbark hickory *(Carya laciniosa)* and an interesting hickory-pecan hybrid called "hican" *(Carya illinoinensis × laciniosa)*. An early-ripening strain of northern pecan *(Carya illinoinensis)*, which Gordon discovered in the upper Mississippi, forms the basis of a significant breeding program.

In recent years, Gordon's attention has turned from mongrel chestnuts and tricky hickories to cantankerous walnuts. His most recent pursuit is improving the "hardy English" Persian walnut *(Juglans regia)*. Gordon views the tree as "a nut from the Garden of Eden" that has, like ourselves, suffered much in exile. Gordon is trying to persuade the New York Nut Growers Association to develop blight-resistant Persian walnuts—a project that could give a meaningful economic boost to upstate nut croppers. The nursery also grows filbert and hazelnut bushes, several strains of native black walnut, and Japanese walnut, or heart nut *(Juglans ailanthifolia* var. *cordiformis)*—a pretty, lush, ornamental tree with valentine-shaped nuts.

Besides nuts, Gordon is known for his breeding work with two obscure native fruit trees, the pawpaw and persimmon. The pawpaw, or custard-apple *(Asimina triloba)*, is the northernmost member of a tropical genus, noted for its exotic flowers and custard-like fruit. Naturalist Donald Culross Peattie once said, "Everything about it is odd and unforgettable." Gordon has developed a line of rich, yellow-fleshed pawpaws called 'PA Golden Strain', based on a Cornell professor's collection of early-ripening Pennsylvania pawpaws. Gordon also grows several less hardy pawpaw varieties with later and larger fruit.

Similarly intriguing is Gordon's cache of hardy persimmon trees *(Diospyros virginiana),* another cold-tolerant native from a tropical genus. As early as the 17th century, Captain John Smith wrote of a "plum" the Indian tribes called *putchamin:*"The fruit is like a medlar, it is first green, then yellow and red when ripe. If it not be ripe it will draw a man's mouth awrie with much torment. But when it is ripe, it is as delicious as an apricot."

Gordon stocks a mix of hardy persimmons selected from wild persimmons native to Illinois and Indiana. These cold-tolerant strains have more chromosomes and are sturdier than Southern populations. A hardy persimmon called 'Szukis Bi-sexual' is a good pollinator both ways—an odd reminder that persimmons, which are dioecious (trees are male or female), have the uncanny ability to change sex.

Persimmon fruits ripen late on the trees, leaving the best fruit hanging after frost. According to Gordon, persimmon pulp contains, ounce for ounce,"more nourishment than any other fruit grown in the United States." In the catalog he writes, "Many wild vertebrate and birds eat the fruit. Domestic animals eat them, including my dog. I have seen a horse that foundered on persimmons." Gordon himself is fond of persimmons, a traditional ingredient of holiday sweets. The highest use for persimmon pulp, he decrees, is as "a topping for ice cream."

Gordon's nursery offers grafted trees, seedlings, scions, and fertile nuts and seeds at modest prices. The stock is in limited supply, especially grafted trees that take several years to establish. Bare-root trees are shipped from late March through May, wrapped in recycled oatmeal cookie cartons. Scion-wood cuttings are delivered in early March. Stratified tree nuts are sent in November, except chestnuts and other freezable nuts, which go out in spring. On his remote nut plantation, Gordon can be hard to reach except by e-mail (or by U.S. mail with a stamped, self-addressed return envelope).

Most of Gordon's stock consists of grafted trees and seedlings that have thrived without much assistance in local conditions. Old refrigerators, half buried in the ground, are used to stratify seed for the nursery. Because the local soil is too sweet for pawpaw and Korean pine nut seedlings, Gordon drenches seeds in battery acid to get them started. Young pawpaws are sent with white garbage bags as protective tree shelters. In an odd flourish, the nursery daubs bark rifts and grafting nicks with hot-pink nail polish.

Directions: The nursery is 10 miles northeast of Buffalo. Call or e-mail for an appointment and directions.

Related sources: The Society of Ontario Nut Growers (www.songonline.ca) has good information on northern nut trees, including Nut Growing Ontario Style, *a congested but erudite nut-grower's manual. Working with similar methods on different species, legendary conifer nurseryman Don Hilliker of Treehaven Evergreen Nursery, 981 Jamison Road, Elma, NY 14059 (716-652-4206; www.treehavennursery.com), has been selecting and growing native and exotic pine, spruce, and fir trees from seed since 1947 on a 300-acre tree farm near Buffalo. This wholesale nursery sells plugs from superior ornamental evergreens selected over many generations (minimum order $100; minimum quantity 10 per species; instructional booklets).*

THE MAGIC GARDEN
358 Benjamin Hill Road, Newfield, NY 14867
(607) 564-9055
www.magicgardenplants.com; e-mail *info@magicgardenplants.com*
Siri Jones and Fritz Schmidt

Annuals, perennials, herbs, and vines. *Organic greenhouses. Seasonal flats and small pots. Free catalog. Photos and catalog on Web site. Mail order, no minimum. Integrated pest management. Gift certificates. Greenhouses open May 1 to July 1, Thursday through Sunday, 10 to 6. Ithaca Farmer's Market on Saturdays.*

The Magic Garden is a small organic greenhouse specializing in flowering annuals, perennials, vines, and vegetable seedlings by mail order. Owners Siri Jones and Fritz Schmidt started the nursery in 1997, after years of working with plants and gardens. "We got our start as landscape gardeners who loved to grow flowers," recalls Jones. "What we really wanted to do was grow varieties we couldn't find, or new plants no one seemed to know about."

In anticipation of starting a nursery, Jones earned a degree in horticulture at Cornell, while Schmidt tended gardens, pored over greenhouse plans, and maintained the couple's burgeoning plant collection. Their first greenhouse was completed in 1996 and a second added later. "Of course, if you are going to grow a *lot* of plants, you'll need to find *lots* of customers," Jones says. "Thus was born the idea of doing mail order."

The Magic Garden offers an eclectic mix of garden perennials, annual container plants, and fast-growing flowering vines, focusing on plants that are "high quality but affordable." Stock is sold in economic 6-packs, 4-packs, 4-inch pots, and flats. For gardeners who are short on time or resources in early spring, the Magic Garden is a direct link to a colorful garden.

The catalog lists nearly 80 annuals and bedding plants with "bright colors and often furious flowering habits." These range from fragrant clove pinks and China asters to sulphur cosmos and Mexican sunflowers. For "fancy annuals," the nursery offers South African foxglove, red butterfly weed, blue pimpernel, and an heirloom heliotrope known as cherry pie. Many are improved varieties, such as 'Lemon Gem' marigold or *Cerinthe major purpurascens* 'Kiwi Blue'. One finds small collections of flowering tobaccos, annual salvias, violas, and snapdragons.

The perennial plant list is equally eclectic, ranging from cottage classics such as black hollyhocks, white foxgloves, and 'Magic Fountain' delphiniums to border stalwarts such as globe thistle, evening primrose, and heliopsis 'Summer Sun'. Among the fancy perennials are columbine, lady's-mantle, larkspur, geum, ornamental rhubarb, various lavenders, and a "chorus of bellflowers." Showy meadow plants feature perennial sunflowers, elecampane, and purple love grass.

It's not always easy to find colorful annual vines, but here are cardinal climber, canary creeper, perennial sweet pea, creeping gloxinia, and purple sweet potato vine in 4-inch pots. The collection is salted with perennial gems such as orange-peel clematis and Chinese purple bell vine *(Rhodochiton atrosanguineum)*—though the small pots probably mandate a season of care to get them established. Collections of plants that collaborate well include "Flower Power" (for long bloom), "Fragrant Garden," "True Blue Garden," and "Summer Paradise of Daisies."

The Magic Garden grows 500 plant varieties from seed each year. Just as the greenhouses fill to bursting in April, it ships happy flats of color all over the country. Occasional extras make their way, as gifts, into larger orders. "We take pride in the healthy, vigorous plants we ship," says Jones. The nursery is committed to using sustainable methods to control greenhouse pests. A unique organic soil mix is used in all outdoor containers.

The Magic Garden is located off the beaten track in the Newfield hills, near Ithaca. It's "relatively tiny compared to others, with less than one acre of gardens and display beds, outdoor container nursery, and field-grown perennials." A late-spring visit reveals a high-hearted effort on a ramshackle farm, where two color-filled greenhouses imply plant magic and hard work.

Although the operation is mostly mail order, visitors can come to the greenhouses on weekends in spring. This saves shipping costs and also allows choice among what the owners call "all the neat stuff we didn't put in the catalog." What's not in the catalog are hanging baskets, preplanted containers, gallon-size perennials, and a few experimental plants in small quantities. Gardeners can seek out the Magic Garden on Saturdays at the Ithaca Farmer's Market, where the owners enjoy meeting their customers and showcasing their prettiest plants.

Directions: From Ithaca, take Route 13 south for 5 miles into Newfield, turn left onto Main Street, turn east onto Shaffer Road, and go straight at the fork onto Benjamin Hill Road. The nursery is 2 miles on the right. From Route I-86 in Elmira, take exit 54 onto Route 13 north, go 20 miles to Newfield, turn right onto Main Street, and follow directions above.

Nearby attractions: Ithaca Farmer's Market (www.ithacamarket.com) is held at Steamboat Landing, April through mid-December, Saturdays, 9 to 2; June through October, Sundays, 10 to 2. According to the Magic Garden (Booth #88), "Friendly people, great food, excellent crafts, fresh organic produce and plants galore are all part of the fun," attracting 5000 visitors a day. A local craftsman makes nice wooden garden seats (www.cedaradirondack.com).

MARLOW ORCHIDS

2272 Scottsville Road, Scottsville, NY 14546

(585) 889-7083

www.marlowsorchids.com; e-mail *jmarlow1@rochester.rr.com*

Jim Marlow

Orchids. *Small specialty nursery. Open daily, 9 to 5. Visitors welcome, but call ahead. Catalog on Web site. Mail order. Sales at major orchid shows. Orchid pots.*

Marlow Orchids is a specialty grower of showy orchids that does a brisk business with customers near Rochester. Owner Jim Marlow is a former Xerox employee whose fascination with orchids dates to the mid-1970s, when he first spied native lady's-slippers in a local bog. He started growing semitropical Asian species—like most of us, he began with a simple moth orchid (phalinopsis)—and eventually built a 2000-square-foot greenhouse to house a burgeoning collection. Hobby status was abandoned in 1999, when he began growing and selling orchids commercially, shortly before accepting early retirement from his day job.

Marlow Orchids' stock list is cleverly designed to appeal to both beginners and seasoned orchid nuts. Choices range from starter orchids to difficult rarities, including many American Orchid Society award winners. Sophisticated hybrids and species can be found in various orchid alliances, including the adaglossum, brassia, cattleya, coeloglossum, cymbidium, dendrobium, encyclia, masdevallia, miltonia, oncidium, and vanda alliances. One exotic vining orchid *(Robiquetia cerina),* seldom available, has curious flowers resembling clusters of grapes. But even Marlow's ordinary windowsill orchids are glamorous. Among the easy moth orchids, for example, 'Brother Sara Gold' has rare peach-colored flowers, while 'Golden Poker' produces stunning red-blotched blossoms that go on for months.

Of particular note is Marlow's strong collection of wild Peruvian orchids. These temperate or "intermediate" mountain orchids prefer a dry season and cool climate. Examples include *Scuticaria hadwenii,* a rare maxillaria orchid, and *Peristera pendula,* whose waxy, spotted flower-jugs smell like burned rubber. The nursery gets its trove from a Peruvian family of orchid growers in compliance with CITES, the treaty regulating international trade in rare plants.

Like many orchid lovers, Marlow dabbles in hybridizing. He generally crosses related orchid species; a current example is described as "intergeneric hybrids in the Zygopetalum alliance." Breeding efforts have produced some plants of transcendent loveliness. In 2004, Marlow registered 'Alice Marlow', a small bollea-type orchid with fan-shaped leaves and small fringed pink flowers, named for his mother. Another happy cross produced a dendrobium orchid stacked with blue flowers up and down its bloom cane.

Marlow's status as a small commercial grower assures a level of plant quality absent from the Home Depot orchid department. While exact size varies with species, all Marlow orchids come as blooming-size divisions. Healthy specimens can blossom for months, making them popular as gifts. The nursery's Web site offers diagnostic advice and detailed beginner instructions. An "Orchids Without Fear" guarantee permits gardeners to contact Marlow regularly for growing guidance and receive free replacement if plants fail within a year.

"I've have been growing orchids for over 30 years, so I know the tricks and secrets of getting these plants to rebloom in New York State's seasonal climates," says Marlow. One great tip is using a small whisper fan to keep the air moving. Because most orchids are air plants, they love a constant breeze.

Directions: From Rochester, take Route 390 to exit 17/Scottsville Road, and turn south onto Route 383/Scottsville Road. The nursery is 7 miles south, next to Doubling Hills Inn. Notice Whele Horse Farm across the street, a picturesque Kentucky-style barn that once housed the Genesee Brewery's 12-horse team.

Nearby attractions: Zantopia Herb Gardens, 1147 Main Street, Mumford, NY 14511 (585-538-6757; e-mail drewzy@earthlink.net; Drew Zantopp), is a delightful small grower of unusual well-priced perennials, herbs, and annuals, set out on tables at an old train depot; open in season, Tuesday through Saturday, 9:30 to 6.

MASTERSON'S AQUATIC NURSERY

725 Olean Road, East Aurora, NY 14052
(716) 655-0133; (800) 259-5026; fax (716) 655-0160
www.mastersons.net; e-mail *pondguy725@aol.com*
Mike Masterson

Aquatic and water garden plants. Perennials, roses. Nursery and garden center. Wholesale and retail. Open year-round, Monday through Friday, 9 to 7, Saturday, 8 to 5, and Sunday, 10 to 4; shorter hours off-season. Mail order aquatics. Catalog on Web site. Annual Garden Fest in late June. Discount coupons. Kid's Club hands-on activities. Pond supplies. Display ponds and garden. Visitors welcome.

Masterson's Aquatic Nursery and Water Garden Center consists of three horticultural enterprises rolled into one. Owner Mike Masterson, a residential landscape contractor, took over an old dairy building in 1986 and opened a small nursery in East Aurora (near Buffalo). The nursery soon ate up the landscaping business, finding its niche catering to the modern zest for water gardens. "We're still family-owned and operated," says Masterson, "but now we run a retail garden center, a wholesale grower of aquatic plants, and a Web site for mail-order aquatics."

For western New York gardeners, Masterson's is the largest local supplier of water garden plants and a respected source of stylish perennials, annuals, and roses. Determined to offer the nontraditional, Masterson constructed the garden center as a family outing destination complete with children's playground, animal pen, gazebo, fountains, and ornamental pond. Black swans and Japanese carp (koi) enliven the display ponds. Banjo bullfrogs add resonance.

For mail-order gardeners, Masterson's is a well-stocked, user-friendly supplier of aquatic plants. An online catalog lists the plants available, along with descriptions and photo portraits: 24 varieties of hardy water lily, 5 tropical water lilies, 16 marginal plants, and various floaters and oxygenators. All are grown in a clean 5000-square-foot greenhouse space equipped with irrigated holding ponds. Orders are processed from April through November, though desirable plants often sell out early in the season.

Hardy water lilies, both frost-tolerant and continuous-blooming, are the jewels of cold-climate water gardens. Masterson's inventory includes select whites, such as the exceptional 'Gladstone' and native *Nymphaea odorata*; pretty butter-yellows, including fragrant 'Charlene Strawn'; and good pink hybrids, such as angelic 'Marliac Rosea' and fresh pink 'Firecrest'. Showy 'Comanche' blooms in what is termed a "changeable" or sunset palate, from yellow-apricot to copper-gold.

Masterson's personal favorite is the hardy white European species, *Nymphaea alba,* which "starts early, flowers like crazy, and goes all season." Miniatures such as 'Baby Red Dwarf' do well in small tubs and patio gardens. On-site, Masterson offers what he calls "a whole bunch of hardy pinks we can't identify." Most water lilies run about $30 for a 2-gallon pot.

Tropical water lilies, such as 'Panama Pacific' and 'Blue Beauty', offer spectacular bloom in shades of electric blue-violet that are unattainable in hardy species. Implausibly lovely floating chalices include tropical lemon 'St. Louis' and salmon 'Colorado'. Evening-blooming water lilies, such as 'Texas Shell Pink' and 'Missouri', pose special delights for night owls. In the north, of course, tropical water lilies are destined for indoor gardens, requiring temperatures of at least 75 degrees to avoid dormancy.

Some of Masterson's most distinguished water lilies were bred by Perry Slocum, a world-renowned hybridizer born on a family farm near Cortland, New York, in 1913. At age 13, Slocum started his first water garden in an iron kettle used for scalding hogs. The first water lilies he ordered from a California nursery—yellow 'Chromatella', double pink 'Conqueror', and tropical 'Blue Star'—are old-fashioned classics still on Masterson's plant list.

Besides water lilies, Masterson's grows marginals or pond-edge plants such as blue flag, yellow flag, Japanese and Louisiana iris hybrids, bulrush, dwarf cattail, and dwarf bamboo. Among the tropical marginals are papyrus and several kinds of taro. Oddball oxygenators include hornwort, parrot's-feather, and something called anacharis. The only thing lacking on the Web site are plant names in horticultural Latin, the key to assuring that nursery "quick spreaders" aren't the world's next kudzu.

Mike Masterson is a hands-on manager with a genial manner and a sturdy grip on business. Water tanks crank out aquatics for Masterson's three enterprises. New pond products are tested to assure quality. Membership in the Home and Garden Showplace co-op group (comprising 300 independent garden centers and 12,000 independent hardware stores nationwide) affords competitively priced pond and garden supplies. Besides splashing fountains and daily antics in the petting zoo, the nursery holds teaching events and festivals through the season. If chain stores pose a menace to the independent nursery trade, Masterson's is ready for them.

Directions: East Aurora is a pretty town southwest of Buffalo. From Route 400, exit onto Route 20A, turn east, and in East Aurora, turn left at the light onto Olean Road/Route 116 south. Masterson's is 2 miles on the right.

Nearby attractions: East Aurora has several bistros, of which Tantalus, 634 Main Street (716-652-0341) and Patina, 687 Main Street (716-652-9008), look especially promising. Vidler's 5 & 10 Store, 690 Main Street (716-652-0481), has needlecrafts and toys in a 1930s five-and-dime store. Roycroft Campus, 40 South Grove Street (716-652-3333; www.roycrofter.com), an early 1900s utopian Arts and Crafts colony, has good art and artisan shops.

Related sources: Lockwood Greenhouses, 4484 Clark Street, Hamburg, NY 14705 (716-649-4684), is a family-owned garden center (and former dairy farm), known for greenhouse-grown perennials, annuals, and good gardening books. Willow Pond Aqua Farms, 3581 Swamp Road, Canandaigua, NY 14424 (585-394-5890; www.willow pondaquafarms.com), is another good upstate source of aquatics.

MILLER NURSERIES

5060 West Lake Road, Canandaigua, NY 14424-8904
(800) 836-9630; fax (585) 396-2154
www.millernurseries.com; e-mail *info@millernurseries.com*
David and John Miller

Fruit and nut trees. Heirloom apples. Grapes, small fruits. *Family-run horticultural farm. Store open February through March, Monday through Friday, 8 to 4:30; April and May, Monday through Friday, 8 to 5, Sunday, 9 to 4. Garden center hours subject to change. Free catalog. Catalog on Web site. Mail order. Shipping mid-March through May; mid-October through November. Sale in late May. Planting guide. Bare-root spring stock at the nursery. PYO fruit. Recipes on Web site. Gift certificates. Visitors welcome.*

Long a staple of New York State agriculture, Miller Nurseries is a well-known source of heirloom fruit trees, nut trees, grapes, berries, and ornamental plants. This family-owned nursery was founded in 1836 by J. E. Miller in the soft microclimate of Canandaigua Lake. The present owners are John and David Miller, the founder's great-great-grandsons. In 2002, Miller Nurseries received an award from the Massachusetts Horticultural Society honoring its horticultural achievements of more than 150 years.

Miller Nurseries' main business is supplying bare-root orchard trees by mail order, with shipments taking place in early spring and, to a lesser extent, in autumn. Although they no longer graft their own stock, the Millers continue their traditional focus on fruit- and nut-bearing plants. Dormant stock is pre-pruned to balance roots and branches. In recent years, the inventory has included shade trees, landscaping plants, bulbs, vegetables, and gardening supplies. Miller's catalog is mailed to gardeners throughout the country. Sale items are listed in a flyer sent in May. Catalog updates can be viewed on the Web site, along with Miller family recipes.

Miller Nurseries is a valued source for fruits, nuts, and vines that are hard to find in garden centers. Its 65 apple varieties include delicious new improvements and heirlooms derived from historic collections—all well suited to low-spray orchards and home storage. Exotic fruit and berry plants include Asian pears, Chinese apricots, white peaches, pink gooseberries, dwarf Japanese gold plums, 'Red Anjou' and 'Beurre Bosc' pears, and 'Kristin' hardy black cherries. Miller's list of small fruits is strong in blueberries, strawberries, and hardy grapes. For beer brewers, they sell mildew-resistant hops. Hardy nut trees include Chinese and Manchurian chestnut, American butternut, 'Fingerlakes' filbert, northern pecan, and Carpathian and black walnut.

Nursery stock isn't confined to traditional varieties. The Millers keep apprised of fruit research developments, offering such intriguing newcomers as Siberian honeyberry (an exotic honeysuckle shrub with blueberry-like fruit) and 'Lapins' cherry (a self-pollinating dwarf black sweet cherry). A new, disease-resistant blue wine grape, 'Frontenac', is hardy to −30 degrees. Pawpaw trees, Chinese kiwi fruit vines, 'SuperMale' purple asparagus, and 'Thunderlake' cranberries ("no-bog" plants suitable for ground-cover use) count among Miller's new introductions.

Visitors are welcome, but because most stock is shipped, nursery traffic is generally light. For those who visit, Miller Nurseries has a retro charm. Set on a knoll overlooking Canandaigua Lake, the retail shop is beset with whirligigs, scarecrows, garden lighthouses, and garden pots. Inside, shop assistants deliver a sunny welcome. Other than modern labels on garden supplies, little seems changed here since the 1960s. A handsome black walnut tree, planted a generation ago by the front door, attracts comment for its autumnal crop of hulls littering the driveway. The shop turns this nuisance into a kindness by offering written instructions on how to garden under black walnut trees.

One of Miller's lesser-known amenities is its policy of opening cold-storage sheds to retail customers in early spring. Most nursery stock is dispatched bare-root by mail order. Opening the storage shed means that local customers can come and pick out their own fruit and nut trees. Those looking for sturdiness, shape, or espaliering potential may find the chance to select dormant stock a real gardening advantage. Potted plants are sold on-site through the season.

Miller also opens its fruit orchards and vineyards to pick-your-own customers in autumn. An old dirt road ascends the hill behind the storage sheds, leading to a magnificent farmscape overlooking the lake. Mature apple trees and evocative twisted grape vines stand in numbered rows. The vineyards are labeled and a map of apple varieties can be obtained in the retail shop, along with loaner baskets for fruit collection. Both apples and grapes are specialty varieties that cannot be had in markets. The orchard probably provided grafting stock in the days when Miller propagated its own apple trees.

We have rarely tasted such delicious fruits as those in Miller's orchard. Flavors are dense and varied. Pick-your-own heirloom apples include 'Newtown Pippin', 'Arkansas Black', 'Duchess of Oldenburg', 'Sheepnose', 'Opalescent', 'Sops of Wine', 'Winter Banana', 'Chenango Strawberry', 'Northern Spy', 'Rhode Island Greening', 'Westfield Seek-No-Further', 'Yellow Delicious' (the original, juicy-crunchy kind), and 'Caville Blanc' (an old French culinary apple that chefs still swoon over). Grape varieties include the beguiling, spicy red 'Canidace Seedless', with sensational winy flavor; the plummy black 'Alden'; delicate rose 'Catawba', and perfumed 'Golden Muscat'. Virtually all these apple and grape varieties are still sold by the nursery. The per-pound price of this fruit is modest and it is a delight to sample its peak flavor on a fine autumn day.

A decade ago, reviews of Miller Nurseries' performance became, for a time, quite mixed. Some customers described wonderful plants, others complained of broken stock and replacement difficulties. The nursery has been diligent in correcting these lapses. A one-year replacement guarantee now accompanies all plant orders, and replacement practices are generous. Nurseries with long histories commonly undergo transitions from which they recover well. With its venerable name and long expertise, Miller Nurseries works hard to remain a reliable mail-order source for unusual fruit plants.

Directions: Millers is in the Finger Lakes region, 8 miles south of Canandaigua. From Route I-90, take exit 44, turn onto Route 21 south, pass through Canandaigua, and turn left onto West Lake Road; the nursery is 8 miles on the right. From the south, follow Route 21 north, turn right onto County Road 16, and follow to the nursery.

Nearby attractions: Sonnenberg Mansion and Gardens, 151 Charlotte Street, Canandaigua, NY 14424 (585-394-4922; www.sonnenberg.org), has period Victorian and Japanese gardens and beautiful mature ornamental trees.

ORIENTAL GARDEN SUPPLY
23 Great Oak Lane, Pittsford, NY 14534
(585) 586-4969; fax (585) 586-8945; toll-free (866) JMAPLES
www.orientalgardensupply.com
Al Pfeiffer

Japanese maples. Dwarf and unusual conifers. *Small specialty nursery. Wholesale and retail. Open mid-April through mid-October, Monday through Friday, 12 to 4; Saturday, 9 to 4; Sunday, 1 to 4. Catalog $5 (refundable with order). Plant list on Web site. Mail order. Large-order discounts. Custom orders. Delivery of large items by arrangement. Gift certificates. Specific requirements for ordering bonsai stock. Visitors welcome.*

Oriental Garden Supply is a small nursery near Rochester specializing in hardy Japanese maples. Owner Al Pfeiffer is a former electrical engineer who started the nursery in 1998 after selling his precision sheet metal business. "I always loved plants and had a small collection of unusual material. One day I sat down with a pad of paper and wrote down what I liked doing and what I was good at," he recalls. "At the end of the day, 'Japanese maples' was circled. I turned my avocation into my vocation."

Pfeiffer perceived the need for a better class of ornamental maples for smaller gardens. "I saw all these guys on the West Coast growing unusual maples," he says. "I thought, 'Why not upstate New York?'" He began visiting maple collections at area arboreta and nurseries, acquired some acreage in Mendon, and began raising unusual maples. Today, Oriental Garden Supply offers 240 different varieties of Japanese and Asian maples, hardy to Zone 5.

Introduced to Western horticulture in 1820, the Japanese maple *(Acer palmatum)* is a beautiful ornamental tree with an energetic breeding history. Today's countless varieties include dwarf forms and weepers; variegated, red-, yellow-, and purple-leaved forms; and the 'Dissectum' group, beloved for its intricate canopies of lacy foliage. Oriental Garden selects the best-performing cold-hardy varieties, such as colorful 'Butterfly', ferny 'Green Filigree', and exquisite 'Kurui Jushi'. A Japanese maple called 'Orido Nishiki' has beautiful pink variegation and long-tapered leaves. The list goes on and on.

The average gardener needs a good reference (such as Timber Press' *Japanese Maples*) to make sense of it all. Or you can just visit Oriental Garden Supply and take a hard look at the stock. "We look for the unusual," says Pfeiffer. "Ninety percent of our stock nobody else has." Because many cultivated maples are not fully hardy, the nursery's Zone 5 climate helps Pfeiffer select robust performers. "I tell people with maples, 'Treat 'em bad!' Trim them hard and they come right back," says Pfeiffer.

Oriental Garden Supply grows other ornamental maples, too, such as paperbark, trident, full-moon, and three-flowered maples—and even some native vine maple cultivars. Its collection of snakebark maples exhibits marvelous winter bark. An Asian snakebark called 'White Tigress', for example, is garbed in sage-green bark with vertical white stripes, while a showy moosewood (*Acer pensylvanicum* 'Erythrocladum') is decorated bright coral.

Pfeiffer took up growing dwarf and unusual conifers to add winter interest to Oriental-style gardens. The conifer listing is long and varied, containing blue, gold, variegated, dwarf, weeping, contorted, and pendulous forms. "The first time I saw Japanese elkhorn cedar [*Thujopsis dolobrata*], I thought it was plastic and had been stamped out of a machine," says Pfeiffer. Especially fine selections of pine and false cypress are present, along with varieties of spruce, fir, larch, and hemlock. Some evergreens, such as cedar-of-Lebanon, Sicilian fir, and Bosnian redcone pine, are virtually unobtainable in ordinary gardening circles. As a sideline, Pfeiffer grows specimen ornamentals—such as Japanese stewartia, *Ginkgo biloba* 'Autumn Gold', and dwarf lacebark elm (*Ulmus parvifolia* 'Frosty')—and sells bamboos, ferns, and grasses.

Nursery stock comes in many sizes, from affordable 4-inch or gallon-size pots, easily mail-ordered, to large-caliper specimens in box planters requiring special delivery. Pfeiffer propagates a mixture of rooted cuttings, grafted stock, and (for species maples only) seedlings. Some stock is bought in, mostly from Oregon. The Web site plant list runs 31 pages; the mail-order catalog is shorter. Plants are well priced, especially smaller stock and species maples seedlings.

Although landscapers and garden centers form a significant wholesale customer base, Oriental Garden Supply welcomes the home gardener. Many maple seedlings derive from exotic trees growing in Durand-Eastman Park, where Pfeiffer has permission to cull samara. "I encourage people to use the species maples," says Pfeiffer. "They're great plants on hardy rootstock and they fit well with a homeowner budget." The nursery is also popular with bonsai artists and enthusiasts seeking starter plants among its rare maples and conifers.

Directions: The nursery ground is located at 448 West Bloomfield Road, Pittsford, NY 14534 (585-586-3850). From I-90/New York State Thruway, take exit 45 onto Route 490 west (toward Rochester). In 2 miles, take the Bushnells Basin exit, turn right on Route 96, and in 0.2 mile, take the first major left onto Thornell Road. At the T-junction, turn left (south) onto West Bloomfield Road. In 1 mile, cross over the I-90 Thruway, and the nursery is immediately on the left.

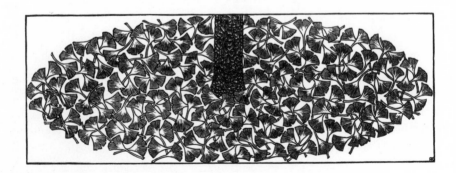

P & P SEED COMPANY

56 East Union Street, Hamburg, NY 14075-5007
(800) 449-5681; (716) 648-7982; fax (716) 532-5690
www.bigseeds.com; e-mail *lgourd@aol.com*
Ray Waterman

Giant pumpkin seed. Big-vegetable seed. Family-run horticultural farm. Open by appointment. Free seed list. Catalog on Web site. Mail order. Sponsor of World Pumpkin Confederation. Annual World Pumpkin Weigh-Off and Fall Festival, late September.

P & P Seed Company specializes in selling seed for giant pumpkins that sweep the big-vegetable awards at county fairs. Only a fascination with monstrosity can explain the popularity of this peculiar pastime. Giant-vegetable seeds produce grotesque, plus-size vegetables subliminally reminiscent of Sumo wrestlers. For most gardeners, autumn is, as Keats described it, a "season of mists and mellow fruitfulness." For growers of monster vegetables, says P & P Seed, "fall is the time of reckoning and, for a lucky few, *glory!*"

Ray Waterman, owner and president of P & P Seed, is the P.T. Barnum of the American seed business. An enterprising farmer in Collins, south of Buffalo, Waterman founded the World Pumpkin Federation in 1983 to promote "challenge gardening" among growers of heavyweight pumpkins. Each September, the Federation holds a World Pumpkin Weigh-Off at Waterman's Great Pumpkin Farm in Clarence, New York, to determine the world's largest pumpkin.

The 1000-pound pumpkin challenge was met in 1996, when two backyard growers won $53,000 for their world-record pumpkin (1061 pounds)—the largest award ever given for a giant pumpkin. The 1998 Guinness Book of Records recorded the feat with a color photo of the pumpkin—a warty, pale, morbidly obese vegetable whose flabby slouch suggested months spent indoors, on a couch, overeating.

Today, growers from more than 30 countries convene in upstate New York for the World Pumpkin Weigh-Off, a fall festival with a side-show atmosphere. Waterman has set a new World Pumpkin challenge of 1500 pounds and predicts a 2000-pound pumpkin (one ton) in 10 years. In 2002, the World Pumpkin weighed in at 1337.5 pounds. To appreciate the feat of growing even a 900- or 1000-pound pumpkin, consider the second-place winner in 1994: a girth of 14.5 feet and enough edible flesh for 900 pies. When carved, the pumpkin held a 60-watt light bulb and a member of the family. At the Topsfield Fair in Massachusetts, 12 men were needed to roll a similar-size colossus onto a tarpaulin and drag it to a cattle scale. In 2000, the World Pumpkin won $25,000 and was flown to Stuttgart, Germany, for exhibition.

Almost all world-record pumpkins since 1982 have been grown in backyard gardens. Howard Dill, a co-founder of the World Pumpkin Federation, held the world record from 1979 to 1982 for his 'Atlantic Giant' series of pumpkins—one of P & P Seed's big sellers. The cost of seed is proportionate to the heft of the mother vegetable. A packet of three seeds from the largest 'Atlantic Giant' (over 800 pounds) costs $10, plus shipping. Seed from other giant pumpkins include World Record champion hybrids and big-pumpkin offspring called 'The Great Ones'.

Pumpkin handling supplies such as tarps and strap lifters are sold, as well as instructional books and World Pumpkin Confederation memorabilia. Tips on rearing giant pumpkins and other hefty vegetables appear on the P & P Seed Web site under the rubric "Growing the Big One."

Besides pumpkins, P & P Seed sells seed from big cucurbits: a 700-pound giant green squash, 200-pound watermelon, 120-pound bushel gourd, and 30-pound cantaloupe. Other big-vegetable seeds include 2-foot long bean, 3-pound giant tomato, and 16-foot giant corn (useful as a windbreak). Without exact measurement, but undoubtedly huge, are 'Pink Giant' banana squash, 'Mammoth' white radish, 'Northern Giant' cabbage, and 'Super Heavyweight' hybrid pepper. P & P Seed also sells 'Waterman' strains for big sunflowers, watermelons, tomatoes, and squashes.

For the more reserved pumpkin grower, P & P Seed sells seed for popular disease-resistant pumpkin varieties from New York's Harris Seeds (see profile). These produce handsome normal-size pumpkins, bred for ordinary human uses, such as pie and jack-o-lanterns.

Directions: The seed farm is located in Collins, south of Buffalo; call ahead for appointment and directions. The annual World Pumpkin Weigh-Off is held in Clarence, 10 miles east of Buffalo. Take Route 1-90 to exit 49 toward Lockport. In 0.5 mile, turn left onto Transit Road/Route 78; in 0.6 mile, turn right onto Wherlec Drive; and in 1 mile, turn right onto Main Street. In 5.5 miles, the Great Pumpkin Farm is at 11199 Main Street.

PALMITER'S GARDEN NURSERY

2675 Geneseo Road (Route 39), Avon, NY 14414
(585) 226-3073; fax (585) 226-6344
E-mail *Palmnsry@eznet.net*
Merle, Sheila, and Marla Palmiter

Perennials, herbs, alpines. Peonies, hosta, daylilies. Annuals and container
plants. Roses. Dwarf conifers. Flowering shrubs and trees. Chile peppers.
Small specialty nursery. Open April through early November, Monday through Sat-
urday, 9 to 6, Sunday, noon to 6. Call for exact dates. No catalog. No mail order. Lists
of peonies, daylilies, hosta. Gift certificates. Visitors welcome.

Many gardeners' first contact with their ideal nursery feels like the ideal
home. The location is comfortably rural; the activity pleasantly old-
fashioned, and the discourse good-humored and sensible. This may
explain why so many gardeners sigh appreciatively when they
speak of Palmiter's Garden Nursery. The nursery is located on
19 acres of quiet, gently rolling farmland southwest of
Rochester, with long views over the western landscape—just
where you might wish your family lived.

"We're a regular Mom and Pop," says Merle Palmiter of
the business he and his wife, Sheila, have operated from their
home for nearly 30 years. They started with a small roadside
stand in the 1970s, selling plants during what he calls "the
annuals craze." Merle Palmiter was working in landscape
maintenance and kept a private rock-garden collection in the
backyard. "People would come to the stand for annuals and
want plants from our rock garden," he recalls. "We started
growing and selling perennials in the 1980s when people
didn't know them well."

Today, the nursery continues to offer refined perennials
and rock-garden plants of unusual diversity to experienced
gardeners. "Our specialty is variety," says Sheila Palmiter. "I'm
an old fogey. I love old-fashioned plants like foxgloves and
Merle likes to try new things." One of the hardest skills in
gardening is discerning meritorious plants. By listening to
customers and keeping up with horticultural developments, the

Palmiters are able to recognize garden-worthy plants that satisfy both longings, old and new.

Palmiter's grows more than 1000 varieties of hardy perennials, from tiny alpines to tall border plants. Some 200 hosta and 150 daylilies have been chosen for looks and durability. High-performance ornamental grasses and flowering herbs are an important percentage of the inventory. Uncommon alpines and hardy sedums populate the rock-garden collection, now dressed up with rare dwarf conifers. The nursery is known for its terrific selection of hardy shrub roses, climbers, and heirlooms. Attractive flowering trees round out the nursery's eclectic bounty.

Perhaps most dear to Merle Palmiter's heart are the peonies—some 50 herbaceous and tree peony varieties. The herbaceous peonies comprise old favorites; stylish newcomers, such as salmon 'Flame'; and elegant Japanese-style singles and semi-doubles, such as 'Krinkled White' and 'Do Tell'. Among the aristocratic tree peonies, Palmiter favors Saunders, Gratwick, and Daphnos hybrids in glorious sunset colors, as well as the sensational yellow intersectional hybrid, 'Bartzalla'. William Gratwick and Nassos Daphnos conducted their breeding at nearby Linwood, where Gratwick's now-mature peony garden retains an enchanted elegance. (Palmiter's first tree peony, 'Gauguin', was a Daphnos hybrid.) For the Palmiters, a 2004 peony-viewing trip to China not only fulfilled a life's dream but immediately attracted a return visit from an elderly Chinese peony collector. The nursery's business card is now bilingual, printed in English and Chinese.

One slightly zany nursery sideline is Merle Palmiter's passion for hot chile peppers. Each year, he grows 4200 perennial capsicums in 60 varieties. When they ripen in summer, he sells colorful fresh chile peppers from a vending stall in the Rochester Farmer's Market. Small pepper plants are also available at the nursery in 4-inch pots. Among them are 'Marbles', 'Jigsaw', 'Thai Hot', 'Tiny Tim', and a best seller, 'Thai Dragon'. Merle Palmiter once grew Jamaican seed for a pepper called 'Super Chili', which he claims was "the first *habanero* in Rochester."

Most Palmiter's nursery stock is grown from seed, cuttings, and divisions in the greenhouses. New cultivars and grafted plants are bought in and fleshed out at the nursery. Plants are set out on tables, in rows. Perennials come in 1-quart, 2-quart, and gallon-size containers, herbs in $3\frac{1}{4}$-inch pots. Consistent with the nursery's old-style demeanor, prices are reasonable. A cautionary sign at the cash register reads, "Roses are red and violets blue, / If your check bounces, we will charge you."

Palmiter's has no catalog, no brochure, no mail order, no fax, and no Web site. "We have a sign," says Sheila Palmiter. They do have a sign. It was missing on our visit. They do have a smart daughter, and therefore an e-mail address, which they do not use. They do have magnificent lush display gardens occupying every planting opportunity on the nursery margins. The gardens seem so Technicolor, so present tense, that visitors are reassured—Palmiter's is not Brigadoon.

Directions: From Route I-90, turn onto Route 390 south and take exit 10/Avon. Turn right onto Routes 5 & 20 west into Avon, past the rotary. At the bottom of the hill, turn left onto Route 39 south. In 4 miles, the nursery is on the left, at the corner of Papermill Road.

Nearby attractions: Tom Wahl's 1955 quilted aluminum diner, Routes 5 & 20, Avon (585-226-2420), makes the Wahlburger, a delicious ground-steak-and-smoked-ham sandwich. Linwood Gardens, 1912 York Road, Pavilion, NY 14525 (585-584-3913), a private garden sanctuary belonging to the Gratwick family, opens for a Tree Peony Festival of Flowers in early June. Linwood's historic gardens frame a renowned collection of mature tree peonies, including original Gratwick and Daphnos hybrids bred on-site. The gardens contain evocative walled gardens, a bewitching dwarf village, and a fine katsura allée. In 1939, visitor Wyndham Lewis wrote, "In the cool of the evening we walked in the gardens. They were of extraordinary beauty. Agatha said to me afterwards that they were the 'purest Chekhov.'" The poet William Carlos Williams wrote that he "was virtually speechless" on entering Linwood "through masonry arches unbelievably romantic in their semi-decay." Linwood is a private residence; visitors welcome at allowed times. Call or write to confirm open days and hours.

PHOENIX FLOWER FARM
2620 Lamson Road, Phoenix, NY 13135
(315) 695-2377
www.phoenixflowerfarm.com; e-mail *phoenixflr@juno.com*
Helen and John Schueler

Historic and bearded iris. Peonies, daylilies, hosta, and grasses. Perennials.
Family-run horticultural farm. Open May and June, daily, 9 to 6; July through Sep-
tember, Wednesday through Sunday, 9 to 6; April and October, weekends, 9 to 6; and
by appointment. Catalog $3. Plant list on Web site. Limited mail order. Spring and
fall garden parties. Daylily Daze clump sale, last week of July. Live music on week-
ends. Slide lectures. Horticultural trips. Gift certificates. Landscaping services.

Phoenix Flower Farm is a small upstate nursery known for its heirloom and
modern iris. Owner Helen Schueler is a respected plantswoman and former
history teacher who became serious about horticulture upon retirement.
"We bought the property 26 years ago with the idea of establishing a Mom
and Pop business," Schueler recalls. "Then in 1988, my job got in the way of
my life, so I gave it up to concentrate on the nursery."

The flower farm occupies two acres of naturalistic gardens behind the
Schueler home in Phoenix, north of Syracuse. Schueler works the nursery
gardens with skilled family help. Husband John is "the tiller," of whom she
admits, "I'd be hard pressed without him." Heavy lifting is accomplished by
Mike and Delos, two energetic, well-educated sons who run a professional
landscaping operation here. The gardens are a tribute to the Schuelers'
commitment to organic mulch, having absorbed three dumpster loads of
composted leaf mold when first established.

Schueler and her husband have grown heirloom, German, and Siberian
iris for more than 40 years. Both are iris judges and life members of the
American Iris Society (AIS). Schueler joined the AIS in 1983, after visiting
the state fair in Syracuse. "A lady there, a neighbor of mine, was manning the
iris booth. She was on the national board of AIS," Schueler recalls. "My
husband turned and said, 'You should join that!'" She did, and proceeded to
amass a collection of more than 1200 iris cultivars. The Schuelers have
collected all the award-winning iris in 11 of 14 recognized classes, from dwarf
and tall bearded iris to Siberian iris and other beardless varieties.

The jewel of Schueler's garden is a collection of some 50 iris antiques.
Many are yellow-and-brown tall bearded (German) iris from the Victorian

period and earlier. Pale yellow 'Flavescens', a tall bearded variety, was brought in colonial ships and officially named in 1808. The heirloom Siberian iris, such as 'Velvet Night', often bloom in drifts and make better garden plants than modern hybrids. Of special charm is Schueler's collection of lovely little violet and yellow "table iris," a type of miniature bearded iris developed in Maine in the 1930s—the only iris class required to be scented.

"I'm a sucker for any historic iris I can find," Schueler says. "I used to put pots of modern tall bearded iris in the car and drive around. Whenever I saw an old iris that interested me, I'd stop and offer to trade one of mine. I got quite a few that way." Schueler's favorites are 1940s tall bearded iris and rock-hardy Siberian iris. "There is the remnant of a famous iris farm (Indian Springs) near us," she notes, "where Siberians are growing and blooming with abandon, untouched by humans since 1947."

Schueler also acquired heirloom iris through the Historic Iris Preservation Society (HIPS), founded by the AIS in 1989. "We joke about 'HIPS' as the name for a group of widening old ladies," she says. When Schueler hosted a HIPS convention in 2000, many members sent sample rhizomes that were later added to her collection. Anyone with an iris over 30 years old is encouraged to come "talk irises" with Helen Schueler.

Nursery treasures are not limited to iris. A good peony collection includes 'High Noon', a 1952 award-winning yellow tree peony bred by Professor Saunders of Clinton, New York, and 'Fiery Francis', a single-flowered magenta peony that has thrived in greater Syracuse for more than 100 years. The nursery grows 800 daylily varieties, emphasizing historic varieties, hybrids from noted breeders, and award winners that perform well in the north. Classy perennials include white lupines, black dahlias, variegated physostegia (obedient plant), dwarf Solomon's-seal, the better cranesbills, and pinellia (an exotic jack-in-the-pulpit relation from China). The rock-garden collection harbors *Phyteuma scheuchzeri*, described as resembling a "mutant bellflower," and some excellent variegated sedges that perform well in shade. Unusual shrubs include a tough little evergreen ground cover called *Paxistima canbyi*, considered choice by garden *cognoscenti*. The nursery sells bags of "Nutri-Brew," a local compost made by Anheuser Busch from discarded beer mash.

Phoenix Flower Farm sells nursery-propagated plants that are grown, as the Web site says, "at a natural pace, outdoors, with the same stresses they will face in your garden." Plants are well labeled and fairly priced. Customer praise confirms the stock's quality and toughness. Bearded irises and daylilies are dug in bloom and transplanted bare-root. Peonies, perennials, and beardless iris are sold in gallon pots for ease of planting during the growing season. Daylilies are available by mail order. While the nursery doesn't normally mail iris, exceptions are sometimes made for collectors who plead for unique plants. The Schuelers are adept at recommending iris and daylilies that do well upstate.

Nursery visitors should not leave without touring Schueler's iris collection in bloom season—a living museum of a beloved garden classic. Antique tall bearded iris are reminiscent of grandmother's garden. Some 19th-century iris bloom in subtle colors, difficult to describe or photograph. A mournful shade of grayish violet called "squalens" or "blend," for example, offers an intriguing window on Victorian color preferences. Schueler hopes some day to find the squalens iris her Swiss grandmother brought from Europe and grew in her garden 50 years ago.

One noted highlight is the hybrids of Dr. William McGarvey, a local breeder who became a leading iris hybridizer of the 20th century. 'Pink Haze' (1969) is his pioneering pink Siberian iris. Dr. McGarvey mischievously named 'Maggie Smith' and 'Lydia Winter' (two nearly identical mauve Siberians) after two local ladies who had a shouting match over their merits in his breeding beds. Schueler is full of such wonderful stories, adding warmth and merriment to an impressive horticultural archive.

Directions: The farm is north of Syracuse. From the east on I-90, exit onto Route 481 north, take the Phoenix exit, turn left off the ramp, and in 1 mile, at the end, turn right onto Route 57 north. In Phoenix, turn left at the second light, cross the bridge, and the farm is 1.5 miles on the left. From the west on I-90, exit onto Route 690 west; at the end, go straight through the intersection, and in 2 miles, turn right at the light onto Lamson Road. The farm is 1.5 miles on the right.

Nearby attractions: Enchantment Acres Flower Farm, 887 County Route 3, Hannibal, NY 13074 (315-598-3346; ron2don@alltel.com; Ron and Donna James; open

May through July, Wednesday through Friday, 4 to 7, weekends, 10 to 5, and by appointment), is a family-owned nursery and Historic Iris Preservation Society display garden with more than 1700 historic and bearded iris; also daylilies and daffodils.

THE PLANTSMEN NURSERY
482 Peruville Road, Route 34B, Groton, NY 13073
(607) 533-7193 phone and fax
www.plantsmen.com; e-mail *info@plantsmen.com*
Rick Hedrick and Patrick Jensen

Uncommon annuals, perennials, biennials, and tropicals. *Small specialty nursery. Wholesale and retail. Open mid-April through July 4, daily, 9 to 6; July 5 through September 30, daily except Mondays, 10 to 4. Call for exact dates. Year-round shop hours. Free catalog. Mail order. No retail pre-season orders. Call ahead for particular items. Imported pottery. Landscape design. Display gardens. Visitors welcome.*

Like Buddhism, horticulture recognizes lineages, special confluences of aptitude and *métier* renewed in each generation. In New York State, no heritage is more eminent than that of Ulysses P. Hedrick, chief horticulturist and director of the New York Agricultural Experiment Station in Geneva from 1905 to 1937. Dr. Hedrick led the institution in its heyday, authoring such authoritative books as *The Peaches of New York* (1917); parallel tomes on grapes, plums, cherries, pears, and small fruits; and *The History of Agriculture in America* (1950). Dr. Hedrick was an active pomologist who had a profound influence on the state's fruit culture.

Dr. Hedrick's great-grandson, Ulysses P. (Rick) Hedrick IV, is a gifted 21st-century nurseryman committed to the superior horticultural traditions of his ancestor's day. Hedrick is a Rhode Island School of Design-trained landscape architect who worked in Manhattan on large urban landscaping projects before coming home to practice landscape architecture on a more human scale. Unable to find local sources for desired plants, Hedrick began growing his own stock—an activity that morphed into a fledgling nursery in 1990. Hedrick has doubled his sales and added greenhouse space every year since then.

Hedrick and his partner, educator Patrick Jensen, are co-owners of The Plantsmen Nursery, a smart specialty nursery set among old farmsteads and wet meadows north of Ithaca. Hedrick is a full-time, hands-on nurseryman.

Nursery manager Barbara Bryant is a devoted plantswoman who propagates annuals and helps manage the greenhouses. (Her obsession is rare pelargoniums, for which Hedrick claims he has her in a 12-Step Program.)

This nursery is a treasure trove of sophisticated garden plants suited to cold Zone 5 conditions. "Our enthusiasm and love of all aspects of gardening is what started us in business," says Hedrick. "We approach gardening and the growing of our plants as a passion." A baroque plant list includes annuals, biennials, tender and hardy perennials, heirloom vegetables, herbs, ornamental grasses, shade plants, ferns, topiary, flowering vines, unusual conifers, and flowering shrubs. Each year, the inventory expands with dozens of new varieties.

To discover new and unusual plants, Hedrick spends a time each year, as he says, "traveling around the world, as well as around the block." Plants are sourced from private collectors, botanical gardens, and eminent commercial sources worldwide—such as the Strybing Botanical Garden, the RHS seed exchange, a Czech botanical garden, and Piet Oudolf's nursery in the Netherlands. Hedrick's most famous contact is British horticulturist Christopher Lloyd, proprietor of Great Dixter and one of the most influential plantsmen of our time. Hedrick cannot resist exotic plants—even customer requests inspire him. The result is one of the most impressive inventories of annuals, tropicals, and perennials in the region.

Although William Morris denounced carpet bedding as "an aberration of the human mind," many of The Plantsmen's showiest annuals are in fact heirloom bedding plants—dwarf impatiens, trailing lobelia, yellow-leaved feverfew, and heirloom marigolds and zinnias. A fine collection of 100 rare pelargoniums ("geraniums") includes zonal, stellar, fancy-leaved, miniature, and scented varieties, often beautifully color-streaked and watermarked. The Plantsmen selected its top-25 flowering maple (abutilon) hybrids, including butter-yellow 'Moonchimes' and lava-red 'Vesuvius'; new brick-red and butterfly-pink forms are bred at the nursery. Vita Sackville-West once considered "how pretty it might be to train abutilon as a standard"—and Hedrick has complied. The vines include a frothy-white tomato relative *(Solanum jasminoides)* and uncommon sweet peas, passionflowers, and morning-glories. Even the vegetables are ornamental—Italian cardoon, Scottish strap-leaved beet, and a variegated chile pepper discovered at the nursery, for example.

Oddity, drama, celebrity, and style—it's all here: a huge castor oil plant resembling a palm tree, angel's-trumpets seeded from plants owned by artist Georgia O'Keefe and dancer Rudolph Nureyev, white leonotis from a Rothschild garden in France, and a large-flowered morning-glory from English designer Rosemary Very. The Plantsmen sells gorgeous urns and jars and container plants to go with them—salvia, coleus, cuphea, begonia, canna, brugmansia, verbena, lantana, and snapdragon.

The Plantsmen also grows hardy perennials. As usual, the list is bewildering, ranging from ornamental alliums and milkweeds to Hungarian violets and gold-leaved columbine. Choice natives include dwarf Solomon's seal, pallid echinacea, variegated turtlehead, and double leopard's-bane. For ground cover we loved the gold-leaved alpine strawberry. Shrubs are judiciously selected to enhance perennial borders: unusual willows, hardy boxwood, and a yellow-berried Siberian called sea buckthorn *(Hippophäe rhamnoides)*.

The Plantsmen grows its plants in a dozen greenhouses. According to Hedrick, "our methods hark back to earlier days, when plants were propagated and nurtured by a nurseryman, not bought in as small liners and sold to you the next week." Annuals and tender perennials are taken fresh from cuttings. Hardy perennials and shrubs are grown from scratch and held for sale until the second season. The result is robust, specimen-quality stock that is well-rooted and correctly labeled. Some varieties are limited and sell out briskly in spring.

The Plantsmen Nursery is set amid gardens on 12 acres of flat, seasonally flooded wetlands, cleared by permission of the local Conservation Commission. It is a plantsman's paradise. An oval entry court embraces a magnificent hallmark urn amid gravel walks. The gardens combine formality and wildness with subtle, impressive panache. Kinetic presences, such as outsized arctic willows and 20-foot plumed grasses *(Miscanthus floridulus),* preside with rustling grandeur over terminal views of marshland. "I started with a strong structural organization and planted self-sowing meadow species, such as inula, helianthemum, monarda, mountain mint, and tansy," says Hedrick. "The teasels blew in from a farm field. So now I'm growing elegant, architectural weeds."

Hedrick's enthusiasm for his work assures a warm welcome to gardeners of all levels. The nursery allows customers to bring in containers for planting; keeps prices reasonable to encourage experimentation; throws occasional garden parties and lectures to make it fun; welcomes questions, whether dumb or difficult; and in July, sometimes gives away extra annuals, in order to hearten gardeners to play around with plants they've never seen before. At the heart of such efforts are the nurseryman's greatest arts— selecting the best plants and growing them well. Hedrick quotes Gertrude Stein on the tease of choice and delight that inspires his work: "When everything is found that is pleasant and when everything that is selected is selected again."

Directions: From Ithaca, take East Shore Drive north and turn right at the end onto Route 34. In 1 mile, at the curve, go straight onto Route 34B/Peruville Road; the nursery is 2 miles on the left. From Syracuse, take Route I-90 west to exit 34A and merge onto Route 481 south. In 10 miles, merge left onto Route 81 south. In 27 miles, take exit 12 and turn left onto Route 281 west. In 3 miles, turn right onto Route 120/Mclean Road. Go straight when Route 120 becomes Route 105, and in 2 miles, turn right onto Peruville Road/Route 107; the nursery is 4.5 miles on the right. From Buffalo, take Route I-90 east to exit 40 and turn onto Route 34 south. In 10 miles, turn left onto Route 38. In 30 miles, turn right onto Route 34B/Peruville Road; the nursery is 2 miles on the right.

Nearby attractions: Cornell Plantations, One Plantations Road, Ithaca, NY 14850 (607-255-2400; www.plantations.cornell.edu), houses Cornell's extraordinary botanical research collections in a 500-acre arboretum and 4000 wild acres (open daily, dawn to dusk). The Greater Ithaca Art Trail (www.arttrail.com) schedules Open Studio Weeks with 50 artists, including Bente Starcke King (bsk11@cornell.edu), a noted botanical illustrator and instructor at Cornell.

ROCHESTER PUBLIC MARKET
280 North Union Street, Rochester, NY 14609
(585) 428-6770
www.cityofrochester.gov

Annuals, perennials, vegetables, and garden items. Public market plant vendors. Market open year-round, Tuesdays and Thursday, 6 to 1, Saturdays, 5 to 3. Market open for "Flower City Days," May through early June, Sundays, 8 to 2. Check Web site for exact dates. Plants direct from area growers. Special Sunday markets; see Web site for details. Some plants and supplies sold on regular market days. Public welcome.

Rochester's century-old Public Market occupies nine acres in the heart of downtown. Operated by the city on the same site since 1905, it is open year-round and annually attracts 1.5 million shoppers. The market has the authentic, earthy atmosphere of a public space long occupied by wholesale vendors of meat, produce, and cut flowers. Touted as "the most diverse place in western New York," the public market's Saturday traffic alone can attract 30,000 visitors. People gather to shop, eat, schmooze, and people-watch. According to the Project for Public Places, a visionary advocate of quality public space, the Rochester Public Market succeeds as "a gathering place, a spot for politicians to campaign, a family shopping tradition, a destination, and part of the weekly routine."

A century ago, the Rochester Public Market served wholesale produce and grocery vendors using horse-drawn carts. Public pressure forced the market to open for retail sales during an inflationary scare after World War I. Today, following a $3.5 million face-lift, the revitalized market is equipped with 300 open-air and indoor vending spaces. The Public Market combines what the City calls "owner-operated family enterprises and healthful farm-fresh quality" with "the values of wholesale shopping and the convenience of modern facilities."

The place is hopping. According to the city, on regular market days (Tuesday, Thursday, and Saturday), visitors can find "fresh fruit, meat, fish, poultry (live and prepared), eggs, dairy products, home baked goods, seasonal produce, flowers, plants, jewelry, dry goods, paintings, crafts, specialty foods, ethnic delicacies, decorative items, curiosities, and bargains, bargains, bargains." A shopper might take home field greens, farm sausage, wild honey, and purple petunias.

Vendors are an ethnically baroque and colorful group of farmers, traders, artists, and entrepreneurs. Many farmers come from nearby Wayne County, which pretty much assures their produce is squeaky fresh. One of the few stands selling organic produce is GRUB (Greater Rochester Urban Bounty), staffed by Rochester Institute of Technology students working with inner-city neighborhoods to develop a successful farm-vendor business. The stand is easy to spot; just look for the slouching teenagers. Merle Palmiter of Palmiter's Garden Nursery (see profile) brings a jewel-like array of fresh hot chile peppers, which he grows as a hobby.

In spring, the Public Market opens on Sundays for "Flower City Days," a series of five Sundays in May and early June devoted to horticultural sales. Just when spring fever becomes a contagion, gardeners flock to the market to stock up on freshly grown annuals, perennials, herbs, and vegetable plants from area growers. Sunday vendors also sell garden-related supplies, structures, art, artifacts, and treasure-trash—what the city calls "lawn figurines, lawn furniture, mulch, topsoil, tools, and trellises." Of course, nothing is really regimented. Gardeners who miss Flower City Days can still buy a few plants and garden objects at the regular market, or on other special Sundays such as "Homegrown at the Market" and "Greatest Garage Sales Ever." (Schedules are listed on the Web site.) But Flower City Days is when eager gardeners really hit the market for plants.

Vendors at Flower City Days change from year to year, but some are regulars. Eaton Farms, a wholesale grower in Ontario, New York, usually shows up with fresh greenhouse-grown annuals, perennials, and herbs at wholesale prices. Wildwood Farms in Williamson sends in quantities of garden plants (and maybe fresh spinach and field greens) with college students working for tuition money running the booth. Cathy and Andy Matulewicz come from Penn Yan in a truck with their two kids, lots of plants, and a plant photo album. Howard Ecker, known as Howard the Hosta Guy, offers hostas, the odd grass plant, and the fun of dealing with a haggler worthy of an Eastern souk.

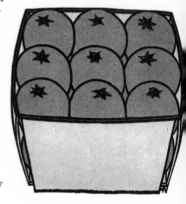

Bustle and elbow-rubbing are part of the public market experience. As journalist Christina Le Beau wrote in the *Upstate Gardener's Journal*, "Most vendors seem to know their stuff. If not, many of the shoppers do. Half the fun of these Sunday mornings is trading tips with fellow gardeners."

Everyone has a favorite spot for a bite to eat after shopping. Some wouldn't miss the Mexican food at Juan and Maria's Empanada Stop, whose owners, Juan and Maria Contreras, sponsor the Spanish festival in September. Others just go over to Scott's for a fried egg sandwich.

Directions: The market is in downtown Rochester, off East Main Street. Local shuttle and bus service is shown on the Web site. Driving from the east, take Route 490 west to Plymouth Street / Inner Loop exit, bear left on Inner Loop Exit, and turn left onto East Main Street. Turn left onto Union Street and right into the Public Market. Bear right to park in a lot or side street.

Nearby attractions: The City of Rochester (www.cityofrochester.gov) and Monroe County (www.monroecounty.gov) together maintain 12,000 acres of public parks— one of the nation's most generous park systems, including three Frederick Law Olmsted-designed landscapes and a world-class arboretum. The Ellwanger Garden, 625 Mt. Hope Avenue, Rochester, NY (716-546-7029; www.landmarksociety.org), once the private garden of 19th-century nurseryman George Ellwanger, is a preserved half-acre "secret garden" of perennials, trees, and shrubs. The George Eastman House, 900 East Avenue, Rochester, NY 14607 (716-271-3361), has a restored 12.5-acre garden and the International Museum of Photography and Film (with cool movie theater and amazing film archive).

SARA'S GARDEN CENTER
389 East Avenue, Brockport, NY 14420
(716) 637-2037
E-mail *sarasgardencenter@msn.com*
Steven and Kathleen Kepler

Perennials, roses, aquatics, and container plants. *Family-run garden center. Open mid-March to December 24, Monday through Saturday, 9 to 6, Sunday, 9 to 5. Extended hours spring. No catalog or mail order. Custom containers and wreaths. Display gardens. Visitors welcome.*

Sara's Garden Center is a small family-run business in Brockport, 20 miles west of Rochester, specializing in hardy perennials, roses, and water garden plants. Owners Kathy and Steve Kepler, who previously operated a nursery, bought Sara's in 1998 from Steve's brother, Frank, who had founded it in 1982 with his wife, Donna, and named it for their infant daughter, Sara. Now grown, Sara works there for her Uncle Steve, along with Frank, who may have burned out as an owner but still likes the work, which is convenient, because he lives next door. In short, Sara's is a classic family enterprise.

Sara's Garden Center combines the ambience and efficiency of an independent garden center with the knowledge and service of a specialty nursery. "Wal-Mart is only two miles from here, so we try to distinguish ourselves by keeping our customer service way up," says Kathy Kepler. "Instead of not being able to find anybody, we're here, and we answer questions. We hold strong on quality, too. Our biggest enemy is the weather!"

Sara's is best known for its outstanding selection of perennials—nearly 3000 varieties. The garden center was among the first in the area to carry perennials in depth, and it remains an exceptionally rich source. Garden-worthy plants seem encyclopedic: 17 monkshoods, 20 yarrows, 40 columbines, 58 primroses, and 68 dianthus, for example. The inventory includes border plants, alpines, ground covers, vines, wildflowers, woodlanders, herbaceous shrubs, grasses, and ferns. Stalwarts of the perennial border—iris, hosta, and daylily—appear in droves. Obscure up-and-comers are tried each year, such as blue poppy and yellow scabeous (*Cephalaria gigantea*). A garden center that bothers to carry 15 horned violets (*Viola cornuta*) and 2 species of pussy-toes (*Antennaria* spp.) has to be paying attention.

Besides perennials, Sara's offers spring container plants, vegetable seedlings, hanging baskets, water-garden aquatics such as lotus and water lily, pond supplies, and Christmas trees. Kathy Kepler is known for custom-planted containers and decorated Christmas wreaths. A strong rose collection focuses on old-fashioned hardy shrub roses and David Austin's English hybrids.

Diverse display gardens embrace the sales area and occupy more than half of Sara's 5-acre site, allowing visitors to view thousands of perennials in a garden setting. These densely planted gardens include flower beds and borders, rock walls, ponds, a bog garden, and alpine scree. Mature plants are a source for cuttings and divisions for the greenhouse. An easy pathway meanders through the site. While plants lack labels (too many were removed by over-enthusiastic customers), Sara's staff can identify whatever is of interest.

Sara's has no plant list or catalog, so most customers just drive over to see what's available. Perennials come in 2-quart or 1-gallon pots; grasses in larger containers. This is not a production nursery, though Sara's does propagate about 30 percent of its own perennial stock and sprouts many annuals from seed. Most plants come in from good growers, such as Sunny Border and Valley Brook for perennials and Weeks for potted roses. The working end of the property contains six large greenhouses. While not exactly organic, "we do the best we can to minimize toxic chemicals," says Kathy Kepler.

Sara's Garden Center is an exception to the common notion that horticulture is merely a lifestyle business. With the Kepler commitment to hard work and plant selection, sales have blossomed. "The male half of the family does it for profit, and the female half does it for love," says Kepler. "It's a great balance."

Directions: Brockport is a college town 20 miles west of Rochester. From Route I-90, take exit 47 to Route 19 north. In Brockport village, cross the Erie Canal and at the first light, turn right onto East Avenue. Sara's is 1 mile on the left.

Nearby attractions: The Apple Tree Inn, 7397 Ridge Road/Route 104, Brockport, NY 14420 (585-637-6440; closed Monday), serves lunch in a cobblestone house surrounded by gardens.

Related sources: Countryside Flower Farm, 1037 York Street, Honeoye Falls, NY 14472 (585-624-5783; www.countrysideflowerfarm.com; open daily, April through October, 8 to 6), sells thousands of nursery-propagated perennials in a clean park-like setting. Cobb Hill Daylilies, 1 Hillside Avenue, Rochester, NY 14610 (585-461-3317; open-house days, July and August), is a home-based daylily nursery and AHS Display Garden of Charlie Zettick, a talented local hybridizer; his long-blooming hybrids grow in the display gardens at Sara's Garden Center.

SENECA HILL PERENNIALS
3712 County Route 57, Oswego, NY 13126
(315) 342-5915; (315) 342-5573
www.senecahill.com; e-mail *hornig@usadatanet.net*
Ellen Hornig

Unusual hardy perennials. Cyclamen, aroids, species peonies, primulas. Small *specialty nursery. Open by appointment. Mail order. Catalog $4. Catalog on Web site. Send SASE for cyclamen seed list. No shipping in summer months. Gift certificates. Display garden. No public restroom. Spring and fall open days. Visitors welcome by appointment.*

Ellen Hornig, proprietor of Seneca Hill Perennials, is a skilled gardener growing superb plants experimentally, largely because she feels like it. Seneca Hill Perennials is an ambitious nursery founded in 1991 on home ground in "snowy upstate New York, just south of the great metropolis of Oswego." Hornig, a former economics professor at SUNY Oswego, took up serious gardening when her children were adolescents. "In middle age," she says, "the hormones turn to horticulture." By 1998, the nursery had become a full-time mail-order operation. Today it occupies seven 48-foot polyhouses and some snow-covered Zone 5/6 testing beds. Nevertheless, Hornig says, "I have no serious mission statement. My basic motivation is playfulness."

Henry Beard once defined a perennial as "any plant which, had it lived, would have bloomed year after year." Turning a frosty climate to advantage, Hornig's genius has been to astonish the meek by growing sought-after plants commonly considered too tender for Zone 5B. In this Hornig follows in the footsteps of Sir Peter Smithers, a noted Swiss plantsman, who said, "I consider every plant hardy until I have killed it myself."

Seneca Hill's quest for cold-tolerant collector's items has produced some notable specialties: hardy cyclamen, hardy aroids, species peonies, primroses, and hardy plants from the botanically rich Drakensberg Mountains of South Africa. "Beyond that," Hornig's catalog announces, "we grow what we feel like growing, and that is definitely a moving target."

The nursery's best-known product, hardy cyclamen, is a delightful member of the primrose clan deserving greater popularity among cold-zone gardeners. Cyclamen produce pink and white flowers, with a curious backward-blown appearance, held above heart-shaped foliage. They resemble the florist's cyclamen but are much smaller and tougher, consenting to grow under trees—at least in England, where they are cherished by connoisseurs. (In middle Europe, the plant was so common that pigs fed on it.) Seneca Hill carries a number of hardy forms, of which only the Neapolitan cyclamen *(C. hederifolium)* and fragrant purple cyclamen *(C. purpurascens)* are considered hardy in Zone 5.

Some years ago, Hornig set out to challenge the hardiness myth by sowing the *Cyclamen coum* outdoors. Far from being finicky, this antic charmer sprouted in the compost heap and broke snow cover with early spring bloom. Seneca Hill offers fancy-leaf forms culled from the survivors. Because *Cyclamen coum* does not breed true, Hornig separates seedlings into distinct strains with silver-pewter leaves, near-white leaves, and most captivating off all, Christmas-tree leaves, so-called because the dark green center of each silver leaf is shaped like a Christmas tree.

Another Seneca Hill specialty is hardy aroids. In *The Collector's Garden*, Ken Druse calls aroids "the collector's collectible." Hornig calls them "truly obscene and wonderful." Popularly known as jack-in-the-pulpit after the uncanny "pulpit" (spathe) enclosing an erect "jack" (spadix), aroids possess the startling glamour of plants resembling the male phallus. Seneca Hill grows an admired hardy aroid collection, including a turgid Russian arum with a maroon spathe (*Arum elongatum* ex 'Krasnodar'), and a gold-splashed Mediterranean aroid discovered in a Sicilian citrus orchard (*Arum italicum* 'Ceni's Spotted'). Another *Arum italicum*, called 'Ghost' for its pale foliage, is a Seneca Hill introduction.

Fooling around with high-altitude plants from South Africa's Drakensberg Mountains must be one of the most entertaining perks of owning a nursery. Seneca Hill offers hardy pink African hairbells (*Dierama* spp.), mat-forming alpine stonecrops (*Crassula* spp.), stunning pineapple lilies (*Eucomis* spp.), and brazen red-hot-pokers (*Kniphofia* spp.). Other little-known Drakensburg natives include *Galtonia regalis*, a bulb with green flowering bells, and a species gladiolus (*Gladiolus oppositiflorus*) with rare salmon flowers.

Seneca Hill is also known for choice woodlanders. Primroses range from a rare fringed *Primula sieboldii* with cherry blossoms to old-fashioned hose-in-hose polyantha seedlings (*P.* × *polyantha*) in mixed colors. Wild peonies, such as the desirable *Paeonia obovata* var. *alba*, are all responsibly nursery propagated. Hornig's *Glaucidium palmatum* is the exquisite pink-flowered species; an even rarer white form sells out in ten minutes. Hellebore hybrids are sorted by color—maroon, blue-black, pink, pink-edged white, red-spotted white, and spotted yellow—but without color guarantee, for hellebores are notoriously loose living.

In recent seasons, Hornig has focused on American native plants, "not because we've gotten religion, but because a lot of them are passed over by gardeners and should not be." Hornig especially admires the milkweeds (*Asclepias* spp.) for their "silky parasols and wandering ways." Other natives include wild lilies, bush clematis, a white form of bluebells, variegated pokeweed, *Iris cristata* hybrids, native sedges, and a weird cousin of Dutchman's pipe *(Aristolochia tomentosa)* from seed collected in odd circumstances in Arkansas.

Hornig has also started growing antique bearded iris obtained from her neighbors at Phoenix Flower Farm (see profile). Other pass-along plants include double tiger lilies from Panther Lake, New York; a mildew-free pink phlox from a gardener in Nashville; and *Centaurea montana* 'Dot Purple', a violet form of mountain bluet from a friend in Ellisburg, New York.

It's hard to summarize the remaining offerings, what Hornig herself calls "bits of this and that." No single class readily admits climbing monkshood, woodland nightshade, and double orange Welsh poppy. A smattering of woody plants includes a Chinese snakebark maple and a shrubby northern strain of American snowbell.

One nursery plant has gone big time: *Buddleia* × 'Ellen's Blue', a fragrant, silver-leaved buddleia discovered by Hornig in her garden. This exceptional blue-flowered plant, introduced by Heronswood Nursery, was recently rated the world's best blue buddleia.

In the end, some nurseries are best explained by poets. Hornig quotes Wallace Stevens' "Table Talk": *But red / Gray, green, why those of all? / That is not what I said. / Not those of all. But those. / One likes what one happens to like. / One likes the way red grows.*

Directions: Seneca Hill is north of Syracuse. Take Route I-90 to exit 34A, turn onto Route 481 north, pass through Fulton, and in 5 miles, turn left on Route 45. At the end, turn right onto Route 57, the nursery is 0.4 mile on the right. From Route I-81, turn onto Route 481 north and follow directions above. Call for an appointment

Nearby attractions: Hi Downing International Hostel, 535 Oak Street, Syracuse, NY 13203 (315-472-5788; www.hiayh.org), offers dormitory-style beds in an 1895

Victorian house at $14 per night. From Oswego, a Lake Ontario scenic byway follows Route 104 east to Mexico, Route 3 north to Sackets Harbor, and Route 12E east along the St. Lawrence River.

SHEFFIELD'S SEED COMPANY
269 Auburn Road (Route 34), Locke, NY 13092
(315) 497-1058; fax (315) 497-1059
www.sheffields.com; e-mail *seed@sheffields.com*
Richard Sheffield

Seed for trees and shrubs. *Small specialty seed house. Open year-round, Monday through Friday, 8 to 4:30. Retail and wholesale. Mail order only. Seed list on Web site. Bulk seed pricing. Shipping and handling charges. Minimum order. Some seasonal seed. Books and seed propagation pamphlets. Visitors welcome by appointment.*

Growing trees and shrubs from seed may seem daunting, but some find it more fun than anything else in gardening. This is not just a nurseryman's game. Seed-sprouting allows a gardener to acquire experimental plants that are out of the realm of commerce, including many worthy natives that deserve a place in gardens. We know of a much-photographed show garden and a famous azalea arboretum grown entirely from seed.

Founded by Rich Sheffield in 1982, Sheffield's Seed Company is an independent seed house specializing in seed for woody trees and shrubs. On a 40-acre farm in upstate New York, an old barn has been converted into a packing room, equipped with storage drawers, drying racks, two coolers, and a freezer. Four employees labor at sorting, grading, cleaning, de-winging, and packing literally tons of tree seed per year.

Sheffield's boasts a huge inventory of high-quality woody plant seed. Its seed list, posted on the Web site, amounts to a long, dense directory of some 2200 trees and shrubs, organized alphabetically in horticultural Latin. An alternate list shows plant common names, to the extent there are common names. The nursery can obtain many species not listed. A separate register of herbaceous plant and grass seed adds 400 species.

Sheffield's Seed today is a leading supplier of woody plant seed to nurseries, foresters, Christmas tree growers, universities, hobbyists, home gardeners, collectors, and seed brokers all over the globe. A recent order from China involved shipping more than a ton of tree seed. Most seed is bought in from independent sources, usually seasonal collectors working solo. Seed for maple, serviceberry, and buckeye trees is taken off the nursery's own land. Even before purchase, all seed is graded, tested for viability, and labeled by name, collection date, and source location. Seed is sold by the packet or pound, with prices ranging from a few dollars to hundreds of dollars. Because collection times and quantities vary, seed for some plants is not always available.

For those who can penetrate the lists, a lavish array of rare and hard-to-find woody plants awaits. For example, Sheffield's offers 148 kinds of maple, 93 oaks, 143 pines, 60 plums, 27 magnolias, 22 crabs, 15 hollies, 13 walnuts, 12 hackberries, 9 eucalyptus, 11 lilacs, and 14 ashes. Plants originate all over the world. Most are species, though some cultivar seed is listed.

There's a generous showing of woody plants native to Eastern North America: Carolina allspice, wild plum, pawpaw, pagoda dogwood, shining sumac, creeping sand cherry, dwarf wax myrtle, hardhack *(Spiraea tomentosa)*, nannyberry, black haw, and arrowwood viburnum—even a rampant vine called moonseed. Southwestern natives include flame bottle tree *(Brachychiton acerifolius)*, desert willow *(Chilopsis linearis)*, tree anemone *(Carpenteria californica)*, and rabbitbrush *(Chrysothamnus nauseosus)*.

The nursery also offers seed for praiseworthy evergreens such as Atlas cedar, Japanese stone pine, false cypress, and dwarf white pine. Precious woody ornamentals include cinnamon tree, dove tree, pistachio, Arabian coffee, cutleaf crab, sapphire berry *(Symplocos paniculata)*, sweet box, and Chinese magnolia vine *(Schisandra chinensis)*. The rare Asian Iigiri tree *(Idesia polycarpa)* resembles a small-leaved catalpa with ornamental fruit clusters.

Sheffield's Seed follows an excellent practice of identifying tree seed by collection location, enabling customers to choose plants suited to their local climate and habitat. For example, seed for Eastern redbud *(Cercis canadensis)* is available from a Zone 5 Northern population, two Zone 6 Northern populations, and two Southern populations. The nursery similarly differentiates Northern and Southern forms of American sweetgum, sweetbay magnolia, and black walnut. Scotch pine seed is collected in 12 European countries, ranging from Belgium to the Ukraine. White pine seed comes from 8 states and 2 Canadian provinces.

The register of herbaceous plant seed is surprisingly interesting, if only for its 20 clematis, 5 yuccas, 3 trilliums, and a Nepalese blue poppy. Seed is available for native herbs such as ginseng, goldenseal, bloodroot, baneberry, bunchberry, American false hellebore *(Veratrum viride),* and Venus flytrap. Grass seed includes, among others, little bluestem, Niagara big bluestem, blue fescue, and switch grass.

One seed in the "poisonous" category caused a stir in early 2004, when a Sheffield's Seed employee reported a large order for Castor bean seed *(Ricinus communis)* to the FBI's terrorist hotline. The deadly ricin toxin, which occurs naturally in Castor bean seed, is 6000 times more powerful than cyanide. The customer, who was later arrested, turned out to be a man who found it "exciting working with poisons."

To assist the bewildered, the Sheffield's Seed Web site allows seed inventory searches by habitat (shade, moisture, rock garden, or acidic soil); by use (street tree, rootstock, bonsai, medicinal, windbreak, ground cover, or mine reclamation); and by characteristic (hardwood, evergreen, fast-growing, ornamental fruit, or edible nuts). Timber Press book titles, including some good propagation manuals, are sold at a small discount. The Web site also has a peculiar set of links for onion seeds, Texas pecans, berry syrup, mailbox flags, quilts, NASA images, online BINGO, and tax advice from a former IRS agent.

Although Sheffield's Seed is open to visitors by appointment, as one visitor remarked, "It's like visiting a mail room—lots of little sheds and drawers and seed-drying racks." It's probably more fun just to order some seed and tinker with it your own backyard.

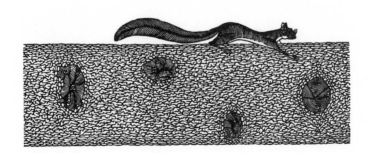

SPRING VALLEY GREENHOUSE

P.O. Box 552, 3242 Daansen Road, Walworth, NY 14568-0552
(315) 597-9816; (315) 597-2704
3100 County Road, Route 10, Canandaigua, NY 14424
(585) 396-1460; fax (585) 396-1461
www.springvalleygreenhouse.com; e-mail *info@springvalleygreenhouse.com*
Irene and Jim Van Laken

Clematis. Flowering vines. *Large commercial nursery. Wholesale and retail. Walworth location open late April through early October, daily, 9 to 8, weekends, 9 to 6. Call for exact dates. Canandaigua location open through Christmas. Wholesale/retail. Catalog on Web site. Limited mail order. Display gardens. Visitors welcome.*

Is there anything prettier than a clematis vine in bloom? Woody twiners of the buttercup family—embracing 300 wild species and 400 cultivated varieties—clematis is the world's most popular ornamental vine. Long ago it was put to work adorning arbors, clambering up fences, ascending treetops, and helping shrubs fake the appearance of a second bloom.

Spring Valley Greenhouse is a large private greenhouse operation specializing in clematis hybrids. Founded in 1981, it is now the country's largest clematis grower. A stunning inventory embraces old-time garden hybrids and brand-new introductions from Japan, Eastern Europe, and Canada. Though it's mostly wholesale, regular gardeners can buy plants at Spring Valley's retail centers in Walworth and Canandaigua and by mail order through the Web site.

Large-flowered clematis are best known to gardeners. Spring Valley's 90-plant list includes 26 large-flowered purples, 23 blues, and dozens of pinks and whites and mauves. While many date to Victorian England, new hybrids are still entering the market. 'Blue Light', for example, is a new chrysanthemum-like sport of what Christopher Lloyd calls "that blowsy old girl, 'Mrs. Chalmondeley'." Pinks include 'Proteus', a rare Victorian double, and 'John Paul II', an angel-pink clematis bred by a Polish monk in honor of the Pope. Two new bicolors are 'Fairy Dust' (pale orchid with a white bar) and 'Piilu' (pink with yellow stamen bosses). Spring Valley's own introduction, 'Cardinal', has blue flowers with purple bars and showy yellow stamens.

The nursery also grows 14 small-flowered clematis—tough little climbers combining wilt-resistance and delicate charm. The sweetest is 'Little Nell', a pale mauve Victorian *Clematis viticella* hybrid. The Chinese "orange-peel" clematis *(C. tangutica)* produces remarkable feathery seed heads that often stock birds' nests. (We were once scolded by a house wren for removing her twig supply during spring pruning.) A festive new hybrid, *C. tangutica* 'My Angel', has nodding flowers that are gold inside, purple outside, and cream on the edges.

Tall clematis vines are in a wildish class by themselves. The nursery grows several kinds of *Clematis montana*, a pink-flowered Chinese vine that grows 30 feet with enough vigor to occupy the canopy of a small tree. The rampant 20-foot 'Sweet Autumn' clematis *(C. paniculata)* easily engulfs an outbuilding; *Clematis spooneri* 'White' is similar but blooms in spring.

Spring Valley prides itself on producing vigorous, healthy stock using state-of-the-art techniques. The nursery sells 3-year plants in gallon containers, 2-year plants in 5-inch containers, and 1-year plants in 3½-inch pots. Excellent clematis photos are posted on the Web site. All plants are flowered before sale to ensure correct labeling.

Spring Valley grows several ornamental vines that perform the same functions as clematis, but with less panache. These include trumpet creeper, silver-lace vine, and eight climbing honeysuckles, at least one of which *(Lonicera japonica)* is considered invasive in New York State. Oriental bittersweet *(Celastrus orbiculatus)* and porcelain berry *(Ampelopsis brevipedunculata)* are also viewed as invasive plants. Clematis is a benign replacement recommended by the New York's Invasive Plant Council *(www.ipcnys.com)*. With such gorgeous alternatives, why mess around with weeds?

Directions to Walworth store: From Route I-90, take exit 43 north, and in 0.8 miles, turn left onto Route 21 north. In 6.1 miles, go straight on Route 210/Church Street. In 3.5 miles, turn left onto Haak Road. In 0.4 miles, turn right onto Daansen Road; the nursery is on the right. From Rochester, take Route 490 south to exit 23 and turn onto Route 441 east. At the intersection of Route 250, take Penfield Road east into Walworth. At the light, go straight for 0.5 mile and turn right onto Daansen Road. The nursery is 1.5 miles on the left.

STONY HILL FARM GREENHOUSES

3801 Brady Hill Road, Binghamton, NY 13903
(607) 669-4187 phone and fax
Dana Keiser

Perennials, alpines, woody ornamentals, and container plants. Small specialty nursery. Open April through June, Wednesday through Saturday, 10 to 6, Sunday, 11 to 4; July through September, Thursday and Friday, 10 to 6, Saturday, 10 to 4; and by appointment. Call for exact dates. No catalog. No mail order. Seasonal newsletter on request. Landscape design, installation, and maintenance. Classes. Lectures and tours.

Stony Hill Farm Greenhouses is a small nursery near Binghamton specializing in artistic plants with distinctive scent, foliage, texture, variegation, and flower form. Owner Dana Keiser took up serious gardening after previous engagements with painting, rug hooking, and wood sculpture. A lifelong plant lover, she began designing gardens and raising unusual perennials in her Zone 4B garden to satisfy the creative urge to work with plants as an art form.

Keiser founded her two-acre nursery in 1994 because, she says, "I couldn't find the rare, weird plants that I'd become addicted to—or if I did, the seller had no clue what they were." Keiser reads voraciously about plants. As the human brain is wired for novelty, so is Keiser compelled toward the cutting edge. "My nickname is 'the weird plant lady,'" she says. "If a plant's name is unpronounceable, I've got to have it."

Stony Hill's inventory includes a diverse palette of flowering perennials, alpines, dwarf conifers, Japanese tree peonies, ferns, trilliums, primroses, and ornamental ground covers. Keiser's favorites include cranesbill geranium 'Victor Reiter', gold-foliage spiderwort, and Italian arums. The nursery also grows textured houseplants, painted begonias, spiky little cactus, tender succulents, desert-candle lilies (*Eremurus* spp.), and fancy-leaf geraniums. Rare herbs include fern-leaf lavender, prostrate Japanese thyme *(Thymus quinquecostatus ibukiensis)*, and grape-scented sage *(Salvia blepharophylla)*, which smells like Kool Aid. Many are plants seldom available in the area. In the manner of small nurseries, the stock list is more broad than deep, and some items sell out quickly.

Stony Hill offers two dozen hardy Weeks shrub roses, propagated on their own roots to avoid winter dieback. Keiser trials Weeks roses each year; her latest favorite is a tough yellow shrub rose called 'Rabble Rouser'. For woody shrubs, Keiser stocks hardy hydrangeas, clematis, and a double-purple wisteria. For trees we spied laceleaf Japanese maples, purple beech, golden rain tree *(Koelreuteria paniculata)*, and Franklin tree, our sole native camellia.

Keiser is relentless in hunting down new and uncommon plants for the nursery. She once discovered a small legacy of miniature pelargoniums in a dilapidated greenhouse, including a Victorian called 'St. Elmo's Fire'. Topiary and Japanese maples derive from a local grower. Keiser accesses rock-garden plants through the Adirondack Chapter of the North American Rock Garden Society, where she is an active member. Stony Hill also brings in exciting plants from Log House Plants, a trend-setting wholesaler of hardy perennials. "My collections keep expanding," says Keiser. "I can't help myself." Rare finds are often scooped up by collectors who share Keiser's fascinations.

The nursery's display gardens function as testing beds, assuring that nursery stock is vetted before being sold to customers. "I love sequence of bloom," says Keiser. "Look at that Dutch iris! I love the peach foxtail lily, too. Firecracker plants interest me, and striped dahlias and the 'schubertii' alliums. I call it my 'Garden of Weedom.'"

Most stock is propagated from "mother plants" grown on-site, except for tissue-culture novelties, which are bought in and grown in the greenhouses. If a customer craves something beyond the budget, Keiser will put her to work in the greenhouse, employing a literal form of sweat equity. In the unconscious manner of a born gardener, Keiser weeds the garden as she walks and talks.

Keiser is a recognized landscape designer and installer who has updated several public gardens in Binghamton. She takes pleasure in planting ornamental container gardens, which she views as "movable landscapes." Customers may bring in pots for planting. "I can take a classy or primitive container and fill it with plants that look totally at home there," she says.

Stony Hill Farm operates three greenhouses and a garden shop next to Keiser's home in Binghamton. The nursery has a loyal following. All plants are sold on-site, though Keiser is contemplating mail order to reach a wider audience. In spring and fall, Stony Hill publishes a newsletter announcing new plants, open hours, design services, lectures, and sales. The garden shop is undergoing expansion, having been crammed to bursting with ornamental pots, statues, tools, books, glitter balls, oversize marbles, mosaic stepping stones, stained glass, flower fairies, amber jewelry, and tiny clay flowers. Among the whimsical *tchotchke* are some stunning copper weathervanes and items in painted tin and wrought iron.

Keiser operates the nursery virtually single-handed. The resulting ornamental jumble is a testament to her energy and enthusiasm. "It takes me forever to pick out the plants I need every year. There's fragrance, foliage, hardiness, bark or leaf texture, flowers, and all-season interest," she says. "I drink a lot of coffee." Her husband is a long-distance truck driver who collects vintage Mack trucks and cars. "He loves machines the way I love plants. When he notices a plant," says Keiser, "I know it's a winner."

Directions: From Albany, take Route 88 west. From New Jersey, take Route 17 west. From Elmira, take Route 17 east. In Binghamton, exit onto Route 81 south. Take exit 1 and turn right onto Route 20/Cedarhurst Road toward Conklin. In 1 mile, cross the river, turn left at the light onto Conklin road/Route 7, and turn right onto Conklin Forks Road. In 3.2 miles, turn left onto Brady Hill Road; the nursery is 2 miles on the right.

Nearby attractions: In Binghamton, Keiser-designed gardens connect the arena and police station, flank the South Washington Street Bridge walkway, and occupy the triangle between the Security Mutual Building and the courthouse. The Cutler Botanic Garden, 840 Upper Front Street, Binghamton (607-772-8954), has an AAS Display Garden and specimen trees within sight of a Mobil station. The Park Diner, 119 Conlin Avenue, Binghamton, NY (607-722-9840; open daily, 7 to 10), is a remodeled chef-owned 1940s diner with panoramic views of the river dam and city skyline. Whole in the Wall Restaurant, 43 South Washington Street, Binghamton, NY (607-722-0006), has natural food and live music on weekends.

THE TEMPLE NURSERY
P.O. Box 591, Trumansburg, NY 14886
Hitch Lyman

Snowdrops "in the green." *Small specialty nursery. Catalog $3. Mail order by overnight mail ($15). Garden design services. Visitors by appointment only.*

Certain plants have an almost magical ability to enthrall collectors. In Britain, where horticultural passions border on madness, no flower is more deeply treasured by its cult of appreciators than the demure snowdrop. Admiring the purity of its late-winter flower, British writer Vita Sackville-West said, "The whole beauty lies in the perfection of line of the single bell." So many eminent writers and bookish folk have fallen for snowdrops, the delirium seems part botany, part literature—let's call it "snowdropsy."

Hitch Lyman of the Temple Nursery is perhaps the foremost American collector of unusual snowdrops. A Cornell-trained horticulturist, fine artist, and garden designer, he first encountered exotic snowdrops on winter trips to London, where the Royal Horticultural Society held flower shows featuring blooming bulbs. As Lyman recalls, "One February flower show, I was staring amusedly at a table covered in snowdrops. A tiny woman popped out of nowhere and asked, 'What do you think?' Within a half hour I had bought ten bulbs." Lyman went home, read the raptures of E. A. Bowles in *My Garden in Spring*, and was hooked. He later acquired a rich collection from three Cornell professors, including some hybrids of historical interest.

Native to woodland slopes and screes from the Pyrenees to the Caucasus, snowdrops (*Galanthus* spp.) are miniature members of the lily family, comprising some 17 wild species and scores of garden forms. Most produce pendulous white bells whose petals are sealed with tiny green chevrons, known as "the family emeralds." Snowdrop frenzy dates to the 19th century, when British soldiers brought bulbs home from the Crimean War. Despite subtle differences, to the average eye snowdrops all look pretty much alike. Indeed, one of the great charms of snowdrop collecting is sharpened perception, without which no gardener could be expected to distinguish the 320 varieties currently recognized by the English Snowdrop Society.

The chief pleasure of snowdrop culture is winter interest, for the plant braves its bloom in the snow, when most plants are still hibernating. As Lyman confirms, "Working with snowdrops adds three weeks to the gardening year and gives interest and variety when nothing else is going on."

Early bloom is achieved by clever internal thermal regulation, which can warm the flower's inner air by as much as two degrees during cold spells. Snowdrops get an early start in late autumn, when they begin to nose up from the ground with what Lyman affectionately calls "their little green snouts." Barbara Damrosch is one of the few writers to keep her head about snowdrops: "Plant them where they will be noticed, or they will just blend in with the snow."

Lyman's plants manifest subtle variety, even within the group of hardy common snowdrops *(G. nivalis)* that comprise the bulk of his collection. Showy doubles, such as 'Floro Pleno' and 'Walrus', add glamour to the flowering pedicel. The emeralds on a "rare, fussy and beautiful" hybrid called 'Lady Elphinstone' are, according to Lyman, "a glowing yellow," while the blossom of 'Virescens' is tinted a "delicate, duck's-egg green." Species snowdrops in Lyman's collection display such quirky traits as twisted bluish leaves and a curious mark that "looks like clip-on sunglasses." One alpine snowdrop is fragrant of bitter almonds, while others emit a honeyed scent specially brewed to intoxicate pollinators in early spring.

Because the bulbs are quite perishable, snowdrops are best transplanted, as Lyman does, in full growth or "in the green." Lyman digs whole plants from his collection in early spring and ships them bare root by overnight mail. A small catalog of remarkable charm describes the nursery's offerings and overnight shipping arrangements. Availability varies and by commercial standards the number of snowdrops offered is quite small. Prices reflect rarity—ten common snowdrops for a modest fee and the vaunted yellow snowdrop (*G. nivalis* 'Sandersii Group', when available) the price of a theater ticket. Because a 1993 CITES treaty prohibits global trade in *Galanthus* bulbs, this may be the only way American gardeners can get their hands on rarities.

It's worth the trouble. As Karel Čapek wrote in *The Gardener's Year*, February gardening consists of "cultivating the weather" and hunting for true signs of spring—garden catalogs and snowdrops; "and I tell you that no victorious palm, or tree of knowledge, or laurel of glory, is more beautiful than this white and fragile cup on a pale stem, waving in the raw wind."

Directions: Write in advance for an appointment and directions.

Nearby attractions: Hitch Lyman's artistry in garden design is evident in the beautiful display gardens surrounding the MacKenzie-Childs studio, Route 90, Aurora,

NY 13026 (800-640-0546; 315-364-7123), on a bluff overlooking Cayuga Lake. MacKenzie-Childs manufactures whimsical handcrafted ceramics and serves an elegant high tea (315-364-9688).

THE-RUN-DE-QUOT GARDENS
242 Hedgegarth Drive, Irondequoit, NY 14617
(585) 342-0895
E-mail: *therundequotgard@aol.com*
Dick Sage

Collector's exotic ornamental trees. Japanese maples. Small home-based nursery. Open weekends during daylight hours, and by appointment. No catalog. No mail order. Plant list available by e-mail. Current stock described on request. Tree seed. Farmer's market sales in Irondequoit and Fairport. Visitors welcome.

The-Run-De-Quot Gardens is a self-described "hobby nursery" specializing in Japanese maples and "collector's exotics." The nursery's name is a play on *Irondequoit*, an Iroquois word for "where two waters meet"—an apt description of the town, north of Rochester, where Irondequoit Creek enters Lake Ontario. For owner Dick Sage, horticulture has been a hobby since he was ten years old. "It's now a very strong hobby," he says. "It took over my back yard."

Sage is a retired Dupont Photochemical research technician and lifelong lover of trees. Some years ago, he began working with a small crew of volunteers in Monroe County's Durand-Eastman Park to clean up and rescue its old tree collections. Tree historians consider the park a forgotten paradise. When the park's importance began regaining recognition, Sage's hands-on knowledge landed him a part-time job with the Monroe County Parks Department—pruning, trimming, identifying, and re-labeling its extraordinary legacy of trees. "It's the same work as before," Sage says, "but now I get to use their equipment."

Sage began The-Run-De-Quot Gardens by growing grafted Japanese maples. He still grows about 30 red, green, and variegated varieties. "We lean toward true dwarfs that mature at 4 to 7 feet," says Sage. "A lot of people think all Japanese maples are dwarfs and are surprised when a tree like 'Bloodgood' grows to 25 feet." After exposure to the Durand-Eastman Park collection, Sage's interests morphed toward unusual species maples. These now include Korean maple *(Acer pseudosieboldianum),* which shares the Japanese maple's charms but is hardy to Zone 4, and snakebark maples, which are basically Asian forms of moosewood with stunning striated bark. The hardiest of these, *Acer capillipes,* is ribbed with white stripes and produces coral twiglets and leaf stems.

Exceptional trees give this miniature nursery its distinction and consequence. The main source of The-Run-De-Quot's "collector's exotics" is Durand-Eastman Park, a 965-acre preserve near Irondequoit that once rivaled the Arnold Arboretum in the diversity and rarity of its tree collection. Bernard H. Slavin, a day laborer who became Monroe County Parks superintendent in 1926, had a visionary interest in native flora. Slavin collected many little-known American tree species in temperate forests from Appalachia to Texas. In the heyday of exotic plant collecting, he managed to trade seed with the Arnold Arboretum and Britain's Royal Botanic Gardens, Kew.

Slavin had an eye for superior seedlings and many of his selections have endured. Sage estimates that 40 percent of the original plantings remain in Durand-Eastman Park, living proof of the trees' durability and worth. "In research, you look for what doesn't belong," he says. "It's the same in nature— it's not just massive green. You look for what is unusual in what survives."

One of the nursery's treasures is the legendary dove tree *(Davidia involucrata),* a dweller of dappled forests in western China, hardy to Zone 6. Its aristocratic beauty and fluttering, handkerchief-like flower bracts inspired zealous collection efforts among 19th-century plant hunters. Rochester's seed came from London's famous Veitch nursery, which had commissioned E. H. Wilson to collect fruit during China's Boxer Rebellion in 1900. Whoops filled the air when Durand-Eastman Park's original specimens finally bloomed in 1955. By some magic common to inspired plantsmen, Dick Sage discovered a way to propagate this notoriously difficult plant. "We've found a way to break double dormancy and germinate it from seed in one season," he says. "It's a little secret that we're going to keep for a while."

The-Run-De-Quot Gardens grows other legacy trees from Durand-Eastman Park that deserve rediscovery. Few trees are daintier than the pink-flowered serviceberry (*Amelanchier* × *grandiflora* 'Rubescens'), and few sights more spectacular than the white bloom cloud of 'Slavin's Snowy' magnolia. Another Slavin find, a gold- and orange-flowered witch hazel

(*Hamamelis intermedia* 'Superba'), emits a fruity aroma at 200 feet. Connoisseurs agree that *Malus ioensis* 'Prince George', a prairie crab with double shell-pink flowers, should never have been allowed to fall from commerce. A lovely old crab, 'Katherine', has survived in the park since 1928; the Arnold Arboretum's specimen, wrote horticulturist Donald Wyman, was "simply covered with flowers and fruits each year."

The-Run-De-Quot Gardens also grows handsome tree species that are inexplicably ignored by the nursery industry. The snowberry mountain ash *(Sorbus discolor)* is a graceful 25-foot Asian tree planted in the park in 1919. "It's an exceptional tree, disease free, open and airy, with heavy flower and fruit set and white berries against red foliage in the fall," says Sage. A similar case can be made for the Texas form of Ohio buckeye *(Aesculus glabra* var. *arguta),* a small horse chestnut with large yellow flower panicles. The nursery has seedlings of giant sequoia *(Sequoiadendron giganteum),* which Sage grows as a lark, having noticed old plantations scattered around town. Sage's collection philosophy is a simple one. "I let Nature do the selection," he says. "She's been at it a lot longer than we have."

As might be expected in response to this inventory, The-Run-De-Quot Gardens attracts an appreciative local following, despite its minute size. The nursery occupies a suburban lot behind Sage's home. Seedlings are sprouted in propagation trays and transferred to containers, where they are offered as one- to five-year-old plants. Grafted trees are spliced onto hardy rootstock and come in several small sizes. The mix changes yearly and rarely contains more than a few plants of any one variety. Prices vary with the difficulty of germination but are universally reasonable, generally escalating $10 per year of growth. As a sideline, Sage collects exotic tree seed and cuttings for specialists and nurseries around the country.

The nursery is too small to have a Web site or mail order, but it does have a plant list and a flexible attitude. "It's mostly word of mouth," says Sage. "We're usually around on weekends and if we aren't around, people can just come and prowl."

Directions: Irondequoit is north of Rochester. From Route I-90, take Route I-390 north (from the west) or Route I-490 north (from the east). Turn onto Route I-590 north, continue when it becomes a limited-access parkway, and at the first light, exit onto Titus Avenue.

Go west four lights and turn right onto Cooper Road; Hedgegarth Drive is the first turn on the right.

Nearby attractions: Local favorites are Keenans Restaurant, 1010 East Ridge Road, Rochester, NY 14621 (585-266-2691); www.keenansrestaurant.com), and Don's Original, 2545 Monroe Avenue, Rochester, NY 14618 (585-244-2080; fabulous burgers). Durand-Eastman Park is an extraordinary arboretum operated by the Monroe County Parks Department (585-244-9023; www.monroecounty.gov). The park has a fine pinetum; a comprehensive tour of its exotic tree collections would occupy days. Take Route I-590 north, go straight when it becomes a limited-access parkway, take the SeaBreeze/Durand-Eastman Park exit, turn left onto Durand Boulevard (becomes Lakeshore Boulevard), and turn left onto Zoo Road; park in the lot on the right.

THE VIOLET BARN

P.O. Box 9, 7209 County Road 12, Naples, NY 14512

(716) 374-8592

www.robsviolet.com; e-mail *robsviolet@aol.com*

Dr. Ralph and Olive Ma Robinson

African violets. Streptocarpus. Gesneriads. *Small specialty nursery. Open year-round, daily, 12 to 5, and by appointment. Closed on major holidays. Free catalog. Catalog on Web site. Mail order. Growing supplies. Expert advice. Group tours. Visitors welcome.*

The Violet Barn is a small mail-order nursery specializing in African violets, gesneriads, and collectible houseplants. Owner Dr. Ralph (Rob) Robinson is a former college professor who began growing and exhibiting African violets as a hobby in 1975. In 1991, he gave up teaching to grow them full-time. Best known for his innovative miniatures, Rob Robinson received a lifetime achievement award from the African Violet Society of America (AVSA) for his breeding work. Olive Ma Robinson began collecting African violets in 1986 and operated Violets Fun, a small urban greenhouse in Taiwan. She and Robinson met at a 1996 African violet convention and it was love at first sight. They married and she moved to America in 1998.

United by a passion for African violets, the Robinsons operate The Violet Barn, an upstate retail shed and greenhouses. Both Robinsons are

African violet judges; both have been cited as Grower of the Year by the New York African Violet Society. Together they regularly attend shows, where their plants have won numerous awards. Since 1998 they've published *Violets Fun*, a subscription newsletter. A 2003 appearance on Martha Stewart Television and flowers on the cover of *Martha Stewart Living* magazine put them in the spotlight and doubled their business.

African violets are the most popular houseplant in America, sold to hobbyists and collectors throughout the country. They're not violets at all, of course, but well-loved hybrids of the *Saintpaulia* genus, tropical gesneriads native to moist woods in East Africa, where they are called *usambara*. Collectors consider them the perfect houseplant because they are colorful, inexpensive, easy to grow, and practically always in bloom.

At The Violet Barn, the Robinsons grow a notable collection of African violets suited to collectors, exhibitors, and windowsill gardeners. Offerings include miniatures, semi-miniatures, standards, trailers, new introductions, award winners, and novelties. The Robinsons take pride in their plants' showy blooms—pink, mauve, red, maroon, purple, sapphire, and rare yellow and green. A few plants are bred for pure weirdness, such as award-winning 'Rob's Sarsparilla', with ruffled flowers "the color of a brown paper bag."

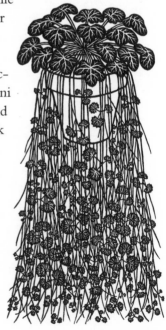

Both Robinsons are active hybridizers. Rob specializes in African violet miniatures and trailing varieties, while Olive works on standard-size plants. Her cultivar names gravitate toward senior proms and corsages, while his are fun and crazy, employing terms like "whoa Nellie" and "humpty-doo." Rob's introductions include 'Rob's Squeeze Toy', a cute semi-mini with coral blooms and gold-variegated foliage, and 'Rob's Twinkle Pink', a tiny show plant with pink bouquet over black foliage. Robinson's best-known chimera, 'Rob's Lucky Penny', is distinguished by its extraordinary foliage variegation. The AVSA Honor Roll recognizes 'Rob's Sticky Wicket', a multiple award-winning trailer with fuchsia blooms. Olive's introductions include 'Ma's Pillow Talk', an award-winning white carnation-type over streaked foliage, and 'Ma's Melody Girl', with semi-double coral stars marked with raspberry "fantasy" (streaking).

Besides African violets, The Violet Barn grows Cape primrose hybrids (*Streptocarpus* spp.). Called "the thinking man's African violet," Cape primroses are pretty little plants with bloom trumpets in white or violet. Graceful cousins of the African violet, they require much the same care— bright indirect light and routine fussing. Unusual hybrids offer variegated foliage or rare red or black flowers, but all are basically windowsill plants, valued for long bloom. The Robinsons' introductions go by the 'Bristol' name, after the Bristol Hills where the nursery is located. 'Bristol's Starlight', for example, is a pure white Cape primrose with no veining; 'Bristol's Black Cherry' has cherry flowers, and 'Bristol's Red Lava' is a stunning double red.

Taken as a whole, The Violet Barn's selection surpasses anything dreamed in the supermarket's houseplant department. According to the Robinsons, "Plants aren't just a business for us; they're a fun hobby, too." Besides African violets and Cape primroses, the nursery grows strange and showy tropicals— alsobia, chirita, codonanthe, columnea, episcia, nematanthus, hoya, miniature begonias, and miniature houseplants. Starter kits for indoor dish gardens are designed by Olive Robinson, like the one she created on Martha Stewart Television.

The Violet Barn operates largely by mail order. A dense catalog includes photographs, but more can be seen on the Web site. The nursery prides itself on plant quality and shipping. Blooming-stage plants are sent in 2½-inch pots, with outer leaves stripped and inner leaves folded like tiny umbrellas for protection. Each year the nursery ships thousands of orders, and tens of thousands of plants, carefully boxed and cushioned in Chinese-language newspaper.

The Violet Barn does occupy a barn, set on a hill in Naples overlooking Canandaigua Lake. In the glasshouses, 20,000 plants sit in alphabetical order under artificial lights. Splendid off-limits show plants can be spied from a distance. Visitors can choose plants off the shelves, including larger sizes or oddball varieties not available by mail order. The Robinsons insist that "It has to be fun." They also say, "It's a modest life, but it's rare that one can live one's dream."

Directions: Naples is 27 miles south of Canandaigua. From Route I-90, take exit 44 and turn onto Route 332 south. In Canandaigua, turn onto Route 21 south, and at the end, turn right onto Route 64. In 200 yards, turn left onto County Road 12. The nursery is 3 miles on the right. From Route I-86/17, take Route 390 north to exit 2/Cohocton and turn onto Route 415 toward Naples. Turn onto Route 371 north and then onto Route 21 north. In Naples, past the village, bear left up a big hill; the nursery is in 3 miles.

Nearby attractions: Naples is a "Swiss village" with homey restaurants. The Sutton Company, Main Street, Naples (585-374-2628), sells fishing tackle from an 1860s dry goods store. Monica's Pies, 7599 Route 21, Naples (585-374-2139; www.monicaspies.com), is famous for fresh grape pies. Mountain Creek Herb Farm, 7556 County Road 33, Naples (585-374-9108; www.mountainrise.com), sells an organic granola touted on The Food Network. Arbor Hill, 6461 Route 64, Naples (585-374-2870; www.thegrapery.com), sells award-winning local wines.

Related sources: The African Violet Society of America (www.avsa.org) has a large photo library on its Web site. Violet Venture, 52 Harper Drive, Pittsford, NY 14534 (585-381-6384; faywagman@mac.com), has 24-page list of African violets; leaves sold by mail order.

WHITE OAK NURSERY
P.O. Box 559, Stanley, NY 14561
(315) 789-3509
Nursery location: 4350 Kipp Road, Canandaigua, NY 14424
www.whiteoaknursery.biz; e-mail *jimengel@whiteoaknursery.biz*
Jim Engel

Native trees and shrubs. *Small specialty nursery. Open by arrangement on nights and weekends. Plant list. Mail order or nursery pick up. Catalog on Web site. Organic. Minimum mail order. Natural landscaping. Visitors welcome by appointment. Two days notice appreciated.*

White Oak Nursery is a small native plant nursery in upstate New York specializing in affordable, nursery-propagated native trees and shrubs. The nursery's proprietor, Jim Engel, was an engineering draftsman who began propagating hardwood trees as a hobby in the late 1980s. Fascination with native trees transformed his life. "I began to research and experiment how to collect, treat, and germinate nearly every type of seed I could find," he recalls.

Engel first began White Oak Nursery as a fledgling operation in 1991, selling tree seedlings on a limited basis. Recognizing that plants were his proper life's work, he returned to school for a degree in ornamental horticulture. Engel now lives with his family in Geneva and works at the prestigious New York State Agricultural Experiment Station, trialing vegetable systems in its Integrated Pest Management Program.

The dream of building a significant nursery never faded. In 1999, Engel bought fifty acres of land outside Canandaigua to expand his repertoire of native woody plants. "My goal is to grow quality shade trees in volume and make them more readily available and affordable to the general public," he says. Most trees and shrubs are grown from seed harvested from local populations; the crop changes each year with the harvest. At present, the nursery's main customers are reforestation projects, land trusts, and arboreta such as Cornell Plantations—as well as enlightened homeowners seeking locally adapted plants to enrich woodland gardens.

White Oak Nursery grows most of the woody species native to the eastern United States and some choice ornamentals from around the world. "I grow over 80 species of shade trees and native shrubs," Engel says. "I started with the easy stuff, oaks and hazelnuts, and it took off from there." Plants come as affordably priced seedlings, root-trained liners, and containerized specimens. Stock can be picked up at the nursery or (for large orders) shipped. A full list of nursery plants is posted on the Web site, along with Engel's advice on natural landscaping and design.

As White Oak's name suggests, the genus *Quercus* is a major interest. In addition to the dignified white oak, the nursery grows such handsome shade trees as native pin oak, red oak, black oak, bur oak, swamp white oak, and chestnut oak. Our most talkative tree, quaking aspen *(Populus tremuloides)*, comes with a red oak planted in the same pot. Other noble giants include American sycamore, yellowwood, basswood, and the underused Kentucky coffee tree. For wild magnolia fanciers there's native cucumber tree and tulip tree *(Liriodendron tulipifera)*. Moosewood and sugar maple, strong presences in our native forests, are grown alongside elegant Asians—Tartarian, Amur, and paperbark maples.

Engel grows hardy nut trees, such as native shagbark hickory, bitternut hickory, and beaked filbert, all important to wildlife and scarce in nurseries. White Oak also offers Chinese chestnut, which survives chestnut blight, and American chestnut, a magnificent doomed forest tree that some hope to revive. For wild fruits, the nursery grows American persimmon, pawpaw, red mulberry, red chokecherry, and fragrant sumac. Slim-stemmed American hornbeam and hop hornbeam give attractive intricacy to woodlands, as do the sweet, black, and paper birches.

White Oak's prettiest performers are flowering understory trees: American fringe tree *(Chionanthus virginicus)*, fragrant snowbell *(Styrax obassia)*, Eastern redbud (singles and clumps), sourwood, and various woodland dogwoods. The rose family contributes flowering shadblow *(Amelanchier arborea)* and red and black chokeberry *(Aronia arbutifolia; A. melanocarpa)*. A few irresistible garden magnolias and flowering cherries supplement the woody ornamentals list.

For shrubs, Engel has a special fondness for native spicebush *(Lindera benzoin)*, which he esteems for bloom, fragrance, toughness, deer resistance, and songbird food—quite a lot to get from one plant. The nursery's native winterberry and viburnum (including hard-to-grow nannyberry and mapleleaf viburnum) have already attracted a following, so handsome is their presence near woodlands and streams.

A scientist at heart, Engel spends a lot of time developing efficient ways to grow woody plants, especially those with a reputation for being difficult. Because each species offers its own challenges, it sometimes takes years to discover the secrets of propagation. According to Engel, "I find the key is to develop an excellent root system. I do a good job on that, because roots are what really drive growth and health. A plant must transplant with ease, establish quickly, and have a high survival rate" to become a practical choice for residential landscapes.

Engel also experiments with native plants to understand their restorative capabilities. He's currently studying how to speed up the process of natural succession in old fields. He also works to restore a six-acre oak-hickory wood at the border of the nursery. "I am learning how to control invasive species such as Japanese honeysuckle, European buckthorn, and Garlic mustard," he says. Adding native shrubs and herbaceous plants to the mix, he combines seeds and transplants to see what works best for woodland restoration.

Underlying Engel's work is a deep desire to protect, preserve, and restore the natural environment. "I want to change the way people relate to their surroundings, particularly in the way they choose to landscape their homes," he says. "The average residential landscape creates a sterile, hostile environment for the majority of native wildlife and plants. I want to demonstrate how one's house and land can become a refuge for native wildlife."

Engel's work is part of an important movement toward sustainable landscapes. "Unless we change the way we grow and sell plants, people won't be able to afford landscaping," says Engel. He considers native plants to be just as attractive as most non-native plants, and far more durable. Unlike the expensive, high-maintenance, lawn-and-specimen gardens promoted by the horticulture industry, native trees and shrubs can be clustered in diverse, multileveled groups that attract wildlife and thrive without fertilizer and coddling.

Such naturalistic gardens impart an ecological richness extending far beyond property lines. For as writer Rick Darke observes in *The American Woodland Garden*, "A garden that is truly reflective of the woodlands is perhaps one of our surest means of learning to appreciate the woodlands itself."

Directions: From I-90, take exit 43 and turn onto Route 21 south. In Canandaigua, turn left onto Routes 5 & 20 and in 3 miles, turn right onto Route 364 south. In 3 miles, turn right onto Powell Road, which becomes Kipp Road. Call ahead for appointment.

NEW JERSEY

NEW JERSEY

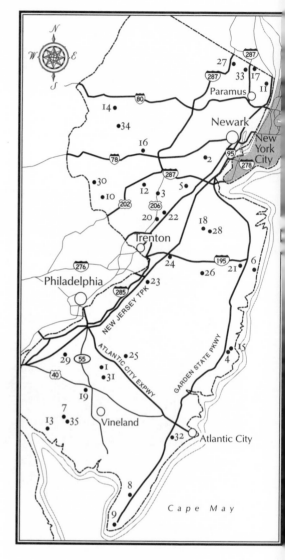

New Jersey

AL DOLINSKI & SON DAHLIAS

779 East Avenue, Franklinville, NJ 08322
(856) 694-1133; fax (856) 694-4368
http://users.snip.net/~dolinski; e-mail *dolinski@snip.net*
Al Dolinski

Dahlia bulbs. Small family-owned bulb farm. Free catalog. Catalog on Web site. Mail order only. Tubers shipped in April. Photos on Web site.

Al Dolinski & Son Dahlias is a commercial bulb farm that has been growing dahlia tubers in the South Jersey flatlands since 1950. For most of its history this 80-acre farm has supplied dahlias to the wholesale trade. In recent years, pressure on wholesale prices led the farm to offer tubers to retail home gardeners. Today, 30 acres remain in production.

Dahlias were the Aztecs' royal flower and still make a splash in their native Mexico. Conquistadors sent them as trophies to Spanish grandees, and like another Aztec delicacy (chocolate), dahlias became a status symbol among European royalty. Dutch breeders eventually got their hands on two species and began an energetic hybridizing effort—thereby democratizing the plant and creating the modern dahlia.

Sun-worshipping dahlias come brilliantly painted in red, orange, yellow, purple, and white. Modern hybrids explore such fashion tonalities as black-red, hot pink, amber, lavender, and showy bicolors with decided Art Deco effect. "Dahlias can be the crowning glory of your cut flower bed," the farm's Web site declares. "Dahlias make a gorgeous display, whether in the garden, or in bouquets and arrangements in the house."

Dolinski & Son specializes in long-stemmed cut-flower dahlias, excellent for home cutting gardens. (A long-standing farm sideline is selling fresh-cut dahlias to florists.) Bulbs are sold by variety—decorative, cactus, and pompom types—as well as in mixed collections. Labeled tubers cost $3 each, with a minimum order of $15. Unlabeled mixed collections run about $2 per bulb. A "virtual catalog" is posted on the Web site, with flower photographs and descriptions.

Waxed tubers are shipped after the customer's last frost date along with cultivation instructions. Being tender, dahlias must be planted after frost and lifted for winter storage, like gladiolus bulbs. Some clever gardeners cultivate and store dahlias in pots; others grow them for bouquets at family weddings. Their profuse blooms brighten late summer gardens. An obliging nature increases flower production the more often they are cut.

Dolinski & Son seems vulnerable (as do most South Jersey farms) to being sold for development. Farming is hard labor and level farmland easy to pave. Stock up on tubers, dahlia devotees—or else, we fear, the farm will disappear.

Related sources: Dolinski & Son sells cut dahlia bouquets at farmers' markets in Collingswood and Ocean City. The American Dahlia Society (www.dahlia.org) has growing information and lists local chapters, including one in New Jersey and six in New York.

AMBERG PERENNIAL FARM
2100 Lamberts Mill Road, Scotch Plains, NJ 07076
(908) 233-0873; fax (908) 233-4540
www.gardennj.com; e-mail *Bob@GardenNJ.com*
Bob Amberg

Field-grown perennials. *Family farm and garden center. Open March 15 to December 24, Tuesday through Saturday, 9 to 5, Sunday, 9 to 1, and by chance. No catalog. No mail order. Some plants listed on Web site. Seasonal items. Visitors welcome.*

The gardener's heart goes out to the farmer who turns to horticulture to keep the family farm. Amberg Perennial Farm is a small, 3rd-generation farm whose main crop is hardy perennials. It's a living remnant of a vanished way of life. Fifty years ago, the Ambergs operated a truck farm growing vegetables, later branching into field-grown perennials and finally potted perennials. Over the same period, Union County farmland shrank to 325 acres, supporting just a few farm families. Bob Amberg's family is one of them, and there's no way he's giving up the farm—even if it's not far from Newark.

"Agriculture has been a driving force in our life," Amberg says. "We have a tremendous love for the earth and the plants and animals on it. We enjoy growing things and seeing them produce."

Amberg Perennial Farm grows a fresh assortment of potted perennials on a six-acre site, combining newer varieties with workhorses that do well in New Jersey. The farm's retail outlet is basically a little garden center, with the adjacent fields offering a modest respite from suburban advance. Most perennials and flowering shrubs are farm-grown, with the rest of the nursery stock coming fresh from regional growers.

Amberg's inventory mostly consists of sun perennials for well-drained soils. The list is strong on plants that are tough, hardy, long-blooming, multi-seasonal, disease-resistant, nature-friendly, and easy to grow. Top choices include Leucanthemum 'Becky', Rudbeckia 'Goldsturm', purple coneflowers ('Magnus' and 'White Swan'), and several ornamental mints. Low-care gardens would be lost without landscaper daylilies ('Stella D'Oro' and 'Happy Returns')—supplemented here with everblooming maroon, rose, red, lemon, and cream varieties. Hummingbird and butterfly plants are given special attention, such as native asters, milkweeds, and joe-pye weeds.

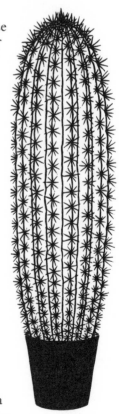

The ornamental grasses are surprisingly hip—Japanese blood grass, airy *Deschampsia caespitosa,* and a red form of switchgrass (*Panicum virgatum* 'Shenandoah'), for example. Nobody can resist 'Little Bunny', a cute miniature fountain grass. Although *Miscanthus sinensis* cultivars don't carry invasiveness warnings (we think they should), the varieties offered here are popular ornamentals. For shade, Amberg grows 20 hosta and a dozen ferns, including the new lady fern ('Lady in Red') and Japanese painted fern ('Ghost').

The farm grows its own flowering shrubs, typically new landscape varieties that won't hit the chain stores for several years. "I try to grow things that look really neat and aren't on the mass market yet," says Amberg. "I'm big on disease-resistance, but I like to keep ahead on selection, too." The clematis list deserves praise for including small-flowered and shrubby varieties. Cyclical items—such as bedding plants, vegetables, pumpkins, poinsettias, and pond supplies—are staples that keep family businesses afloat off-season.

Amberg has no catalog or plant list, but a general idea of what is offered can be gleaned from the Web site. Not everything is available at once, and selection changes with the seasons. As you'd expect when buying directly from the grower, quality is good and prices reasonable. A gallon-size perennial typically runs $6.95 and a 2-gallon pot twice that. Although the farm isn't organic, Amberg tries to limit pesticide use and grow things that are pest-free. A small band of African guinea hens is employed chasing the farm's unwanted bugs.

The Web site shows evocative photos of Bob Amberg's father tilling soil on an old tractor, and two Amberg children admiring a crop of winter pansies in the greenhouse. The farm is part of the state's "Jersey Fresh Plants and Produce" program and actively supports local agriculture. Bob Amberg has served on the Union County Board of Agriculture and works hard to keep New Jersey the "Garden State." He views the farmer's life as heroic. "Insects, deer, drought, floods—New Jersey gardeners and farmers alike are tested in many ways," he writes.

Despite the challenges, Amberg remains optimistic. "One area that has changed for the better is the fact that more people are putting their hands in soil and gardening," he says. "Maybe in today's high-tech, high-speed life, we all need gardening more than ever."

Directions: The farm is located in central New Jersey. From the Garden State Parkway, take exit 135. At the traffic circle, turn onto Central Avenue toward Westfield, and turn left at the second light onto Terminal Avenue. Turn right onto Westfield Avenue (becomes Rahway Avenue at the railroad tracks). Turn left onto Lamberts Mill Road; the farm is on the left, after a sharp right bend. From Route 22 in Scotch Plains, take the Terrill Road exit onto Terrill Road, which becomes Raritan Road. At the end, turn right onto Lamberts Mill Road; the farm is on the right.

Nearby attractions: Dreyer Farms, 831 Springfield Avenue, Cranford, NJ (908-276-1290; www.gardennj.com), is a 4th-generation family farm founded in 1905—the last working farm in Union County, with fresh produce, vegetable plants, herbs, and landscaping plants (open mid-March through December 24, daily, 8:30 to 6; call for directions).

Related sources: Union County is actually upscale garden center territory, with good independently owned examples at Williams Nursery, 524 Springfield Avenue, Westfield, NJ 07090 (908-232-4076; www.williams-nursery.com), and The Farm at Green Village, 403 Green Village Road, Green Village (near Summit), NJ 07935 (973-377-8703; www.thefarmatgreenvillage.com).

AMBLESIDE GARDENS
Box 220, Route 206, Hillsborough (Belle Mead), NJ 08502
(908) 359-8388; fax (908) 904-0678
www.amblesidegardens.com
David Scudder

Unusual annuals, perennials, trees, and shrubs. Japanese maples. Family-run garden center. Open March through December, Monday through Saturday, 9 to 6, Sunday, 10 to 5. Extended hours in spring and at Christmas, Wednesday through Friday until 8. Winter hours "irregular at best." No catalog or mail order. Award-winning landscape design. Gift shop and supplies. Garden ornaments. Seasonal and holiday items.

A small oasis on a busy roadside in central New Jersey, Ambleside Gardens is an independent garden center known for its superior plants and landscaping services. Townsend and Mary Scudder founded Ambleside in 1966, when Route 206 was a quiet road between Somerville and Princeton. They named it after a charming town they'd visited in England's Lake District. Perhaps for this reason, it has the look and feel of a British garden center—sophisticated, homey, and full of exceptional garden plants.

Ambleside has the comfortable air of a plant center run by tried-and-true nurserymen, people who know and care about plants. Although the owners buy in much plant material, it's beautiful stuff from excellent sources, and they still grow quite a bit themselves in greenhouses in Neshanic. Expertise is everywhere evident, from intelligent garden supplies to a roadside berm and waterfall alive with frogs. Pergolas, raised beds, plant tables, and alpine troughs are used to organize and display nursery stock. A metal heron sculpture stalks fish in a small lily pond. Nothing is dowdy, edgy, or showy— just thoughtfully chosen, attractive, and robust.

Landscape design and construction are a major part of Ambleside's business, now run by David Scudder, the founders' son. He trained at various landscape firms and toured the sacred gardens of Japan before assuming responsibilities at Ambleside. One result is a clear preference for using elegant Asian ornamentals—Japanese tree lilacs and stewartias, for example—in place of the typical lackluster repertoire. Landscapers who know little of horticulture may give clients a false sense of security, but Ambleside is master of the subject. Its design-build team has won five "Best in Show" awards at the New Jersey Flower Show and is respected both for its design skills and its plantsmanship.

Ambleside's refined, well-priced nursery stock spans everything from rock-garden miniatures to giant metasequoias. Unusual annuals are ready in May. There are 1000 varieties of perennial flowers, ferns, grasses, and wildflowers, in sizes ranging from 3-inch pots to 3-gallon containers. The exotic conifers include blonde and blue-haired varieties, some trained as topiary. A fine collection of woody plants, supplied by 50 growers, includes native azaleas, fragrant viburnums, and multiseason shrubs (such as blueberry and winterberry) pruned as small trees. Ambleside's rare Japanese maple collection makes the tree yard a competitive hot spot in spring.

We're not big on gift shops, but Ambleside's International Gift Shop deserves mention—if only for its classical leaden urns, medieval-style stone planters, and hand-painted Moroccan pots. We wish we'd bought a curious Chinese birdbath. Even at Christmas, when most nurseries betray their standards, Ambleside offers handcrafted nativities from 25 countries— miniature Bethlehems such as jeweled Polish manger scenes, banana-fiber sets from Africa, and nativity yurts from Kyrgyzstan, rendered in felt.

Directions: Ambleside is on Route 206 in Hillsborough (Belle Mead). From Route 287, take exit 17 onto Route 202/206 south; in 1 mile, bear right onto Route 206 south. In about 19 miles, just past Route 514, the nursery is at the intersection of Oxford Place. From Jersey City, take Route 78 west to Route 287 south and follow directions above.

Nearby attractions: Ash's Flower Farm, 135 Route 206 south, Hillsborough, NJ (908-218-7844), sells flowering plants and hanging baskets by the thousand in an open-air lot that was once Old Packard's Market.

ANYTHING GROWS FLOWER FARM

127 South Main Street, Barnegat, NJ 08005-9809
(609) 698-1060; fax (609) 660-9232
Stephanie Lopez and Julie McKendry

Annuals, perennials, and seasonal plants. Open daily, 9 to 5, mid-March through December. No catalog or mail order. Greenhouse-propagated plants. Newsletter.

Anything Grows Flower Farm in seaside Barnegat is an appealing nursery and landscaper specializing in flowering plants. From the road it's a yellow ranch house with a large plastic sign, cute mailbox, and front yard full of neon flowers. Out back, where you park, it opens up to reveal a large greenhouse, three cold frames, and a delightful sales yard crammed with intriguing plant stock. This reverses the typical commercial garden-center experience, which gets more boring the longer you're there. Anything Grows just gets more interesting.

Owners Stephanie Lopez and Julie McKendry are plant lovers who met at a commercial greenhouse in Wisconsin, moved to New Jersey, and founded Anything Grows in 1996. Lopez is a propagation powerhouse of 20 years' expertise who runs the greenhouse operation. McKendry handles landscaping jobs and writes a monthly "Plant Chat" column in the *Ocean County Journal.*

Lopez and McKendry take pride in owning one of the few garden centers on the Jersey coast to grow its own flowers and constantly experiment with new and uncommon varieties. Staff members refer to plants as "Stephanie's babies." Intimate oversight from infancy onward is one of its great assurances of plant quality. Like toddlers who are regularly fed, bathed, and taught good manners, the nursery's seedlings and divisions respond to coddling with a flourish of health and good looks that promise to last a lifetime.

Anything Grows manages to cram into its congested inventory the area's hottest flowers and plants. Fancy annuals and clever seasonals are so wide-ranging that, as one staff member said, "It's easier to say what we *don't* have." Popular hanging baskets offer unusually pretty plant combinations. Colorful bedding plants include variegated pelargonium, fruit-colored diascia, African daisies, and a rainbow of exotic coleus. Victorian pansies appear in spring—and again in autumn, with winter pansies. In autumn the named chrysanthemums include 'Corinne', an unusual white spoon-bill daisy mum. Luscious poinsettias include cream, peach, speckled, and variegated hybrids, all greenhouse-grown for the holidays.

The nursery emphasizes plants that survive seashore conditions—that "flourish in our climate of high winds, sandy soil, and salt air," the owners say. These plants swell in importance as New Jersey struggles with development and drought. Every year, the owners play around with unusual dry-land material, such as epilobiums or agastaches, in search of a new treasure.

Even when plant stock is bought in, quality remains high. A gorgeous medley of 'Happy Ever Appster' daylilies were bred by Darrel Apps at Woodside Nursery (see profile). Choice trees and shrubs for sandy soils include Chinese seven-son flower, crape myrtle 'Natchez', and native fringe tree and black gum. A few lush hydrangeas feature a cherry-colored variety and the renowned ever-blooming blue mop-head, 'Endless Summer'.

Anything Grows takes the time to befriend its customers by offering amenities that are genuinely useful and enjoyable. These include a newsletter, a little garden shop, seasonal sales and specials, and a well-equipped potting bench. The staff is knowledgeable and nice, jumping to help at need, but leaving browsers and camera bugs alone when appropriate. Although there are few open spaces on the 1¼-acre site, tucked-in container displays are charming. Autumn visitors can cast votes in the staff's scarecrow contest. "Customers just get in the moment and buy what strikes them," says McKendry. "People really like being here."

Directions: Take the Garden State Parkway to exit 67, turn east onto Route 554, and in Barnegat, turn right onto South Main Street/Route 9 south. The nursery is 2 miles on the right.

Nearby attractions: In Barnegat Light, Mustache Bill's Diner, 8th and Broadway (609-494-0155), is a 1959 Fodero lunchcar where breakfast is king; try the potato-skin omelet (open daily; 6 to 3). Reynolds Garden Shop, 201 East Bay Avenue, Manahawkin, NJ 08050-3316 (609-597-6099; www.reynoldsgardenshop.com), is a large high-end garden center/landscaper on Long Beach Island (open daily, 9 to 6, Sunday, 9 to 5).

ATLOCK FARM

545 Weston Canal Road, Somerset, NJ 08873
(732) 356-3373; fax (732) 868-0831
E-mail *kenselody@aol.com*
Ken Selody

Topiary and conservatory plants. Annuals, perennials, and herbs. Small spe-cialty nursery. Open from April through July 3, Monday through Saturday, 8 to 5, and Sundays in May and June, 10 to 4. Open from July through December, seasonal hours; from January through March by appointment. Closed for lunch, 11:30 to 12:30. Free plant list. No mail order. Spring Open House, Father's Day weekend, 12 to 4. Winter Open House, Saturday after Thanksgiving, 10 to 4. Garden design. Garden ornaments. Formal gardens. Visitors welcome. No dogs.

Atlock Farm is an artisan nursery in Somerset offering beautifully grown plants in a garden setting. Ken Selody founded the nursery on his family's sod farm, expanding over 20 years into 7 greenhouses, formal gardens, and a refined garden-ornament shop. A prominent supplier of topiary, Atlock Farm supplies stylish conservatory plants, unusual perennials, and fine garden herbs in changing array. "Our goal is to make interesting and unusual plants that are not found in average nurseries," says Selody. Considering the quality, prices are unexpectedly modest.

Atlock Farm's history parallels the story of land use in New Jersey. Atlock Farm was originally named for its location "at Lock 10" on the Delaware & Raritan Canal, the 1834 fluvial artery connecting inland produce farms with markets in Trenton and Philadelphia. Once a dairy farm, it was transformed when Staten Island landscapers came to buy turf. "My great-grandmother told the men to follow the landscapers and see what they were doing," says Selody. "My grandfather became one of the first sod farmers in New Jersey." Today, Selody Sod Farm produces flawless carpets of emerald turf on some 350 acres.

Selody's nursery is a cutout, sliced from the surrounding sod. He studied photography at Pratt Institute, and when he needed flowers as film subjects, his father paced out five strides from a farm shed. After the sod was cut, rolled, and sold, he used the plot to cultivate calla lily, bird-of-paradise, and *Sisyrinchium striatum* from seed. "I had so much fun," Selody recalls. "But then I couldn't buy the plants that interested me, so I asked for more growing space." His father paced another 100 feet for boxwood hedges and fruit trees; paced again for an asparagus patch, and finally for the nursery greenhouses. "It took ten years," says Selody. "The nursery literally grew step by step."

At the nursery he opened in 1987, Selody applied his art-school training to craft fine topiary for tables and gardens. The Roman art of training plants into shapes gives an elegant formality to cultured landscapes. Atlock Farm grows living spirals, triples, and columns of French lavender, rosemary, germander, and *Geranium maderense*. Its ivy tabletop topiary and red-and-green coleus standards make elegant Christmas decorations. Selody's skills have been demonstrated on Martha Stewart Television and his topiary featured in *Martha Stewart Living*.

Tender perennials, which Selody has been collecting and growing for years, are another nursery treasure. "Tropicals used to be considered house-plants," he says, "but now they're put in gardens for a wild-African-safari look." Selody grows pastel angel's-trumpets and solanums with yellow thorns or purple fuzz. His best tropical grasses include palm-leaved *Setaria palmifolia rubra,* a 3-foot stunner with red midribs and pleated foliage that seems to be crafted from crepe paper. "People stop and stare in late summer and fall, when it gets most *zaftig,*" he says.

Atlock Farm's container plants include scented and fancy-leaf zonal geraniums; frosted and rouged rex begonias; fan-leaf, stippled, and striped forms of plectranthus (Swedish ivy); fuchsias and flowering tobaccos; the red 'Bishop of Llandaff' dahlia; and more than 30 tender salvias. A collection of 130 coleus (with names like 'Tilt a Whirl', and "Flirtin' Skirts') is among the finest in the region.

Selody's current passion is tender ligularia (farfugium), especially its crested forms, which he uses for foliage effects after removing the flowers. Tanzanian starfish plant *(Stapelia gigantea)* is a strange, clustering succulent whose liverish flowers emit a rotten-meat odor, specially brewed to attract flies. Other remarkable plants are plum-colored leatherleaf sedge *(Carex buchananii),* African climbing onion *(Bowiea volubilis),* and living baseball plant *(Euphorbia obesa).*

Atlock Farm's hardy perennials reflect the same artistry. Daylilies are the small, dapper kind you almost never see, such as 'Siloam Virginia Henson' and 'Mary's Gold'. Variegated Solomon's-seal is used inventively as a shade container plant. The sales beds are adorned with hellebores, primroses, epimediums, rare gingers, and ladybells. Desirable herbs include fruit-scented mints, colored sages, and all the good lavenders. Well-priced Japanese tree peonies and clematis are sold in generous pots. Hardy sempervivums (hen-and-chickens) resembling roses, pinecones, and artichokes do well in sun-scorched xeriscapes. Uncommon woody plants occasionally creep into the farm's inventory, such as white camellias, dainty climbing roses, and double-flowered hydrangea.

Selody labors to breed new strains of dwarf amaryllis, mixing desirable traits from known cultivars. His hybrids of Amaryllis × 'Scarlet Baby' have already produced dwarf plants with crimson blooms, purple stems, and 16 flower stalks. While breeding is tedious work, amaryllis seedlings "pup up" quickly to produce saleable stock. Atlock Farm offers its own radiant hybrids—the ones that Selody can part with—in handmade terra-cotta pots.

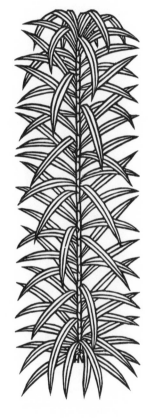

Selody is a consummate plantsman, well capable of continuing Atlock Farm's creative trajectory. He works tirelessly. He collects cool plants. He lectures. He designs gardens for importunate clients. He continually experiments in the greenhouse, choosing, editing, and selecting, as artists do. Whenever he travels, he visits nurseries. On vacation, he visits botanical gardens. "I absolutely love being in a greenhouse around plants," says Selody. "It's like having children. It's hard to leave."

The farm's display gardens comprise a formal oasis blending art and artisanship, a Matisse cutout in the surrounding turf. Visitors are greeted by wandering guinea fowl and the sacramental odor of boxwood. Epimediums and hellebores form drifts under a canopy of flowering trees. Summer heat supports a red border with tropical flourishes. Handsome lead urns give visual clues to treasures in the garden shed—Siebert & Rice pots and other elegant accessories. A formal parterre of chocolate barberry and salmon opium poppies is punctuated with blue Lutyens benches, where visitors may rest.

This is a fine spot to contemplate the gardens, in the very place where they began. Transcendent shadows show a man pacing out room for a son's artistry. A grown son, continuing the family *métier*, working hard, making it new.

Directions: From Route 287, take exit 12 in Somerset and turn left off the ramp onto Weston Canal Road. The nursery is 1.5 miles on the left.

Nearby attractions: Selody Sod Farm (908-725-0823) sells sod for about 20 cents a foot. Atlock Farm is named for Lock 10 on the Delaware & Raritan Canal, directly across West Canal Road from the nursery. A public parking lot behind the old toll-house permits public access to the towpath. Colonial Park Arboretum, 156 Mettler's Road, East Millstone, NJ 08873 (732-873-2459), has a formal rosary garden with 4000 roses (peak bloom in June).

BARLOW FLOWER FARM
1014 Sea Girt Avenue, Sea Girt, NJ 08750
(732) 449-9189; fax (732) 449-2757
www.barlowflowerfarm.com
Stephen and Leslie Barlow

Flowering annuals and perennials; fresh nursery stock. Family-run greenhouses and garden center. Open year-round, Monday through Saturday, 9 to 5:30. Closed Sunday in January. Free perennial and rose lists. Annuals list on Web site. No mail order. Classes and workshops. Potting bench services. Most Beautiful Garden photo contest. Gift shop. Florist. Visitors welcome.

Barlow Flower Farm is a vibrant family-owned garden center and green-house in Sea Girt, a fashionable shore town in an area whose affluence extinguishes all "Joisey" jokes. Steve and Leslie Barlow bought the 7-acre farm in 1983 when it was nothing but a produce sales shed and a huddle of run-down greenhouses. It took years to install heating systems, build production greenhouses, construct an enlarged sales yard, and find parking for 100 cars.

Today, the farm is a sophisticated enterprise with 32 greenhouses, a European glasshouse, an acre of retail space, a large shop, and a full-time professional staff. It dominates garden-center popularity contests and has won many quality awards. Fully 80 percent of its plant material is grown on-site, making it the largest retail flower grower in New Jersey. The only reminder of the site's rural past is the dirt road between the retail yard and greenhouses, retained to safeguard "farm" status with local authorities.

Barlow Flower Farm specializes in growing flowers, flowers, and more flowers—1000 varieties of flowering annuals, perennials, herbs, and shrubs. On any given day just about everything is in bloom. Vivid outdoor displays juxtapose moss baskets, potted plants, and elaborate planted containers, all filled to the utmost with flowers—or if not flowers, with painted or variegated foliage that passes for flowers. Colorful exuberance gives the farm a naïve, happy air, like a toddler's color-crayon garden or a folk-art image of paradise.

The farm works hard to spread the gospel of flowers. It holds popular promotional events and sponsors a Better Gardening and Design Series of classes and workshops for home gardeners. It teaches horticultural skills to high school students in an award-winning vocational program. It offers a popular potting service, including container pick up and delivery. It holds a home-garden contest, with merit points given—well, for flowers, of course.

Nursery stock is bright and fashion-forward. Spring annuals include not just 32 kinds of pansy but 'Red Madness' petunia, 'Daybreak Orange' gazania, and solar coleus in lime and ruby. Big-flowered hibiscus novelties boost the merriment, along with sky-blue Chilean glorybower standards and pale-pink Martha Washington geraniums in 3-tiered baskets. What *fashionista* could resist 'Flamingo Feather Pink' celosia—not to mention 'Champagne Bubbles' poppy and 'Cocktail Vodka' begonia? The sales yard is as festive as a yacht club cocktail party.

Perennials, too, stay abreast of fashion developments with the latest chartreuse columbine, blackberry corydalis, and mango coneflower. You'll find pretty pastels, too, such as pink gaura and white physostegia. A perennial-plant list reveals the inventory by name, variety, flower color, bloom time, and site requirements. Because Barlow grows practically everything in its own greenhouses, the stock stays fresh and the selection good throughout the season.

Considering Barlow's amenities and high level of care, prices are good. Gallon-size annuals typically run $6.95 or 2/$12, gallon-size flowering herbs $9.98, and 2-gallon perennials $13.95. Bedding plants and vegetables come in 6-packs. Prices will only ascend with the price of fuel, of course, but sales offer bargains later in the season.

Because Barlow is only a mile from the sea, it necessarily grows plants that thrive in seashore conditions. The ornamental herbs and prairie perennials (such as coreopsis and rudbeckia) pay little attention to drought and heat. Shrubs are mostly sunny long-bloomers, such as yellow and purple butterfly weed, and plants that look like long-bloomers, such as variegated lacecap hydrangea. The roses are chiefly carefree beach-rose hybrids that bloom openly in tough circumstances.

Even in winter Barlow Flower Farm doesn't run out of flowers. It sells greenhouse-grown holiday plants and flower pots for Valentines. The floral staff makes creative cut-flower bouquets, gift baskets, and silk flower arrangements. In a pinch, you can always find flowers displayed on the Web site.

Directions: From the Garden State Parkway, take exit 98 onto Route 34 south, and after the overpass, turn right onto Atlantic Avenue. In 1 mile, at the traffic circle, turn right onto Route 35 north. At the first light, turn right onto Sea Girt Avenue; the farm is 1 mile on the left. From the New Jersey Turnpike, exit onto Route 195 east; turn right at the end onto Route 35 south; and at the fifth light, turn left onto Sea Girt Avenue. The farm is 1 mile on the left.

Nearby attractions: Curtis' Central Market, Main Avenue at Mount Street, Bay Head, NJ (732-899-0068), a cornerstone of Bay Head since 1910, is where everybody goes for breakfast or a quick sandwich. Recycling The Past, 381 North Main Street, Barnegat, NJ 08005 (609-660-9790; www.recyclingthepast.com; open daily, 10 to 5), is an architectural salvage company with an eclectic mix of old wrought iron, bronze, terra-cotta, urns, and garden furniture.

BLUE STERLING NURSERY
372 Seeley-Cohansey Road, Bridgeton, NJ 08302
(800) 526-6433; (856) 451-2259; fax (856) 451-2442
www.bluesterling.com; e-mail *conifer@bluesterling.com*

Dwarf conifers. Japanese maples. Large wholesale grower and supplier. Open to wholesale customers, year-round, Monday through Friday, 8 to 12 and 1 to 4:30; Saturday by appointment. Closed at 3:30 in winter. Open one Retail Day per year, late June or early July, 11 to 4; exact date on Web site. Wholesale catalog. No mail order. Retail outlets listed on Web site. Online newsletter. Plant photos on Web site.

Conifers are called "the palm trees of the Northeast" for the evergreen architecture they give to landscapes. In their natural state, though, they're often too big for gardens. Dwarf conifers are modern substitutes—smaller evergreens for smaller gardens. Of course, a crowd of dwarf conifers can resemble a little shop of horrors. But in the right place, dwarf conifers make fine garden structures, perennially fresh and green. And they stay within bounds.

Blue Sterling Nursery is a prominent wholesale grower of exotic conifers. Founder Jim Smith is a former landscaper (and Grateful Dead fan) who couldn't find a good East Coast grower of these plants. In 1982, in frustration, Smith and his wife, Barbara, founded Blue Sterling on 24 acres of fenced South Jersey cow pasture—gradually transforming its barbed-wire grid into "a rather nicely laid-out container production nursery."

Since then, the Smiths have added 36 acres of production fields, dazzling display gardens, a modern office, and an expert support staff. In 2000, they built a state-of-the-art propagation house—a gleaming 21,000-square-foot greenhouse facility constructed by a Dutch specialist. Blue Sterling serves independent garden centers and commercial landscapers. Retail gardeners are not officially allowed inside this wholesale emporium—except once a year.

On a designated "Retail Day" (usually in late June or early July), Blue Sterling opens its doors to all visitors, wholesale and retail. Retail Day is coordinated with open-house days at two area nurseries: Woodside Nursery, a noted daylily farm, and Fairweather Gardens, a prominent mail-order nursery (see profiles). This open-house trifecta has become something of a pilgrimage route for sophisticated plant shoppers of the Northeast and

Mid-Atlantic regions. (We hear that gardeners can sometimes talk themselves in during off-season as well.)

Blue Sterling's inventory focuses on slow-growing, rare, and unusual conifers—what it calls "Genetically Superior Cultivars." Its 75 selections of false cypress, for example, probably represent the full range of conifer charm and weirdness. They include pygmy, prostrate, and pillar varieties of Lawson's cypress *(C. lawsoniana);* twisted and dwarf forms of Hinoki false cypress *(C. obtusa);* and cream-ball, baby-blue, and curly-top versions of Sawara cypress *(C. pisifera).*

Selection for appealing oddity governs in all conifer groups. Midget Atlantic cedar, spiral cryptomeria, and cream-flecked Japanese arborvitae (thujopsis)—everything's a bit abnormal. In all, the nursery grows 51 blue, 58 yellow, 24 purple, and 42 variegated plants. Like many exotic conifer collections, this one harbors lots of little cosmic buns (63, in fact) with names like 'Teddy Bear' and 'Leprechaun'. Dwarf plum yew and other spiky, bitter, and hard-to-chew plants are popular for their disrepute with deer.

One of Blue Sterling's best professional accomplishments is identifying dwarf conifer classics that have become confused in the nursery trade. The nursery grows the true 'Kosteri' false cypress and the true *Chaemacyparis obtusa* 'Nana', for example, not the faster-growing, erroneously named forms sold in nurseries. Blue Sterling also offers fine forms taken from botanical gardens, many dating to the 19th century. A few indigenous New Jersey treasures came from legendary nurseries a generation ago, such as 'Verkade's Sunburst' false cypress, 'Okken Selection' blue spruce, and some fine Vermeulin Nursery discoveries.

Besides grafted conifers, Blue Sterling grows grafted Japanese maples (40 varieties), unusual witch hazels, and dwarf hollies. Connoisseur plants include items like witches'-broom ginkgo and 'Gumball' dwarf sweet gum. Fernleaf and roundleaf beech are the kind of thing collectors travel across state lines to acquire.

Blue Sterling has all the amenities of a good wholesaler. Plants are container-grown in a range of 1- to 10-gallon pots. Stock is propagated from grafts or cuttings (not seedlings) to retain desirable characteristics. Plants are well labeled and guaranteed true to name. For clarity, Blue Sterling follows American Conifer Society height standards to define its inventory (in 10 years, a "miniature" conifer grows 2 to 3 feet; a "dwarf" 3 to 6 feet; an "intermediate" 6 to 15 feet; and a "large" 15 feet). Knowledgeable staffers can guide customer choices based on hardiness, color, texture, form, growth rate, best planting location, and current availability. The wholesale catalog (accessible to retail customers online) notes important plant awards, such as the Pennsylvania Horticultural Society's Gold Medal.

Blue Sterling's "idea garden" consists of landscaped stone terraces artfully clad in dwarf and unusual conifers that are being tested for the catalog. Here visitors can view slow-growth conifers at maturity—especially what are called "little gems" (or faintly comedic pet names) because they stay pat over decades of growth. More than plant tags or digital photos, such living examples give invaluable clues to what exotic conifers will look like in 20 years.

Ideas come and go, but this garden is truly handsome and inspiring—far surpassing the ubiquitous "New Jersey combo" (i.e., blue spruce, yellow-thread false cypress, and red Japanese maple) installed beside every new meadow-mansion in the state. No landscaper will admit to inventing the New Jersey combo. It all started, we're told, on Staten Island.

Directions: Blue Sterling is in South Jersey, an hour south of Philadelphia and an hour west of Atlantic City. From the New Jersey Turnpike, take exit 2 and turn right onto Route 322 east. Turn right at the light onto Route 45 south, follow about 1 mile through Mullica Hill, where the road becomes Route 77 south. In 12 to 15 miles, in Deerfield, pass Pole Tavern Circle and turn right at the second blinking yellow light onto Route 540 west. In 2 miles, turn right on Seeley-Cohansey Road. The nursery is first on the left. From Atlantic City, take Route 40 west to Pole Tavern Circle, turn south on Route 77, and follow directions above.

CAPE MAY BIRD OBSERVATORY
600 Route 47 North, Cape May Court House (Goshen), NJ 08210
(609) 861-0700
www.njaudubon.org/Centers/CMBO; e-mail *cmbo2@njaudubon.org*
New Jersey Audubon Society

Native perennials for wildlife. Open year-round, daily, 1 to 4:30. Plant sales from late April through autumn; call for exact dates. Plant list on Web site. Selection changes in season. No mail order. Web site information on the center's "World of Backyard Habitats" quick-link pages. Classes and workshops. Visitors welcome.

Cape May is a renowned birding area at the southeastern tip of New Jersey, where prevailing winds and peninsular geography create a "migrant trap" unmatched in eastern North America. In autumn, tens of thousands of migrating birds (including 16 species of hawk) journey to Cape May before crossing the Delaware Bay. The bayshore is also home to an astonishing wild fauna, animating its windy expanse with singing, nesting, fluttering, and soaring in every season.

The Cape May Bird Observatory, founded in 1975 by the New Jersey Audubon Society, opened its Center for Research and Education in 1997. This 8600-square-foot facility, surrounded by 26 acres of marsh and upland, is the perfect place to study the natural richness of the Delaware Bay shore. It focuses on bird watching and backyard habitat, with natural-history displays, a lecture hall, an outside observation deck, a wildlife art gallery, and a little store offering feeders, binoculars, maps, and books. Naturalistic outdoor landscaping uses native plants to demonstrate model backyard habitat for the center's classes and workshops.

Gardeners seeking to attract airborne wildlife can purchase suitable native plants in a dedicated nursery area outside the center's building. "Plantings beneficial to butter-flies, hummingbirds, and fruit-eating birds are not always easy to find," says Program Director Pat Sutton, who teaches the center's backyard-habitat curriculum, writes a popular wildlife book series, and is herself an ardent birder. "People sometimes see native plants as weeds, without appreciating the role they play in sustaining wildlife," she says.

Plants are supplied by Flora for Fauna, a nursery in

Woodbine operated by Karen Williams, formerly a marine biologist. Williams is a master seed-collector who grows an admirable short list of ecologically important plants from local populations maintained for that purpose. The focus is on "nectar plants, caterpillar food plants, and fruit- and seed-bearing native trees and shrubs." Helpful labels describe each plant's habitat value, proper landscape placement, and ornamental assets. Though small, these locally adapted plants often "take" better and grow faster than the exotic, instant-landscape specimens sold in many garden centers. Selection changes each season, making it worthwhile to stop by regularly for the freshest choices.

The center sells about 40 varieties of perennials, trees, shrubs, and vines— mostly New Jersey natives. Some locals, such as Pine Barrens blazing-star *(Liatris spicata),* dwarf beach plum *(Prunus maritima),* and dwarf hackberry *(Celtis tenufolia),* are almost never seen in nurseries. Meadow plants include wild bee balm, milkweeds, New England aster, New York ironweed, and such towering charismatics as joe-pye weed and cup plant *(Silphium perfoliatum).* Attractive berried shrubs include silky dogwood, cranberry viburnum, shadbush, and black chokeberry. Hints of architectural grandeur can be achieved with festooning native trumpet creeper (a hummingbird lure) and lofty tulip magnolia (whose seeds are relished by songbirds, game birds, rabbits, squirrels, and mice).

Anyone harboring doubts about the consequence of gardening with these plants need only visit the center's backyard-habitat gardens to witness their extraordinary appeal to butterflies, bees, songbirds, hummingbirds, moths, and dragonflies. "Classroom" gardens weave together wildflower-and-bunchgrass meadows, butterfly and hummingbird habitat, a dragonfly pond, a bog garden, and breeding grounds for purple martins and blue jays. Such gardens not only provide wildlife food and nesting sites but offer their keepers positive dividends—bird song, plumage display, flight acrobatics, and the promise that the birds alone will consume many times their weight in nasty insects. On the Jersey shore, the bug-control effect alone should be enough.

Directions: From the New Jersey Turnpike or Route 295 near Philadelphia, take Route 55 south to its end and merge onto Route 47 south. Turn left onto Route 347 south and follow until it rejoins Route 47 south. Pass through Dennisville and pass by Route 83. At the traffic light at Route 657 (Southville Restaurant on corner), continue straight for 1 mile. The center is on the left, past a bend in the road. From the

Garden State Parkway, take exit 17 and turn west off the ramp. At the first light, turn left onto Route 9 south. In 2.5 miles, turn right onto Route 83 west. In 4 miles, turn left onto Route 47 south and follow directions above.

Nearby attractions: The center holds a Backyard Plant Swap in late April and sells an excellent Delaware Bayshore Birding and Butterflying Map of southern New Jersey. Cape Island Garden Shop, 720 Broadway, Cape May, NJ 08204 (609-884-4210), carries a good selection of butterfly and hummingbird perennials and salt-tolerant plants. The New Jersey Coastal Heritage Trail Route (www.nps.gov/NEJE) lists local wildlife trails, old lighthouses, and bald eagle nesting sites.

CHURCH'S BEACHGRASS AND NURSERY
522 Seashore Road, Cape May, NJ 08204
(609) 884-3927; fax (609) 884-7738
www.churchsbeachgrass.com; e-mail *info@churchsbeachgrass.com*
Paul Church

Native beach grass. *Family-owned nursery and garden center. Open Monday through Saturday, 8 to 5. No catalog. Mail order. Local delivery or pick up available. UPS delivery for smaller orders. Grass dug to order October through March. Advance notice required for orders of 1000 plants or more. Wholesale and retail. Beach grass nursery not open to the public.*

Church's Beachgrass and Nursery is a state-certified grower of American beach grass *(Ammophila breviligulata).* Native to sand dunes of the Atlantic coast and Great Lakes, this long, slender grass is used as a sand-binder for dune stabilization and restoration. (*Ammophila* means "sand-lover.") While not exactly ornamental, salt-tolerant beach grass has great character and can be used effectively in naturalistic seaside plantings.

Church's is a family-run garden center that has been growing American beach grass as an important sideline since 1962. "We had a Nor'easter that wiped out the dunes in Cape May, Avalon, and Stone Harbor. People woke up and realized they needed to build up the sand dunes to protect from storm surges," recalls owner Paul Church. "We're the first commercial nursery to grow native beach grass as a field crop." Today Church's beach grass, derived from Cape May genotypes, is used from South Carolina to Maine and west to the Great Lakes.

Church's sells American beach grass plants in bulk during winter dormancy. Planting season is October through mid-April. Grasses are shipped bare root in stout bundles of 100 plants. Each double-stem grass is cut to 16 inches for planting in staggered rows, 12 to 18 inches apart.

Because American beach grass is largely unavailable in the trade, Church's is one of the few places where salt-spray gardeners and native plant enthusiasts can acquire this handsome grass. Most bare-root orders are for widespread dune plantings, but Church's will sell a bundle or two to the ordinary gardener. Church's garden center also offers containerized beach grass.

Directions: Cape May is at the southern tip of New Jersey. From the Garden State Parkway, take exit 4A onto Route 47 north, and in 0.2 mile merge onto Route 47/Delsea Drive. In 0.5 mile, turn left onto Route 9 and in 1.2 miles, bear right onto Cresse Lane. Turn immediately left onto Seashore Drive; the garden center is at #522. Call ahead for beach grass pick up.

CROSS COUNTRY NURSERIES

P.O. Box 170, 199 Kingwood-Locktown Road, Rosemont, NJ 08556-0170
(908) 996-4646; fax (908) 996-4638
www.chileplants.com; e-mail *janie@chileplants.com*
Janey Lamson and Fernando Villegas

Chile pepper plants, tomato plants, and supplies. *Small specialty nursery. Open mid-April through June, Monday through Friday, 9 to 5, Saturday and Sunday, 10 to 6. Open evenings and other times by appointment. Free catalog. Catalog on Web site. Mail order. Seasonal. Books and organic growing supplies.*

Cross Country Nurseries is a small organic nursery with a big collection of chile and sweet pepper plants—alleged to be the "world's largest selection." Owner Janey Lamson and her husband, Fernando Villegas, operate the nursery on an old farm in Rosemont, west of Flemington, where Lamson once grew flowering perennials for a predecessor nursery. Villegas came to work for her and in 1996 they started growing chile peppers for sale, using seed his mother sent them from Oaxaca, Mexico.

In 1997, the couple grew 101 mail-order varieties, including 'Costeño', a hot little chile pepper from Villegas' home state that is good for drying.

Today, Cross Country Nurseries offers more than 500 kinds of chile and sweet peppers—known collectively as capsicums—from a collection of some 750 varieties. The catalog lists the peppers available by name and use; the Web site provides color photos and a searchable database.

Here chile lovers, affectionately known as "chile heads," can find peppers of every description, sorted by shape, heat, color, length, cuisine, use, and place of origin. The temperature gauge starts low, with sweet bell peppers and poblanos; ascends through warm jalepeños, serranos, cayennes, and tabascos; and tops out with mind-boiling habaneros at 200,000 heat units.

As writer Jean Andrews records in *Peppers: The Domesticated Capsicums*, chile pepper cultivation began in Peru with the ancient Incas and spread throughout prehistoric South America. The ancient Aztecs used them in *mole poblano*, Mexico's signature condiment consisting of crushed dried chile peppers combined with pulverized chocolate. (Every mother in Mexico has her own recipe.) Culinary uses, which are prolific, include salsa, seasoning, roasting, pickling, drying, stuffing, and frying.

Such is the pepper's allure that it has been incorporated into practically every cuisine. While most chiles are South American or Mexican, today's hybrids come from all over the planet—Trinidad, Romania, Italy, China, Guam, Hungary, Turkey, Indonesia, Japan, Russia, and the United States. India alone grows more than 2 million acres of chile peppers per year.

Most of Cross Country's peppers are destined for the kitchen. The top sellers are high-alarm habaneros, so blistering they're said to make consumers feel cool in hot weather. Especially popular are exciting new habaneros rated "extremely hot" in the catalog. These include 'Fatalii', a South African tongue-scorcher that promises a near-death experience, and 'Habanero-Red Savina', listed in the *Guinness Book of Records* as the hottest pepper in the world.

The nursery owners themselves consume no such fire. "It's my big secret," says Lamson. "The Chile Goddess eats no heat!" Instead, Lamson and her husband, who are vegetarians, prefer flavorful poblano peppers such as 'Yellow Cheese' (a sweet, scalloped chile that looks like a mini-pumpkin) and some lovely ancho roasting peppers, which they use for grilling.

Besides culinary peppers, Cross Country offers 70 ornamental peppers for use as container plants, including 'Brazilian Rainbow', Texas Black', and 'Peruvian Purple'. As tender perennials, peppers can, with care, be overwintered as pretty houseplants for their white blossoms and colorful fruit. Indeed, one of the pleasures of growing them is the amazing color and shape of their fruits. Culinary curiosities such as 'Hungarian Banana', 'Tiger Teeth', 'White Wax', and 'Brazilian Starfish' seem like art objects, offering a feast for the eyes as well as the tongue. A seasoning pepper called 'Bird Dung' probably looks the part when dried.

Cross Country Nurseries is an organic hoophouse operation that uses beneficial insects to control greenhouse bugs. Baby chiles are spawned in the *chilarcito* ("little chile") greenhouse until hardened and ready for potting. At nine weeks, mature seedlings are sold in deep, 2½-inch square pots, which afford a good-size root and perform better than vegetable plugs. Packing is careful, earning customer accolades for the state of shipped plant material on arrival. All plants come with growing instructions—the most critical is to plant peppers late, when the ground is well warmed. A clearance sale offers bargains on orders placed after June 1.

Cross Country cultivates some field-grown peppers to maturity, not only for photos and testing but to perpetuate seed for the next year's crop. Boxes of fresh organic peppers are sold by mail order in September, offering those with daring palates an appealing way to taste test a number of varieties. The owners also sell a collection of organic field-grown tomatoes at the nursery—80 kinds, mostly delicious heirlooms that are hard to find in grocery stores.

Although the nursery is small and operates largely by mail order, visitors to the farm are given a warm welcome during growing season. Chile lovers often travel long distances, down from Connecticut or up from Virginia, to pick out their own plants. One year, some chile fanatics drove an RV from South Carolina just to see the farm. Late afternoons are a nice time to visit, when Lamson and Villegas are free of chores and a warm light descends on their pre–Civil War farmstead. Those who miss a visit can catch Lamson over Labor Day weekend at the Bowers Chile Pepper Festival in Fleetwood, Pennsylvania. In late September, she also mans the "Ask the Chile Goddess" booth at the Brooklyn Botanic Garden's Chile Festival.

Cross Country is an exceptionally clean nursery with a special spiritual sweetness. Before leaving the nursery, Lamson blesses her plants with an invocation to the Virgin of Juquila, a miraculous icon that attracts an annual pilgrimage to a shrine in Oaxaca's mountains. (Many years ago, Villegas' grandfather carved the doors on the sanctuary church.) Lamson's prayer is as follows:"Virgin of Juquila, be with these plants as they travel across the country. May they arrive safely in their new home. May they bring joy, peace, love, and happiness to their new owners." When Lamson sits on her porch at day's end, she senses a satisfied "connection" to the pepper plants she and her husband send cross-country. Even the UPS driver waits for the blessing before retrieving the shipping boxes.

Directions: From Route 78, take exit 15 and turn left at the light toward Pittstown. In 10 miles, at a stop sign, turn right onto Route 12 west, and then left at the light onto Route 519 south. In 4.1 miles, turn left onto Kingwood-Locktown Road. The nursery is 0.3 mile on right. From Route 202 in Flemington, take Route 12 west, and in about 8 miles, at the third light, turn left onto Route 519 south and follow directions above. From Route I-95 south, take the last exit in New Jersey and turn north onto Route 29 toward Lambertville. In 10 miles, follow signs to stay on Route 29 north. In 5 miles, bear right onto Route 519 north. In 4.7 miles, turn right onto Kingwood-Locktown Road; the nursery is 0.3 mile on right.

Nearby attractions: Cravings, Route 29, Stockton, NJ 08559 (609-397-2911), is a nice little café, just north of the village (7 to 9 daily).

D'ANGELO FARMS
546 Washington Avenue, Dumont, NJ 07628
(201) 385-7788; fax (201) 385-9040
www.dangelofarms.com; e-mail *info@dangelofarms.com*
The D'Angelo family

Quality nursery stock. *Family-run greenhouse and garden center. Open year-round, daily, 9 to 4. Extended hours in spring and on holidays. No catalog or mail order. Landscape design. Garden supplies. Florist and flower shop. Seasonal plants. Visitors welcome.*

Can local horticulture survive, or are we doomed to get garden plants from Big Box stores? Using today's interstate highway system, national chain stores treat plants as commodities—fungible goods to be purchased in bulk and trucked anywhere and everywhere, like so many cases of soda. Suburbia expands, chain stores occupy shopping malls—and local nurseries close, beaten down by commodity prices. It's a national story that's playing out in every neighborhood. Gardeners buy goods at chain stores because they're cheaper. But are they any good? Does what work for canned soft drinks work for garden plants?

Real gardeners know in their hearts that if they want good plants, they need a local grower. It's axiomatic that the best plants for any garden are propagated within 100 miles. This isn't just local chauvinism—it's because locally grown plants are generally fresher, healthier, and better adapted to local conditions. Chances are they're more beautiful and unusual, too, because they were chosen by somebody who was thinking about plants rather than plant sales.

D'Angelo's is a family-owned nursery founded in 1923 in Dumont, 13 miles north of the George Washington Bridge and a half-hour's drive from Manhattan. So far, this 7-acre mom-and-pop nursery has withstood competition by offering fresh locally grown plants, tended by people who know plants and have worked with them all their lives. Owners August and Emmanuela D'Angelo and their son, Glenn, are dedicated growers who have a direct, hands-on approach to the plants in their greenhouses. Unlike commodity stores, they take questions and graciously share their knowledge.

D'Angelo's specializes in annuals, perennials, and ground-cover plants, all grown in the family's clean, bright greenhouses. Also available are spring vegetables, hanging baskets, and foliage houseplants—even cactus for apartment dwellers who hate to water. Seasonal items—fall mums, creamy or peachy poinsettias at the holidays—spice up the dull months, as do cut flowers, a florist service, and all sorts of garden supplies. It's open year-round, seven days a week.

Although D'Angelo's doesn't produce its own ornamental trees and shrubs, even these are in good supply—architectural plants from worthy sources, carefully tended after reaching the nursery. Home Depot may open a store an hour, but it doesn't carry 'Whitespire' Japanese birch, golden rain tree, weeping autumn cherry, scarlet fire thorn fans, or spiral topiary in generous pots.

Besides lush plants, there's something friendly and warm here, beginning with the road sign announcing "D'Angelo Floral Acres"—the kind of mid-century backlit plastic sign that collectors will deem priceless any day now. Area garden clubs uniformly praise the farm's "very nice plants," good prices, and well-informed staff. This is writer Ken Druse's local garden center, and his patronage is in itself assuring.

Display gardens and ponds offer diversion, but it's really the greenhouses vibrating with flower and foliage plants that impress the visitor. Commodity stores are an economic powerhouse, but for living, breathing plants, you'll have to spend a few dollars on horticulture, and here's a convenient place to do it. As Druse remarked in his gardening column in the *New York Times*, "There's no such thing as a dead bargain."

Directions: From the George Washington Bridge (upper level), turn south onto Route I-95 and in 3 miles, exit onto Route 4 west. In 2.8 miles, turn onto Teaneck Road toward Bergenfield (becomes South Washington Avenue); the nursery is 4 miles on the left.

DAVE'S NURSERY
818 Amwell Road, Hillsborough, NJ 08844
(908) 369-0267; fax (908) 369-0268
www.davesnursery.com; e-mail *davesnursery@verizon.net*
David Verkade

Dwarf conifers, Japanese maples. Unusual grafted plants. *Small specialty nursery. Wholesale and retail. Open by appointment. Retail price list and photos on Web site. Mail order. Shipping from April through June. Garden books. Stock display garden.*

Dave's Nursery is a one-man nursery in South Jersey specializing in dwarf conifers, Japanese maples, and other grafted exotics. Owner David Verkade is an 8th-generation plantsman of the Verkade clan, one of New Jersey's most eminent nursery families. The present operation started in 2000, when Verkade, having outgrown his former site in Pompton Lakes, moved home, nursery, and stock-plant collection to a new 10-acre location. It took several years to get reestablished.

Verkade's expertise is grafting exotic trees and shrubs onto hardy rootstock—a difficult, hard-won skill that involves a lot of bloody fingers. "I've been working with a grafting knife since I was five years old," he says. "I'm what we call in the trade a propagator. Simply put, I manufacture plants." Verkade has been a professional grafter for 30 years. His wholesale customer base includes nationally known collectors' nurseries. More recently, retail sales through the Web site have gained importance, too.

Verkade's grandfather started the family's first nursery in New Jersey, growing what may be called "meat-and-potatoes" plant varieties. His father, John Verkade, became fascinated with exotic plants, discovering many dwarf and unusual forms that are now industry standards. "He was a bit of a dreamer, and my grandfather and uncle snickered at him," recalls Verkade. "Who could have imagined how important his plants would become?"

Many of Verkade's stock plants derive from his father's collection, but he waves away the notion of inheritance. "You don't inherit plants," he says. "You just make new ones." Other grafting stock comes from the rich holdings at Skylands, a public botanical garden in Ringwood to which Verkade donated a large collection of witch hazel plants.

The pride of Dave's Nursery is a stunning assortment of 70 Japanese white pine *(Pinus parviflora)* varieties, each distinguished by some unique feature—dwarf, spreading, twisted, or weeping habit, or blue or variegated foliage, for example. Verkade also grows 50 Norway spruce *(Picea abies)*, a dwarf conifer often derived from witches'-brooms (irregular twiggy growths, reproduced by cutting and grafting). Other valued specimens include a yellow spiral Korean fir, golden dwarf Scotch pine, and pygmy Swiss stone pine.

Verkade also prizes his 50 Japanese maple cultivars, each with unique filigreed, veined, or painted foliage, as well as his exotic beeches. Verkade's exceptional witch hazels include dwarf, weeping, and even purple-flowered forms. A rare cutleaf Japanese emperor oak *(Quercus dentata* 'Pinnatifida')— with scaly silver bark the Japanese call *nishiki* (brocade)—was first acquired by Verkade's grandfather. Verkade hopes for enough stock to sell in a few years, when the tree recovers from the move.

Nursery VIPs ("Verkade-Introduced Plants") form their own subsection. Nine dwarf Hinoki false cypresses and seven dwarf Eastern hemlocks are Verkade-family finds. A rare witches'-broom form of red Japanese maple ('Fire Ball') and a variegated Chinese dogwood ('Verkade's Multicolor') are also Verkade discoveries. Dave Verkade is proud of finding a Norway maple with cream-bordered leaves in North Jersey ('Verkade's Albright').

In short, there's so much cool stuff here that it's impossible to choose, especially for collectors who want at least one of everything. Some customers just order 10 conifers a year. Others ask Verkade to pick whatever items he considers best and send them along.

Dave's Nursery occupies a half-acre of greenhouse space, two cold frames, and a 1½-acre stock-plant garden. Because operations recently restarted, grafted plants are still quite small—most inhabit 2¼-inch pots. Container production is underway, though, and in no time customers will be able to buy gallon pots. In 5 years, Verkade's goal is to double his cultivation space and stock multi-gallon containers.

Almost all sales take place by mail order. Plants are small but sturdy and affordable. "If you follow instructions, chances are excellent that plants will do well. If you don't, they won't," says Verkade. Because dwarf exotics grow slowly and become quite valuable at maturity, it's worth starting a collection early, like a retirement fund. Dave's offers the chance to acquire choice plants at reasonable cost, starting with small fry. Excellent garden books are also available to customers whose zeal exceeds their wisdom on such subjects as propagation, rare conifers, maples, and collector's plants.

Because the nursery is home-based, Verkade is cautious about accepting retail traffic. "We have no store, and I'm the only guy here besides my wife," he says. Outside of the busy season, though, Verkade welcomes customers (by appointment) who want to examine his display gardens and see how plants will perform in years to come.

As a grafting expert who appreciates the open traditions of horticulture, Verkade offers a special service to anyone who discovers a unique collector's plant—he'll graft multiple copies. Exchanging his labor for a share of the litter is a good way for him to acquire new things. "I keep half, there's no money involved, and everybody's happy," he says—with one caveat. He refuses to handle patented plants, no matter how unusual. "Paying royalties just makes nurseries charge more. It's nonsense," Verkade says. "If you want to keep a plant to yourself, fine, go ahead and patent it. But if you want to put it out into the world, I'll help you do that."

Directions: The nursery is 20 miles northwest of Trenton near the junction of Routes 202 and 206. From Route 78, take exit 29 onto Route 287 south. In 4 miles, take exit 17 onto Route 202 south, and in 6 miles, turn left onto Old York Road/Route 637. In 0.2 mile, turn right onto South Branch Road, and in 5.5 miles, bear right onto Amwell Road. The nursery is at #818. Call ahead.

FAIRWEATHER GARDENS

P.O. Box 330, Greenwich, NJ 08323
(856) 451-6261, (609) 451-6261; fax (856) 451-0303
www.fairweathergardens.com
Robert Hoffman and Robert Popham

Distinctive trees and shrubs. Fine perennials. Small collectors' nursery. Retail only. Open only on designated Open House days. Catalog $3. Catalog on Web site. Mail order. Shipping February through April. Plant reservations, minimum $50. Pick up on designated days; no nursery access. Open House and plant pick up days posted on Web site. Map mailed by request; ask well in advance. No pets or unrestrained children.

Owners Bob Hoffman and Bob Popham, affectionately known as "the Bobs," are plant fanatics who began Fairweather Gardens when their own collection exceeded its bounds. "Years ago, we found ourselves gardening on a postage stamp–size bit of ground in Brooklyn, in the shadow of the Williamsburg Bridge," they recount. "After we had finally used up the last square inch of ground, we knew we had to either acquire more real estate or give up gardening." Giving up gardening wasn't an option, so they moved to a small plot in New Jersey: "Boy, were we going to garden!"

As many gardeners discover, though, it isn't that easy. Frustrated by the lack of variety on the local market and disgusted with mail-order deliveries of "anemic little plantlets that had to be put on life-support," the Bobs began thinking about starting a nursery. In the late 1980s, they moved to a 6-acre site in South Jersey intending to grow plants "to a size and quality that we ourselves had been hoping to receive when ordering by mail"—a principle that still guides Fairweather Gardens. Their first catalog ("a black-and-white 10-page job") came out in 1992. The nursery has been busy ever since.

Today, the nursery's glossy 80-page catalog ignites what one competitor calls "catalog envy." Its depiction of its trees, shrubs, vines, and perennials is delectable, bordering on prurient. Luscious photographs treat each open blossom like the sultry centerfold of a soft-porn magazine. Plants are listed by botanical name, accompanied by mouth-watering descriptions and hardiness ratings based on nursery experience (Zone 7). Such evaluations are valid for the Mid-Atlantic region but should be viewed with a gimlet eye in tougher climes, especially with rare collectors' items not well-known to Western horticulture.

Fairweather Gardens is a nationally recognized source of fine ornamental trees and shrubs. Its plant list is intended to gratify gardeners who have been bit by what the owners call "the gardening bug"—presumably the same creature that spreads collection fever. The magnolias, for example, include two double-flowered sweet-bays, nine yellows, an extremely rare Chinese species *(Magnolia zenii)*, and many stunning hybrids set with coral, purplish-black, and ruby flowers. Red-flowered wood lotus *(Mangliatia insignis)*, a little-known magnolia relative, was admired by plant explorer Reginald Farrer as "a plant to dream about." Camellias are also in fine supply, including the U.S. National Arboretum's magnificent cold-hardy camellias (Zone 6).

The owners have the knack of skimming the cream from overcrowded cultivar groups—Japanese maples, hydrangeas, and evergreen hollies come to mind. They savor elegant showy shrubs, such as a yellow-twig Japanese kerria, blue-leaf dusty zenobia, and white enkianthus *(Enkianthus perulatus)*. Acquisition trips to Asia must account for the Eastern joy lotus tree *(Parakmeria lotungensis)*, Chinese falsepistache *(Tapiscia sinensis)*, and twiggy Chinese shrub with blue tubular flowers *(Leptodermis oblonga)*.

Exceptional Southeastern native plants are a nursery specialty—such as Virginia stewartia, white-flowered Florida anise *(Illicium flordanum* 'Alba'), and Alabama snow-wreath *(Neviusia alabamensis)*. The Franklin tree and Georgia plume *(Elliottia racemosa)* are horticultural legends. Connoisseurs lust after double-flowered *Cornus florida,* blush-pink Eastern redbud, and purple-leaved Carolina allspice. The plant list is jazzed with the odd bigenic cross, such as catalpa/desert willow (producing an ever-blooming catalpa). Fairweather even champions leatherwood *(Cyrilla racemiflora)* from the New Jersey swamp. A growing perennials list offers plants of comparable finesse, including wild gingers and pitcher plants.

Fairweather grows plants in limited quantities, and some catalog items are not available every year. Threat of scarcity makes spring ordering something of a blood sport among collectors. To keep peace, early orders and substitution lists are strongly encouraged.

Handling practices are all that could be wished for. Plants are container-grown in natural conditions, fertilized lightly, and winter-hardened in unheated polyhouses. "We send healthy, vigorous plants that are ready to set out in the garden," the Bobs say proudly. Most plants are grown to a bushy size, though the nursery uses small "tree tubes" to ship some slow-growing exotics. "Specimen" items consist of instant-impact plants for the deep-pocket client. These, as the owners admit, are "a dickens to pack and ship," justifying surcharges that might finance another plant somewhere else.

Fairweather Gardens is located in the old flat farmlands of South Jersey, down near the Delaware Bay—still the seat of much authentic farming and horticulture. The owners operate mainly by mail order. When they do open to visitors, on Open House days, the greenhouses are literally mobbed with gardeners. On our visit, cars were parked a mile along the road and the purchase line was two hours. But as one visitor remarked to his friend in the magnolia house, "Only fifty bucks apiece here—you won't see 'em again."

"We think of ourselves primarily as gardeners," the Bobs announce a bit testily, almost in defense of the feeding frenzy their Open Houses inspire. Yet the plight is grasped by any working gardener—"there are still only two of us." A genuine devotion to fine plants is, of course, what inspires this popular outpouring. And boy, do they garden.

Directions: From Route 295 or the New Jersey Turnpike, take exit 1 (just before the Delaware Memorial Bridge) onto Route 49 south. In Salem, take signs to Route 623 south and follow to Greenwich. Contact the nursery in advance for local directions.

Nearby attractions: New Gardens, 1118 Sheppards Mill Road, Greenwich, NJ 08323 (856-455-7368; Gretchen Niedermayer; by appointment only), has a small inventory of elegant boxwoods and woody ornamentals, in-ground and "sensibly priced." A state-record cucumber tree (Magnolia acuminata) grows on Bacon's Neck Road, Greenwich; it's on the right, a block west of Route 623. The Bait Box Restaurant, Bacon's Neck Road, Bridgeton, NJ (856-455-2610), has good water views. Mood's Farm Market, 901 Bridgeton Pike (Route 77), Mullica Hill, NJ (856-478-2500), is an authentic "time-warp perfect" family farm with fresh-picked fruit, pies, and pumpkins.

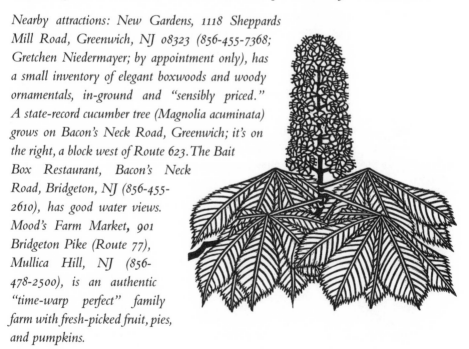

GODLEWSKY FARMS AND GREENHOUSES

196 Alphano Road, Great Meadows, NJ 07838
(908) 637-4927 (farm); (908) 637-6167 (office); fax (908) 637-6190
www.godlewskyfarms.com; e-mail *info@godlewskyfarms.com*

Annuals, perennials, herbs, vegetable seedlings, hanging baskets. Family-run horticultural farm. Wholesale and retail. Open year-round, Monday through Friday, 9 to 7, Saturday, 10 to 4. No catalog. No mail order. Plant information on Web site. Pick your own pumpkins. Seasonal plants and Christmas trees. Visitors welcome.

No gardener can resist a bargain, which is probably why Godlewsky Farms is thronged with gardeners every spring. This family-owned greenhouse complex is in western New Jersey, not far from the Delaware Water Gap. The Godlewskys are 3rd-generation farmers who emigrated from Poland 80 years ago and built a farm on what they call "strong traditional Catholic values, hard work, and complete trust in God."

The Godlewsky family owns a 60-acre produce farm in Great Meadows, a lake bottom drained by the U.S. Army Corps of Engineers during World War I. The family started growing wholesale produce (the area is noted for celery and onions) and branched into horticulture in the late 1970s to make ends meet. Today their 42 greenhouses look like an airplane-hanger complex, filled to the rafters with annuals, perennials, and hanging baskets. The surrounding acreage (known locally as "black muck") continues to support vegetable, sod, and cut-flower production.

In a world increasingly dominated by counterfeit experience, it's refreshing to see a family greenhouse operation run the old-fashioned way—big practical growing houses cranking out plants at grower's prices. Greenhouses brim with "annuals, perennials, herbs, and vegetable plants, hanging baskets, mums, poinsettias and seasonal favorites." While much of the stock looks a bit like horticultural fast food—nameless petunias and geraniums in crayon colors—some of it is quite fine. There's something here for everyone.

A random list of spring annuals includes New Guinea and rosebud impatiens, diverse pansies, and nonstop tuberous begonias—even "needlepoint" ivy and flowering maples.

Colors veer toward fluorescent but often include pretty pastels for subtler tastes. Seedling grape tomatoes, head endive, red cabbage, kohlrabi, and iceberg lettuce come in flats. For cutting gardens, the farm grows competent assemblies of dahlia, calendula, stock, chrysanthemum, and sunflower.

Perennials in flats are a special bargain for those with patience to grow them to maturity. Lists tacked to greenhouse doors tout Shasta daisies, veronicas, columbines, English daisies, sea pinks, geums, and dragons-blood sedum. Easy self-seeders include hollyhocks, poppies, and lupines. Culinary herbs feature anise, sage, thyme, lemon balm, and chamomile. A big surprise is the rose collection, containing hardy miniatures and modern favorites such as 'Carefree Beauty', 'Mr. Lincoln', and 'Climbing Peace' ($12 each).

The farm has its rough side. It's an accomplished growing operation, but this isn't sophisticated horticulture. Lush greenhouse growth is probably due to repeated applications of Miracle-Gro. Cheap trees and shrubs, some shoveled into plastic soda bottles and recycling jugs, apparently emanate from a local source. As on real farms, nothing is prettied up. Weed-engulfed sheds house string, tacks, and used hardware. Rusted farm equipment looms like abandoned sculpture along edges of the parking lot.

But consider the farm's biggest draw—its price tags. A flat of annuals runs $7 for a single variety, $10 for a mixture. Flats of year-old perennials are generally $12; for 2-year plants, $22. Most potted perennials run $4, peonies $7, and clematis vines $10. Herbs in 4-inch pots are $1.50 apiece. Hanging baskets cost $9 and big moss or cocoa baskets about $25. Prices vary, but even with gasoline at $30 a tank, it's easy to see why gardeners in SUVs show up for a day's bargain hunting.

You have to hand it to the Godlewskys. Many small growers try to compete with chain stores on plant selection, but few have the nerve to compete on cost. We can't think of another nursery that beats big retailers on price. Nor do big chains sell farm-grown vegetables, pick-your-own pumpkins, or poinsettia standards. Hard work and traditional values may triumph after all. It's enough to restore faith in the family farm.

Directions: The farm is south of Blairstown, 1¼ hours west of New York City. Take Route 80 west to exit 19/Hackettstown, turn right off the ramp, and go straight onto Route 667/Hackettstown Road. Pass Route 517 north and turn left onto Route 612/Johnsonburg Road. In 0.2 mile, turn left onto Alphano Road. In 3.7 miles, turn into the driveway, pass the greenhouses (unrelated), and drive down the long driveway to the large greenhouse complex.

Nearby attractions: Don't miss The Runway Café at Blairstown Airport (908-362-9170), where you can lunch and watch the airplane gliders in an atmospheric setting. Genesis Farm, 41A Silver Lake Road/Route 608, Blairstown, NJ 07825 (908-362-6735), is a noted 226-acre ecological and spiritual learning center. Hope is a 1769 Moravian village; a nice inn occupies the old stone mill (908-459-4884; www.innat millracepond.com). Landscape stone is sold by the forklift at Wicki Wholesale Stone, 17 Cemetery Road, Great Meadows, NJ 07838 (908-637-6004; www.wickistone.com).

GUNNING RIVER HERBS
163 Gunning River Road, Barnegat, NJ 08005
(609) 698-1921; fax (609) 698-5019
www.gunningriverherbs.com; e-mail *info@gunningriverherbs.com*
Carla and Howard Effron

Herbs, vegetables, and flowers. *Small specialty nursery. Open from late April through September, daily, 9 to 5. No catalog or mail order. Some plants on Web site. Organic grower. Garden shop. Visitors welcome.*

Gunning River Herbs is a home-based nursery behind a ranch house in Barnegat, not far from Long Beach Island. A few polyhouses and sheds on a backyard lot accommodate its supply of "culinary, medicinal, and ornamental plants." Blackjack oak and pitch pine confirm the proximity of the Jersey Pine Barrens. Tough, attractive herbs are among the few garden plants with prospects in such infertile sandy conditions.

But gardening isn't what lured owner Howard Effron into growing herbs—it was cooking. Effron is a professional chef who became intrigued with growing fresh-cut herbs for restaurants. He and his wife, Carla, grew 2000 basil plants in 1996 but found it easier selling them to gardeners. Since then, Gunning River Herbs expanded its repertoire to 150 herb plants, supplemented with vegetable plants, vines and flowers, and even woody plants bought in from local growers.

Today's inventory includes 15 varieties of basil and many lavenders, sages, and thymes. It's easy to love the fragrant mints—variegated, orange, pineapple, Korean, and Corsican mint—and scented geraniums. Here's a source for lemongrass, sweet marjoram, fernleaf dill, and garlic chives. Vegetables favor such chef's favorites as pickling cucumber, Japanese eggplant, and yellow and red grape tomatoes. There's something congenial, too, about the farm's hollyhocks, hyacinth beans, lemon marigolds, and Mexican sunflowers.

Gunning River has been written up in many newspapers and styles itself "the biggest little herb farm in New Jersey." Herbs and vegetables are grown in 4-inch pots and are priced reasonably. Conditions are organic—a welcome assurance of quality in edible plants. High season is late May. Despite expansion, it's still a family operation, with the Effrons functioning as "owners, growers, sales force, and the resident herbal enthusiasts."

Gunning River's intimate herb gardens, filled with flowering mints and buzzing bees, are a seasonal destination for visitors heading to the Jersey shore. Golden thymes creep along its walkways. Small signs describe plants' uses in herbal medicine. A small garden shop sells organic supplies, deer repellant, and nursery-crafted products such as "Gardeners Healing Salve."

Howard Effron is an herbal evangelist who loves telling herb stories and persuading people to expand their palates. Ever the chef, he encourages visitors to pinch and test kitchen herbs (such as lovage or coriander) that may be unfamiliar to some gardeners. "Here, try this," he'll say. "You've got to taste this." Or as he once remarked, "Herbs look nice, smell nice, a lot of them put up a good bloom—and then you can dig them up and eat them."

Directions: Take the Garden State Parkway to exit 67, turn east onto West Bay Avenue, and turn right at the third light onto Gunning River Road; the nursery is 0.2 mile on the right.

Nearby attractions: Barnegat is an atmospheric fishing village with antique stores and a famous lighthouse. Hurricane House, 688 East Bay Avenue, Barnegat (609-698-7808), is the oldest ice cream parlor in Ocean County.

HILDEBRANT NURSERIES

P.O. Box 52, Main Street, Oldwick, NJ 08858

(908) 439-2256 phone and fax

Charles Hildebrant

Fine trees and shrubs. Boxwood. Japanese maples, conifers. Commercial grower. Wholesale and retail. Open in season, Friday and Saturday, 9 to 2, or "whenever the gate is open"; otherwise by appointment. Closed last two weeks of July. Wholesale plant list. No mail order. Landscape design. Plant rentals. Call ahead if coming a distance.

Hildebrant Nurseries is a commercial grower of trees and shrubs based in Oldwick, an historic town off Route 78 in northern New Jersey. Owner Charles Hildebrant inherited the site along with his occupation—the nursery was established by his great-grandfather. Early ancestors cultivated fruit orchards in Oldwick and discovered a clingstone peach that is still in commerce. Hildebrant continues to graft selected peach trees, but his main interest is in fine ornamental trees and shrubs—especially those that survive in deer country.

Charles Hildebrant is a noted boxwood expert, and shrubby boxwood is his leading product. Enthusiasts view aromatic boxwood as "man's oldest garden ornament," cultivated in North America since the mid-1600s. Its main use was in Colonial-style gardens—until the deer population exploded. Because pungency makes it unpalatable to wildlife, boxwood has soared in popularity. As one arboretum director remarked, "It's now the only broadleaf evergreen you can grow unprotected in New Jersey—the deer eat everything else."

Hildebrant grows notable boxwood cultivars—English, American, and Korean; variegated, blue, and dwarf; and hardy cultivars like 'Winter Gem'. Some come from local sources, such as 'Morris Midget' and 'Willowood #1644' from the Morris County Arboretum. Hildebrant's own discoveries include 'Appalachian Pyramid', which makes a handsome 6-foot wedge, and a proprietary form of 'Northern Emerald', as neat as a bandbox.

Years of effort give Hildebrant an expert appreciation of what it takes to grow boxwood successfully. "Its only weakness is sensitivity to drainage," he says. "It can't stand wet feet." He wryly quotes the maxims of boxwood culture—"Plant 'em high / Or watch 'em die," and "Prune in June / In the light of the moon."

Plants are propagated and grown at the nursery in the field and in pots. Boxwood comes in a wide range of prices and sizes, with a 2-year difference between each pot size. As with all the nursery's stock, prices are good but not low, reflecting the plants' slow growth and high quality. Nursery customers include notable botanical gardens. Hildebrant's Japanese hollies (known as "poor man's box") share boxwood's merits but not, alas, its deer resistance.

Hildebrant is a recognized grower of Japanese maples, especially rare variegated forms such as 'Tamukeyama' and 'Tsuma Beni' (red nail). He describes the grafting process as one requiring "infinite patience," which may account for why such beautiful trees are hard to find in nurseries. Other woody plants include Japanese tree lilac, stewartia, unusual beeches, and choice magnolias, hollies, and viburnums. Many are Gold Medal Plants recognized by the Pennsylvania Horticultural Society for their fine points in Mid-Atlantic conditions. Inevitably, there are quite a few dwarf, yellow, blue, and contorted conifers, for it seems the old Dutch growers just can't leave weird conifers alone.

Hildebrant Nurseries is not simply a nursery but a mature private arboretum surrounding Charles Hildebrant's home. The sacramental odor of boxwood pervades the formal gardens, whose legacy trees and shrubs make profoundly beautiful presences. Because Hildebrant operates mostly wholesale, gardeners shouldn't absorb too much of the owner's professional time in choosing plants—though garden clubs and rare-plant enthusiasts will find a warm welcome. The owner's wit is an antidote to the gardens' copious ornament. A favorite Hildebrant axiom, which pretty well summarizes gardening in deer country, is "Man proposes, Allah disposes."

Directions: From Route 78, take exit 24 onto Route 517 north. In Oldwick, pass the junction of Route 523; the nursery is a block north on the left. Call ahead to make sure it's open.

Nearby attractions: Bamboo Brook, 170 Longview Road, Chester, NJ 07930 (973-631-5396; open to the public), is an important early 20th-century garden designed by Martha Brooks Hutcheson, which retains a remarkable collection of original plants. Hearts Ease Greenhouses & Nursery/Tewksbury Orchids, 213 Old Turnpike Road/Route 517, Califon, NJ 07830 (908-832-2708; www.tewksburyorchids.com), are twin nurseries operated for 40 years by horticulturist Hildigarde Howell, known for her choice perennials and orchids; it's a treat to visit the 7-acre mini-botanical gardens and orchid house. Dale and Carol Davis at Stony Hill Gardens, 8 Route 24, Chester,

NJ 07930 (800-525-6128; www.ftdfloristsonline.com/stonyhillgardens), grow seasonal annuals, perennials, cut flowers, and potted orchids in 18 greenhouses; surrounding fields have pick-your-own apples and pumpkins.

INTERNATIONAL BULB COMPANY
P.O. Box 545, 5 Worlendyke Avenue, Montvale, NJ 07645
(201) 573-0306; fax (201) 573-8885
E-mail *info@internationalbulb*.com
Jan Doornbosch

Wholesale flower bulbs and perennials. *Wholesale bulb importer. Business hours Monday through Friday, 9 to 5. Free bulb catalog. Mail order only. Detailed lists, on request, for perennials, potted dahlias, lilies, and freesias. Most items sold 100 per variety. Packing quantities sold as listed, no exceptions. Minimum order $150, shipping excluded. Payment due with order. No credit cards.*

International Bulb Company is a wholesale flower bulb company based in Montvale, New Jersey. The business is owned and operated by Jan Doornbosch, a professional bulb importer from the Netherlands who has been surrounded by flower bulbs all his life. "My father was a bulb grower and exporter in the Netherlands," he recalls. "It used to be that exporters owned their own fields. I grew up in the business and my family was my supplier."

Today, IBC imports hundreds of flower-bulb varieties from growers in the Netherlands, France, New Zealand, and Chile; some also come from the United States. Bulbs are purchased in huge quantities and sold wholesale, in lots of 100 per variety, to retail garden centers and large landscapers. Somewhat gingerly, IBC also accepts orders from individual customers who meet minimum order requirements and don't expect retail services. Payment accompanies all orders, and there are no cancellations. The bulb stock is so luscious, it is no chore to meet IBC's $150 minimum.

"We are bulb people. We have honest service and a good product," says Doornbosch. "But this is a seasonal business and it gets very hectic. Our prices are based on supplying the product only. We cannot deal with smaller customers who change their orders. We have no design information. We cannot advise on what goes with somebody's blue mailbox." Serious gardeners who do their homework and behave professionally can expect superb selection on wholesale terms. Gardeners who require advice and attention should look elsewhere for bulbs.

Despite the anonymity of the Dutch bulb auction, Doornbosch may be one of the few importers who actually knows his suppliers—a fact that helps assure the freshness and quality of IBC's bulbs. "Everybody goes to auction. We make long-term contracts with growers, but they can never meet it all. We need 100,000 'Queen of the Night' tulips, he has 90,000 or 120,000. We go to auction for spot purchasing and selling," he says. "The growers live in remote areas and they feel great if people come. We visit the fields, have tea and a cookie, ask about his dog, walk the fields. There is always something new—a color, a mutation they have not named yet. They love what they do."

IBC offers rich choices of aristocratic tulips: 150 Darwin, emperor, Kaufman, gregii, botanical, fringed, lily-flowering, peony-flowering, Rembrandt, parrot, green, and multi-flowering tulips, together representing a satin rainbow in every color but blue. Tulip bulbs, as all others, are top-size and healthy. IBC's blue-flowering bulbs include captivating hyacinths, glory-of-the-snow, and large and small anemones. Two beautiful American natives, Virginia bluebells *(Mertensia virginica)* and quamash *(Camassia esculenta)* make a lovely show in wet meadows.

IBC sells daffodils in the recognized tribes: trumpets, large-cups, butterflies, poeticus, doubles, jonquils, triandrus, and paperwhites. Some 60 narcissus are offered, including pink-cup varieties, an orange-and-white split-corona ('Broadway Star'), and some good rock-garden and naturalizing mixtures. Among the 16 crocus are white 'Joan of Arc', purple-and-white 'Lady Killer', metallic violet *C. tomasinianus*, fall-blooming saffron crocus, and a white form of autumn crocus *(C. kotschyanus).*

Although equally alluring, IBC's summer bulbs may be too much for the average gardener. They include alliums, calla lilies, canna lilies, hardy lilies, tender amaryllis, gladiolus, tuberous begonias, dahlias—even hardy cyclamen and the odd Italian arum. But it's one thing to buy 100 daffodils and another to buy 100 of the same non-stop pink tuberous begonia. Gardeners with roomy cutting gardens might be able to absorb 100 white 'Casa Blanca' oriental lilies or red cactus dahlias. Clubs might share an order or sell bulbs at a plant sale. Even a small garden could digest 100 small pink alliums or *Crocosmia* 'Lucifer' plants.

IBC is the exclusive importer of 'Manhattan', a glowing orange tulip created to commemorate the 300-year historic relationship between the Netherlands and Manhattan, where the Dutch founded today's New York City. Developed by a Dutch breeder over a ten-year period, 'Manhattan' tulip was introduced in 2003, at the 100th birthday of The Netherland Club of New York and the Netherlands Chamber of Commerce. Presiding over its black-tie debut were HRH Crown Prince Willem-Alexander and HRH Princess Maxima of the Netherlands. In the fashion of tulips, 'Manhattan' attended all public events arrayed flamboyantly in vermillion satin.

"It was really a labor of love," says Doornbosch, one of the tulip project's principal sponsors. "We were looking for an orange tulip, because the flag of New York is orange, and Holland's royal family is from the House of Orange." Donation of 5000 bulbs to the New York City Parks & Recreation Department could explain the astonishing May-time radiance in Manhattan's Stuyvesant Square (2nd Avenue and 16th Street).

JAPAN NURSERY
314 Dey Grove Road, Monroe Township (Englishtown), NJ 08831
(732) 446-2186; fax (732) 446-2358
Hiro Aso

Bonsai plants and supplies. Japanese garden materials. Specialty grower and importer. Wholesale/retail. Open year-round, Monday through Friday, 9 to 4, Saturday, 9 to 12. Closed for lunch, daily, noon to 1. Closed on holidays. Catalog $5. Mail order. Minimum order $150. Shipping and packing charges extra. Free local delivery. Visitors welcome.

In his poem, *Bonsai*, poet Billy Collins captures the mysterious distorting lens that a single dwarf potted plant turns upon its surroundings. "All it takes is one to throw a room / completely out of whack. / Over by the window / it looks hundreds of yards away," he writes. "Up close, it draws you in, / cuts everything down to its size."

The art of bonsai, developed centuries ago in China and Japan, is a studied method of pruning live trees into miniature shapes. Bonsai, meaning "potted plant" in Japanese, are kept in shallow containers to restrict root growth, thereby dwarfing the plant. Bonsai trainers strive to create, within a reduced context, a powerful illusion of age and dignity in a mature tree. It's one of the few forms of gardening where men outnumber women.

Japan Nursery is a bonsai grower, supplier, and importer established in 1974 in central New Jersey. It grows plants known to perform well as bonsai—olive and pomegranate trees, brush cherry *(Eugenia myrtifolia)*, Camellia 'Sansaka', dwarf podocarpus *(Podocarpus alpinus)*, and Fukien tea *(Carmona retusa)*. Such plants are, of course, real miniaturized trees possessing the same requirements as their full-size counterparts. Bonsai such as Chinese elm and juniper are hardy trees that must stay outdoors and be kept cold in winter. Conversely, semi-tropical bonsai, such as fig trees, are houseplants requiring freeze protection.

The nursery is in high repute with area bonsai clubs and sells plants to a number of well-known bonsai nurseries. Unlike inferior "cutting" growers who know little about true bonsai practice, Japan Nursery is the real thing. It is owned and operated by Hiro Aso, a Japanese horticulturist and garden designer who may speak English with difficulty, but provides genuine materials and expertise.

Japan's prices for finished bonsai vary with plant size but are uniformly reasonable. Any customer who meets the $150 minimum can buy plants at wholesale rates, making this a good source for individuals and small groups. Many bonsai cost from $20 to $40 for a well-developed specimen. Mature bonsai are valued as fine art—a 45-year-old five-needle pine *(Pinus parviflora* var. *pentaphylla)* at $4900, for example, and a 25-year-old dwarf *Schefflera arboricola* at $999.

Starter plants in 2½-inch pots cost $2.50 apiece, less in 32-piece flats. These "pre-bonsai" offerings include pungent Shimpaku juniper (*Juniperus chinensis* 'Shimpaku') and small-leaved Catlin elm (*Ulmus parvifolia* 'Catlin'). Prices rise modestly with pot size. A Sago palm "with baby" (offshoot) in a 4-inch pot costs $4.50. Boxing and shipping charges are extra, often adding 15% to an order.

The nursery's catalog is essential in the absence of a Web site. It lists sizes and prices but omits botanical names, leaving neophytes to wonder what "Satsuki chinzan" might be and whether "Serissa rose" is indeed *Serissa foetida* (a common Oriental dish-garden plant). The nursery supplies imported precision tools—bonsai nippers, knob-cutters, and root-picks—and appealing accoutrements—volcanic soil, moss, and stones.

Japanese ceramics are of special interest. Small bonsai pots, glazed and unglazed, come in characteristic flattened shapes to restrict the plants' bound feet. Hard kiln-fired ware from fine Japanese potteries seems a bargain. Used bonsai dishes can run as little as 50 cents.

Japan Nursery is an excellent source for authentic, full-size, imported Japanese garden materials, such as stone lanterns, stone bridges, *natsume* water basins, and wooden *sishaku* (dippers). Hiro Aso is a skilled Japanese garden designer, and to supply such projects, he shapes Japanese black pine specimens in an outdoor area. Visitors are likely to spy him indoors, deftly root-pruning bonsai at the potting bench. His wife, Mi Tsu, works hard in the hot greenhouses in her straw coolie hat.

The nursery leaves visitors to wonder at the curious power of bonsai to contort perspective. Evocative twisted shapes—especially of the "forest" bonsai—seem to warp the very atmosphere. As Billy Collins writes of bonsai in his poem: "The button lying next to it is now a pearl wheel, / the book of matches is a raft, / and the coffee cup a cistern / that catches the same rain / that moistens its small plot of dark, mossy earth. / For it even carries its own weather / leaning away from a fierce wind / that somehow blows / through the calm tropics of this room."

Directions: The nursery is east of Englishtown. Take the New Jersey Turnpike to exit 8 and turn east onto Route 33. At the intersection of Perrineville Road (Lobster Shanty restaurant on left), keep right and use the "jughandle" to turn left onto Perrineville Road. Turn right onto Dey Grove Road; the nursery is on the left. Go slowly, for the driveway entrance is easily missed. Hiro Aso owns Japan Nursery, 5300 Orange Boulevard, Sanford, FL 32771 (407-328-9793).

Nearby attractions: There's a Japanese garden (with bonsai) inside the greenhouses on the 2700-acre Duke Farm and Gardens estate, Route 206, Somerville, NJ 08876 (908-722-3700; www.njskylands.com/atdukgar.htm).

Related sources: Other respected bonsai sources are Oriental Gardens, 307 Disbrow Hill Road, Perrineville, NJ (609-490-0705; owner Xilaopo Li) and Jiusan Bonsai Co., 1243 Melville Road, Farmingdale (Long Island), NY 11735 (631-293-9246; www.jiusanbonsai.com; owner John Capobianco; chrysanthemum bonsai) The MidAtlantic Bonsai Societies (http://midatlanticbonsai.freeservers.com) hold classes and plant sales; recommended vendor links are posted on the Web site.

JERSEY ASPARAGUS FARMS

105 Porchtown Road, Pittsgrove, NJ 08318
(856) 358-2548; fax (856) 358-6127
www.jerseyasparagus.com; e-mail *jaf@jafink.com*
The Walker family

Asparagus crowns. Strawberry, blueberry, and raspberry plants. Family-run horticultural farm. Retail and wholesale. Open year-round, Monday through Friday, 8 to 5. Catalog on Web site. Mail order. 25-crown minimum. Plants shipped March 1 through May 1. Early-order and online-order discounts. Plant pick up by arrangement. Fresh cut asparagus by mail order (www.asparagusguy.com). Cooked asparagus products (www.bettersalsa.com). Farm stand. Call ahead for a tour. Visitors welcome.

Once a regional delicacy, asparagus today is a major vegetable crop and South Jersey's sandy loam a near-perfect growing medium. Asparagus is a perennial vegetable that throws up edible stalks for 15 years or more. The Romans ate asparagus as early as 500 B.C., and if you wanted, you could still use Roman instructions for raising it. Commercial farmers usually grow it from seed, but the fastest way for homeowners to establish a patch is to plant roots (crowns).

Jersey Asparagus Farms, a 300-acre family farm near Bridgeton, is a major national producer of high-quality 'Jersey Male' asparagus crowns. The Walker family has operated a vegetable and grain farm here for 160 years. In the early 1970s, Rutgers University chose their virus-free ground as a testing site for its asparagus hybrids. The Walkers grew it as a vegetable crop until 1987, when they received an exclusive license from Rutgers to grow asparagus seed. In 1990, the farm became a full-time mail-order nursery selling asparagus crowns and seeds.

Rutgers' patented 'Jersey Male' asparagus hybrids are widely recognized as the finest in the world. More than 30 years ago, the late Dr. J. Howard Ellison pioneered the university's asparagus breeding program. Poking in old fields for genetic material, he discovered a unique asparagus that produced all-male offspring—the ancestor of Rutgers' first 'Jersey Male' hybrid. The Walkers have since collaborated with Dr. Ellison's successors to develop still better asparagus—'Jersey Knight', 'Jersey Giant', 'Jersey Supreme', and ongoing iterations.

Oddly enough, with asparagus, male is better. A female asparagus plant's energy is devoted to the strenuous work of producing seeds for baby asparagus plants. The male does nothing but sit around erecting big, husky asparagus spears. Male spears have greater vigor, better disease resistance, and tighter heads. They taste better, too. Because they produce no messy babies, male asparagus can also be grown organically, without pesticides.

Over 30 years, Jersey Asparagus Farms has devised diverse ways to sell 'Jersey Male' asparagus. Year-old crowns are dug in spring and shipped around the country. Seed is sent to farmers worldwide. Fresh-cut spears are sold at Walker Farm's roadside stand and are sent out by priority mail. In 2004, the Walkers began selling asparagus guacamole and salsa in glass jars. (The farm also sells dormant strawberry crowns, blueberry bushes, and raspberry canes.)

The only mystery is why no one sells asparagus as an ornamental plant. Its 4-foot ferny foliage makes a delicate green "hedge" in a vegetable garden, turning golden in autumn. Consider an ethereal stand of asparagus in a potager with the farm's other edibles—ground-cover strawberries (with scalloped, weed-suppressing leaves), raspberries (with red, yellow, and purple fruit), and blueberry bushes (turning scarlet in fall). The light-footed asparagus might even intermix with a bed of daffodils, emerging just in time to cover the fading bulb foliage.

Directions: Pittsgrove is in South Jersey. From the New Jersey Turnpike or Route 295 near Philadelphia, take Route 55 south and in 20 miles, at exit 39B, turn onto Route 40 west. In 1 mile, turn left onto Porchtown Road/Route 613; the Walker farm stand is 0.5 mile at #105.

Nearby attractions: General Custard's Restaurant and Ice Cream, 2578 East Chestnut Avenue, Vineland, NJ 08361 (856-696-2992), is a popular family restaurant (with ice cream). Wheaton Village, 1501 Glasstown Road, Milltown, NJ 08332 (800-998-4552; www.wheatonvillage.com), features traditional Down-Jersey glassblowing and crafts in an historic village (take exit 26 off Route 55 and follow signs).

KALE'S NURSERY AND LANDSCAPE SERVICE

133 Carter Road, Princeton, NJ 08540

(609) 921-9248; fax (609) 497-0266

www.kalesnursery.com; e-mail *office@kalesnursery.com*

Douglas Kale

Specimen trees and shrubs. *Large nursery, landscaper, and garden center. Retail and wholesale. Open year-round. Garden center open Monday through Saturday, 9 to 6, Sunday, 10 to 5; closed on major holidays. Shorter hours in winter. Business office open Monday through Friday, 7 to 4:30. No retail catalog or mail order. Retail tree list at the garden center (ask at the desk). Discount 15% to landscape professionals. Free festivals, seminars, and plant shows. Christmas shop. Visitors welcome.*

"Suburbia," writes journalist Bill Vaughan, "is where the developer bulldozes out the trees, then names the streets after them." The progression is ironic. New homes emerge in a landscape scoured of soil; homeowners hire landscapers to replace trees destroyed for development. New trees screen the neighbors, restoring the dream of suburbia as a place of greenery and refuge—as it was before the bulldozers arrived.

This drama takes place at a curiously brisk pace in New Jersey, where demand for instant landscapes seems to outpace any other in the region. Legions of landscapers "install" horticultural scenery around homes, at offices, even in gas stations. As in any real-estate game, some players are more capable than others.

Kale's Nursery & Landscape Service is one of the best nursery and landscaping operations in the region. Kale's was founded in 1956 on a 12-acre site in Princeton and converted to an upscale garden center in 1978. Its off-site nursery supplies field-grown trees to its garden center, landscaping arm, and wholesale customer base. Owner Douglas Kale, son of the founder, runs this network of businesses with the help of a talented professional team of landscape architects, designers, and horticulturists.

Kale's has been praised in the *New York Times* as the county's top landscaper and in *New Jersey Monthly Magazine* as one of the five best garden centers in New Jersey. The garden center is large and well provisioned. Stock includes fine potted perennials, ornamental shrubs, and container plants from first-rate suppliers. Tree selection is exceptional. Free seminars, festivals, and plant sales—including a spring hellebore festival—boost the garden center experience. The staff is intelligent and well informed.

As a nursery, Kale's is best known for (and justly proud of) its large, high-quality specimen trees. A 90-page retail tree list, available for consultation at the garden center, shows a bewildering array of some 1000 tree species and cultivars. Native, exotic, evergreen, shade, flowering, winter-interest, and street trees are all featured. Rarities are present, but most are garden-worthy trees used and appreciated by the region's best landscape architects and designers—Japanese stewartia, ruby horse chestnut, 'Autumn Gold' ginkgo, 'Allée' lacebark elm, and 'Rohan' purple-leaved beech, for example.

Princeton, New Jersey, has the densest deer population in the United States, so most of Kale's trees possess good-to-excellent deer resistance. Evergreens include the desirable Swiss stone pine, Bosnian redcone pine, and weeping Atlas cedar. Unless first-year watering chores are neglected, it's hard to go wrong using the classiest and most reliable local stock.

Kale's grows nearly all trees on 400 acres of farmland in Bucks County, Pennsylvania, and Hunterdon County, New Jersey. Prices are good, considering the stock's amazing size and quality. A vibrant, 15-foot, multistem 'Heritage' river birch, for example, retails for $319. A big 4-inch caliper golden rain tree (Koelreuteria paniculata) goes for $629—well below what many retailers charge. Trees are uniformly healthy, well pruned, and heavily rooted. Most specimen trees are sold through Kale's garden center, but customers seeking especially large quantities or sizes (6- to 10-inch caliper) can choose trees directly from the growing fields by arrangement.

Kale's landscaping department offers expert consultation on the right choice and siting of tree specimens. The trucks, pallets, dollies, and tree spades in the landscaping yard attest to the staff's gargantuan capabilities. Any tree they plant comes with a one-year guarantee. Kale's Web site advertises the firm's design-build accomplishments, including much important residential landscaping and a Healing Garden at the Robert Wood Johnson University Hospital.

One of the most cheering aspects of Kale's tree list is the presence of elegant, hard-to-find native species such as hop hornbeam, sweet gum, tulip poplar, and Eastern red cedar. Kale's nursery also excels in native oaks—pin, red, scarlet, sawtooth, and swamp white oak—that make excellent landscape presences. Such trees developed in New Jersey naturally, in the ages before suburban development. As nursery stock, they establish well, restoring the soul of the landscape, looking at once dignified and, miraculously, at home.

Directions: From Route I-287, take the Somerville/Princeton exit and turn onto Route 206 south. In Princeton, pass the Nassau Street junction and continue on Route 206 south toward Lawrenceville. In 3.8 miles, turn right at the light onto Carter Road. Kale's is 1.2 miles on the left. See the Web site for directions from other points.

Related sources: Just west of Jersey City, DuBrow's Nurseries, 251 West Northfield Road, Livingston, NJ 07039 (973-992-0598; www.dubrows.com), is one of the state's largest and most successful horticultural enterprises, including an award-winning retail garden center backed by staff horticulturists, designers, and two huge commercial farms supplying fine trees and shrubs. Having a party this weekend? They can rip out your whole garden and replant it with 10-inch blooming annuals. Rutgers Landscape & Nursery, Route 31, Ringoes, NJ (800-422-6008; www.rutgersln.com; south of Flemington), is a landscaper/garden center dedicated to helping do-it-yourselfers with home landscaping.

LITTLE ACRE FARM
223 Victory Road, Howell, NJ 07731
(732) 938-6300; fax (732) 938-6340
www.littleacrefarm.com; e-mail *littleacrefarm@yahoo.com*
Ed Woolley

Bamboo. *Small specialty nursery. Retail and wholesale. Open by appointment. Catalog on Web site. Mail order of smaller stock. Larger items available by delivery or pick up. Delivery charges, distances up to 150 miles. Design, maintenance, and eradication services. Barriers, supplies, dried bamboo poles.*

Little Acre Farm grows hardy bamboo for gardens, offices, and privacy screens. Owner Ed Woolley is a Rutgers-trained horticulturist who converted his father's farm in Howell, near the Jersey shore, into a bamboo nursery about a decade ago. The original farm was called "Little Acre" because—in the days before rampant housing development—19 acres was considered small for a produce farm. (Before that, it was a chicken farm.) Today, Little Acre Farm is New Jersey's largest source of hardy bamboo.

Bamboos are, of course, elegant, restless, woody grasses long used in Asia for buildings, tools, food, and ornament. Woolley was introduced to bamboo by his uncle, an urbane art director who built a Japanese garden at his home, complete with bamboo and raked gravel. "When I was 17, I visited my uncle's garden and brought back some bamboo," he says. "I've been growing it ever since." At Rutgers, Woolley studied bamboo culture and oriental garden design. He's now a certified nurseryman active in the American Bamboo Society.

During years as a propagator and grower, Woolley has expanded his bamboo collection to more than 70 varieties. Most are listed on the farm's Web site. Inventory includes tall, medium, and low hardy running bamboos; clumping bamboos; and near-tropical varieties, which can almost be grown as houseplants. Unlisted collector's treasures are available in small quantities at the nursery, with grasses, hosta, and ferns as companion perennials.

Little Acre propagates bamboo plants in several greenhouses, one a converted chicken coop. Five acres of running bamboo, controlled by strategic mowing, is organized into 40 groves of planting stock. Most bamboos are hardy to Zone 7 (some to Zone 5) and succeed in coastal areas. Bamboo poles cut from farm acreage are bundled for use in staking and trellising. (A local children's camp used them to make rafts on Survivor Day.)

Cane samples illustrate the merits of Little Acre's tallest bamboos (20 to 35 feet) for privacy screens and fishing poles. Popular yellow-groove bamboo (*Phyllostachys aureosulcata*) has yellow-striped stalks. Golden bamboo *(P. aurea)* has bright yellow stalks and black bamboo *(P. nigra)* polished ebony poles. Lofty varieties develop a desirable zigzag in their culms, so that stalks kink at the knees or, in bamboo parlance, "genuflect."

Low bamboos present a decorous way to fill blank garden spaces. Dwarf fernleaf bamboo (*Pleioblastus distichus* 'Mini'), for example, makes a vigorous 10-inch ground cover, handsome near stonework. Low bamboos have the most attractive leaf variegation, such as dwarf white-stripe bamboo *(P. fortunei)* and dwarf green-stripe bamboo *(P. viridistratus).* In European gardens, they are sometimes mowed to 3 inches and used as a lawn.

Little Acre gets its stock from American Bamboo Society auctions, bamboo nurseries, and as imported rarities just out of quarantine. Some bamboos self-sow after bloom, opening the possibility of exciting mutations. All living forms of Muriel bamboo *(Fargesia murieliae),* for example, bloomed on a genetically fixed cycle in 1998 (once a century) and then died; new-generation seedlings are now being tested by those lucky enough to have owned seed-bearing plants. New arrow bamboo seedlings *(Pseudosasa japonica)*—the source for Samurai arrows in medieval Japan—are similarly under surveillance for attractive new forms.

The only drawback is bamboo's headstrong tendency to bolt off and invade areas where it's unwelcome. Running bamboo can become a vicious landscape pest if not sited correctly and rigidly restrained. Delicate clump-forming bamboos, arching and shimmering in the slightest breeze, maintain a refined demeanor without developing imperialistic ambitions. But the hardier, tougher running bamboos are more popular, despite their aggression.

Woolley deals with invasiveness issues by offering planting advice (water, for example, will restrain a running bamboo); incarceration tricks (3-foot underground barriers); and bamboo maintenance services, derived from his experience managing in-ground nursery stock. If these don't work, there's always the annihilation program. Woolley is practically the only gardener on the planet who succeeds at this heroic task—kill a running bamboo, dead in its tracks.

Directions: The nursery is located in north Jersey near the shore, by the junction of Route 195 and the Garden State Parkway. From the Garden State Parkway, take exit 98 and follow signs for Route 195 toward Trenton. Take exit 31A onto Route 547 south/Lakewood Farmingdale Road. In 2 miles, bear right onto Victory Road; the nursery is at #223. From Newark, take the New Jersey Turnpike/Route I-95 south to exit 11, turn south on the Garden State Parkway, and follow directions above. From Trenton, take Route 195 east to exit 31A and follow directions above.

Nearby attractions: The entire town of Ocean Grove (an 1880s camp meeting with Victorian cottages) is on the national Register of Historic Places. In the faded resort of Asbury Park, The Stone Pony, 913 Ocean Avenue (732-502-0600; www.stonepony online.com), is a top destination for rock-music lovers; Bruce Springsteen got his start here and still pops in for occasional jams.

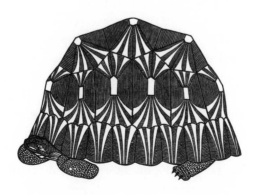

MAPLETON NURSERIES
P.O. Box 396, 140 Mapleton Road, Kingston, NJ 08528-0396
(609) 430-0366; (888) 239-7567 (outside NJ); fax (609) 430-0367
www.mapletonnurseries.com; e-mail *mapletonurseries@hotmail.com*
David Reed and William Flemer IV

Trees and shrubs. Deer-resistant and native plants. *Small specialty nursery. Wholesale, limited retail. Open in spring and summer, weekdays, 8 to 5, Saturday, 8:30 to 3:30, and by appointment. Check for exact dates. Free catalog. No mail order. Plants held by 50% deposit. Delivery available for large orders. Custom-grown container plants.*

Mapleton Nurseries is a wholesale grower of ornamental trees and shrubs, with special emphasis on native and deer-resistant plants. The nursery was founded in 1998 on land in Kingston, outside Princeton, that once served as seedbeds for Princeton Nurseries. Its presence is poetically just, for one of its principals, Bill Flemer IV, belongs to the eminent clan that owned Princeton Nurseries in its heyday. "I was born and raised in this business," Flemer recalls. "My first job at age 10 was pulling weeds."

Mapleton's approach can be characterized as "retail-tolerant" wholesale. Its catalog is intended for industry professionals, but as the staff concedes, "We won't run anybody off." Because it's wholesale, Mapleton is not open extended hours and lacks retail guarantees or the time to counsel visitors. It does offer a warm welcome, though, to plant fanciers who know what they want and can perceive the value of its stock.

Mapleton is a sleeper nursery that grows what plant geeks call "cool stuff." This may partly be Flemer genes at work, for what characterized the old Princeton Nurseries powerhouse—a sharp eye for improved varieties—is true at Mapleton on a lesser scale. We once chose a fringe tree *(Chionanthus virginicus)* from what looked like a thriving group of equals in the sales yard. Without hesitation, Flemer singled out a different specimen and asked, "Don't you want this one? It's got lots of fruit, so it's female and will flower heavily."

Mapleton grows about 300 varieties of trees and shrubs for ornamental landscaping. Some are species, others cultivated forms. Perusing the list, it's obvious why each was selected—beauty, rarity, talent as a filler, or some elegant feature that makes it irresistible. A few vines, perennials, ferns, grasses, and ground covers sweeten the inventory for landscapers, but Mapleton is essentially a specialty grower of ornamental trees and shrubs.

The stock of deciduous trees, for example, is rich in aristocratic dogwoods and magnolias. Side by side with American natives are uncommon giant dogwood *(Cornus controversa)* and the Oyama magnolia *(Magnolia sieboldii)* of Japanese tea gardens. Flowering cherries have been whittled down to great performers, such as 'Okame' and Sargent cherry. Few commercial nurseries bother to grow water ash *(Ptelea trifoliata)* or the mountain ash known as white beam *(Sorbus aria),* never mind a native hydrangea vine called wood-vamp *(Decumaria barbara).* Other underused natives include the black gum tree for its autumnal scarlet, the elegant American hornbeam, and silver-bells and snowbells, enchanting in groves.

The dawn redwood and bald cypress will grow to mighty Jurassic towers in swampy ground. Other Mapleton conifers feature exotic Asians, such as Japanese black pine, and tough customers, such as Russian arborvitae (for dry shade) and Western arborvitae (deer resistant).

Mapleton also grows exceptional viburnums, boxwoods, and witch hazels. Ground-cover shrubs include Japanese skimmia and drooping leucothoe. If you're looking for the self-fertilizing holly called 'Nellie Stevens' ("Nellie don't need a guy!"), or the popular 'Snow Queen' oakleaf hydrangea, or the elusive Chinese sweet shrub *(Sinocalycanthus chinensis),* you're home.

Nursery visitors should seek out items not in the catalog—unique plants that are in short supply or have been hidden away as treasures, such as variegated false holly *(Osmanthus* 'Goshiki'). Because the owners are plant geeks, if you frisk the place you'll find things that collectors crave for their gardens—or would, if they knew they were here.

Directions: From the New Jersey Turnpike, take exit 8, turn west on the Route 133 bypass, and take Route 571 west toward Princeton. At the circle, turn right onto Route 1 north, and in 3 miles, take the College Road West exit. At the second light, turn right onto Seminary Drive and pass the second light (becomes Mapleton Road). The nursery is 0.7 mile on the left, down the drive to the right. From Trenton, take Route 95/295 to exit 67, turn onto Route 1 north, in 7 miles, take the College Road West exit, and follow directions above.

Nearby attractions: Princeton is an elegant college town with good cafés. Princeton University's campus is a graceful horticultural landscape designed by Beatrix Ferrand, a visionary landscape architect whose plan is still visible; many consider it the most beautiful campus in America.

PINELANDS NURSERY

323 Island Road, Columbus, NJ 08022
(800) 667-2729, (609) 291-9486; fax (609) 298-8939
www.pinelandsnursery.com; e-mail *info@pinelandsnursery.com*
Donald and Suzanne Knezick

Native conservation plants; trees, shrubs, perennials, and grasses. *Large whole-sale nursery. Catalog $3. Catalog on Web site. $500 minimum. No mail order. Plant pick up daily, 7:30 to 3. Delivery by arrangement. Site engineering. Erosion control products. Visitors welcome; call ahead.*

Pinelands Nursery is a leading propagator of native and wetland plants for conservation projects. Its central New Jersey headquarters—a large, sophisticated greenhouse complex—was expanded in 1998, the same year it opened an auxiliary facility in the Virginia swamp country. A third nursery in western New York now collects seed for regionally adapted species. This far-flung enterprise began 20 years ago with a few blueberry bushes.

In 1984, owners Donald and Suzanne Knezick began marketing small fruit plants to local garden centers—especially blueberries. Few people knew it, but an important national movement had just begun. The wetland conservation industry was in its infancy. Federal and state environmental laws had begun mandating public reclamation efforts. Landscapers with mitigation projects in the fragile, ecologically sensitive Jersey Pine Barrens needed masses of wild blueberry bushes—one of the few natives suited to acidic wetlands.

The Knezicks recognized that a revolution was underway and promptly converted their fledgling nursery into a production facility for native trees, shrubs, and wildflowers of the eastern United States. They named it after New Jersey's unique sour-water pinelands. Incorporated in 1989, Pinelands has been growing faster than a bald cypress *(Taxodium distichum)* ever since.

The Knezicks did another smart thing. Shortly after founding the nursery, they sponsored a Native Plant and Restoration Symposium to encourage the use of native plants. Now an annual event, it's a magnet for conservation professionals. As such ecological awareness expands, wild species gain stature. Public highway departments stir. Private landowners commit to ecological landscaping. Even die-hard ornamentalists seek less exhausting, more successful ways to garden. The basic problem, though, remains much the same: Where to buy blueberry bushes?

In professional circles, Pinelands is regarded as the best native plant source in the Mid-Atlantic region. Among hundreds of offerings, it makes an admirable effort to grow species that are often invisible to mainstream horticulture. False indigo *(Amorpha fructicosa)* is an adaptable shrub with showy purple flower spikes. Winged sumac *(Rhus coppalinum)* creates a handsome grove. Silky dogwood has red twigs and white flowers. Arrowwood viburnum—well, any native viburnum—can turn a wasteland into a wild garden. The staff recommends Virginia sweetspire *(Itea virginica)* as an ornamental wetland ground cover—or swamp azalea, or *Rosa virginiana,* or an attractive mix of grasses, rushes, and sedges.

Pinelands is an inspired source of native flora for anyone with wet ground. As a large wholesale grower, Pinelands is not really set up for small-scale retail service. Yet individual gardeners can usually penetrate the New Jersey greenhouses if they do their homework, prepare to handle plug-trays, and buy lots of plants. (A $500 minimum is customary, though not always enforced.) The staff is enthusiastic about experimental home plantings. "People shouldn't worry about native plants," nursery manager Dan Segal told us. "Just go ahead and plant them! Restoring nature makes people feel good."

The catalog lists Pinelands' impressive inventory alphabetically and by habitat. Stock is sold in containers, flats, and tubelings (tall narrow pots). Some plants are small plugs, others 4-foot saplings. Most are grown from seed and a few from cuttings—willow and clethra, for example. The nursery does site engineering and handles a line of erosion-control products, mostly coconut-fiber blankets and mats of jute and straw.

Pinelands grows 100 percent of its stock from wild sources of known provenance. Plants are not nursery-grade, but irregular saplings and herbs of the kind growing wild in wetlands. To ensure a range of genetics, seed is collected legally from large plant populations on the Jersey shore, the Delaware River delta, and an area between Camden and Burlington. The nursery stock is deliberately left with natural, asymmetrical jigs and jags. That's the idea, though—not to decorate but to replicate nature, which is after all the toughest kind of gardening.

Pinelands today is not simply a nursery, of course, but part of an important ecological movement. Civic concerns about drought, storm water, erosion, stream ecology, and noxious invasive plants gain urgency in New Jersey. Even gardeners seeking to be part of the solution have a hard time finding truly local plants—the native genotypes preferred by biologists. Such plants can be used to enlightened purposes, teaching us how to keep our water clean, attract birds, shelter wildlife, and generate a little biological music.

Lest native plants sound too politically correct, consider the practical loveliness they offer in harsh conditions—red chokeberry holding a gravel bank, yellow birch steadying a slippery hollow. Consider the merits of sassafras and chestnut oak—what Michael Dirr calls "noble trees." Or consider blueberry pie. Pinelands still sells lots of wild blueberry bushes, too.

Directions: Pinelands is in central New Jersey. From the New Jersey Turnpike, take exit 7 and turn south on Route 206. In 3 miles, take the Columbus/Burlington exit (Route 543) and turn left onto Route 543. Pass the light in Columbus and in 1 mile, turn right onto Island Road; the nursery is 0.2 mile on the right. From Route I-195, take exit 16 and turn left onto Route 537. Turn right onto Route 68 and in 0.5 mile, at the first crossroad, turn left just before the Victory Baptist Church. At the second crossroad, turn left onto Island Road; the nursery is 0.2 mile on the right. See the Web site for directions from South Jersey, Pennsylvania, Delaware, and Maryland.

Nearby attractions: Locals like the good home-cooked meals at the Columbus General Store, 266 Atlantic Avenue, Columbus, NJ 08022 (609-298-1499; across from the post office).

PLEASANT RUN NURSERY
P.O. Box 247, 93 Ellisdale Road, Allentown, NJ 08501
(609) 259-8585; fax (609) 259-6044
www.pleasantrunnursery.com; e-mail *pleasantrunnursery@juno.com*
Richard and Heidi Hesselein

*Fine trees and shrubs. Magnolias. Roses. Perennials. Specialty nursery. Whole-
sale only, except for designated open days. Open March through December, Monday
through Friday, 7 to 12 and 1 to 4; Saturday, 7 to 12; and January and February by
appointment. Free wholesale catalog. Availability list on Web site. No mail order.
Retail visitors welcome on open days sponsored by the Allentown Garden Club (P.O.
Box 74, Allentown, NJ 08501). Garden club and group tours by arrangement.*

Located near Princeton, on ground bordering Pleasant Run Creek, Pleasant
Run Nursery is a wholesale grower of choice and sophisticated flowering
trees and shrubs. This specialty nursery opens discreetly to the Allentown
Garden Club and groups on special sales days in spring and fall. At that time,
retail visitors can examine the operations of a top-notch grower and buy
garden treasures that are rarely available, except to specialists and collectors.

Pleasant Run was founded in 1998 by Richard Hesselein, former
president of Princeton Nurseries. He works with his wife, Heidi, and her
sister, Louise, of the talented Flemer clan that founded Princeton Nurseries
and gave it prominence. All are 4th-generation horticulturists with exceptional industry credentials and contacts. At Pleasant Run, they're growing
some of the best nursery stock in the state.

British gardener Vita Sackville-West once wrote, "Gardeners who want
the maximum reward for the minimum of labor would be well advised to
concentrate on the flowering shrubs and flowering trees." That's exactly what
Pleasant Run is doing—focusing on exotic trees and shrubs from high-end
breeding programs, botanical gardens, plant collectors, and other illustrious
sources. Fellow nurserymen concede the clout of Pleasant Run's plant list.
"We can't compete with Big Box stores, so we try to grow weird stuff that's
not generally available," say the Hesseliens. "We love the fun of the chase."

Like many of the best nurseries, Pleasant Run is both propagator and
grower—assuring fresh, healthy stock that is correctly labeled and of
excellent garden merit. Rick Hesselein is an expert budder and grafter who
understands how to propagate tetchy plants that larger nurseries don't have
the skill or patience to handle. The nursery maintains 40 greenhouses, a

propagation facility, sophisticated drip irrigation, and a state-of-the-art iron-removal system (assuring stain-free foliage). Pot sizes range from 3 to 30 gallons.

Pleasant Run is a good place to scan the horizon for exciting new botanical superstars, such as Dr. Thomas Ranney's large-flowered Carolina allspice (*Calycanthus* 'Venus'), the J. C. Raulston Arboretum's stunning red-flowered version (*Calycanthus* × *raulstonii* 'Hartlage Wine'), and Dr. Elwin Orton's latest breakthrough dogwood (*Cornus kousa* × *nuttallii* 'Venus'). Other collector's plants include a dazzling form of snowdrop tree (*Halesia diptera* var. *monticola*), wild Chinese redbud, and four kinds of Japanese kerria (hardy shrubs that bloom in shade).

Sovereign among flowering trees, the magnolia is a clear nursery favorite. From shrubs to towers, its ancient lineage produces more conspicuously beautiful trees than any other genus. Pleasant Run's magnolia list—including the Brooklyn Botanic Garden's rarer yellow magnolias and glamorous new hybrids developed here and in Japan—makes collectors hyperventilate. Sweet bay magnolias include a gold-variegated variety (*Magnolia virginiana* 'Maggie Smith') and forms hardy to Massachusetts. Here's where to find a double pink star magnolia (*M. stellata* 'Chrysanthemumiflora'), an Oyama magnolia with immense semi-double flowers (*M. sieboldii* 'Colossus'), and a cucumber tree whose creamy blossoms open in a pale blue shade (*M. acuminata* 'Blue Opal').

Pleasant Run grows excellent roses—some 50 varieties of highly rated shrub roses and climbers, some in tree form. Unusual species from Asia include the red-prickled Omei rose *(R. omeiensis)*, a blood-red Moyes rose (*R. moyesii* 'Geranium'), and the canary-yellow Father Hugo rose *(R. hugonis).* Rose expert Steven Scanniello says, "Their roses are incredible. Roses come out of the pots as real plants because they actually grow them here, using first-rate potting mix. You can't get this quality of roses anywhere else in the Northeast." Scanniello's favorites include 'White Cap', 'Trier', 'Casablanca', 'Autumn Bouquet', and 'All That Jazz'.

Richard Hesselein belongs to the "distinguished committee of knowledgeable horticulturists" who select each year's Pennsylvania Horticultural Society Gold Medal winners. Pleasant Run is itself a recognized source for many Gold Medal favorites, including dwarf sweet box, bottlebrush buckeye, and seven-son tree. The nursery also grows fine inventories of crape myrtle, camellia, dogwood, witch hazel, holly, buddleia, and viburnum. The hydrangea list is full of top performers—'Limelight', 'All Summer

Beauty', 'Annabelle', 'Snow Queen', 'Blue Billow', 'Tokyo Delight', 'Unique', and 'Endless Summer'.

Pleasant Run grows fine perennials, grasses, and ground covers in an apparent concession to landscaper demand. The hellebores are particularly nice. Japanese tree peonies come from Klehm Nursery stock. Perennials selection and prices are excellent, though one suspects that the Hesseleins' hearts are elsewhere—perhaps in the magnolia greenhouse. Or maybe in the office, where an amusing sign on Rick Hesselein's desk reads, "Teamwork is a lot of people doing what I say."

Directions: The Allentown police ticket energetically, so observe local speed limits. Take the New Jersey Turnpike to exit 7A and turn onto Route 195 east. At exit 8, turn right onto Main Street, pass the turnoff for Route 539 south, and take the next left onto Ellisdale Road. The nursery is in 1.7 miles on the left ("Richard Hesselein" sign at the road). Go straight down the dirt drive to the house on the left and follow signs for the office.

Nearby attractions: In Allentown, you can eat pretty well at La Piazza Ristorante Brick Oven Pizza, 11 Church Street (609-208-0640) or the Black Forest Restaurant, 42 South Main Street, in The Old Mill shops (609-259-3197; German food).

POPES' GARDENS
1146 Old White Horse Pike, Waterford, NJ 08089
(856) 767-3343; fax (856) 767-2270
www.popesgardens.com; e-mail *pope@eticomm.net*
James and Joan Pope

Perennials. Annuals, vegetables, herbs, shrubs, vines. *Small family-owned nursery. Open March through October, daily, 9 to 6. Longer hours in June and July; call for exact hours. Plant lists on the Web site. No mail order. Organic grower. Farm animals. Exotic pheasants for sale. Sales and specials. Gift certificates. Visitors welcome.*

Founded in 1990, Popes' Gardens is a family-oriented nursery with amusing diversions for the visitor. In this pleasant area of South Jersey, most residents still grow backyard vegetables. Owners James and Joan Pope live and work on-site, and it's their husbandry that provides all the amusement—Scottish Highlander cattle, pet emus, silver pheasants, and lots of nursery stock.

Popes' Gardens specializes in garden-worthy perennial plants—some 850 varieties. Jim Pope has a degree in horticulture and brings professional skill to the couple's nursery operations. Friendly bugs and companion plantings allow the Popes to operate an "all natural" nursery and greenhouse—no mean feat, especially with a greenhouse. Plants are set out in alphabetical rows on an acre of black plastic, covering an old farm field.

"We grow everything we sell, so that keeps the prices down," says Joan Pope. "People come a distance! Two guys from Philadelphia come every week and a schoolteacher visits every Saturday night." Prices are an important draw—a gallon-size perennial may go for $6 or a banana tree for $9.99. Flats of annuals and vegetables are priced modestly. Bunnies are only $10.

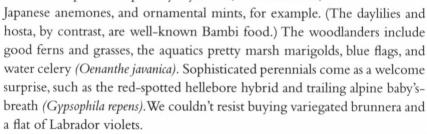

The Popes' selection strikes a healthy balance between common and unusual garden plants. Garden mules that survive drought, stress, and deer predation are an important specialty—yarrows, monkshoods, Japanese anemones, and ornamental mints, for example. (The daylilies and hosta, by contrast, are well-known Bambi food.) The woodlanders include good ferns and grasses, the aquatics pretty marsh marigolds, blue flags, and water celery *(Oenanthe javanica)*. Sophisticated perennials come as a welcome surprise, such as the red-spotted hellebore hybrid and trailing alpine baby's-breath *(Gypsophila repens)*. We couldn't resist buying variegated brunnera and a flat of Labrador violets.

Besides perennials, Popes' grows common and unusual annuals designed to give splash to the flower bed. Telling examples are flowering tobaccos, cardinal vines, geranium standards, luffa sponge plants, and mix-and-match verbenas. Urbane tropicals include solar coleus, cannas, and passionflower vines. Vegetable selections stress no-nonsense zucchinis and Burpee tomatoes—stuff people can eat for dinner every night. Some 150 varieties of flowering shrubs, landscape roses, and woody vines complement the perennials list.

The nursery's Web site combines informative plant lists with bold, almost childish graphics. Pictures of Popes' favorite farm animals appear alongside "natural remedy" recipes to evict woodchucks and deer from gardens. Plant descriptions are edifying yet friendly. The Popes describe purple coneflower, for example, as an "outstanding sturdy summer-blooming perennial bearing raspberry-colored daisies in July and August," adding, "Goldfinches, our New Jersey state bird, enjoy their seed heads, so don't remove spent flower heads."

Directions: From the Garden State Parkway, take exit 38A onto the Atlantic City Expressway north. At exit 31, turn onto Route 73 north, turn right onto Waterford-Blue Anchor Road, and turn left on Route 30/White Horse Pike. At Geneo's Tavern, turn right onto Pennington Avenue, cross the railroad tracks, and at the stop sign, turn left onto Old White Horse Pike; the nursery is third on the right.

Nearby attractions: Silver Coin Restaurant, Routes 30 and 206, Hammonton (609-561-6974), is a long-hours diner with good cheese ravioli. Krissy Lee's Garden Ornaments, 702 White Horse Pike, Elm, NJ 08037 (609-704-7077; Beverly Scanga), sells cast-concrete garden items, some handsome (large planters), others grotesque (outsized concrete golf balls).

RAREFIND NURSERY

957 Patterson Road, Jackson, NJ 08527

(732) 833-0613; fax (732) 833-1965

www.rarefindnursery.com; e-mail *info@rarefindnursery.com*

Henry (Hank) Schannen

Rhododendrons. Unusual trees, shrubs, and perennials. Collector's nursery. Retail and wholesale. Open late March through Thanksgiving, Wednesday through Saturday, 10 to 4, and by appointment. Shipping March 1 through Thanksgiving. Call or check Web site for exact dates. Catalog $3. Catalog on Web site. Mail order. Open house days. Group tours by arrangement. Display gardens effective April though mid-July, peak bloom in May. Visitors welcome.

The French describe falling in love as *le coup de foudre*—a clap of thunder, signifying that you've been hit by a lightning bolt. That's what happened to Hank Schannen when he attended an American Rhododendron Society meeting in 1966, spurred by a fancy for bonsai. Schannen, founder of a successful market research firm in Princeton, was struck with a passion that has endured for 40 years. He ditched bonsai and began amassing what became a vast rhododendron collection, systematically choosing the finest and rarest plants of the genus. Among Schannen's holdings are collectors' trophies, important wild species, interspecies hybrids, his own original hybrids, and some fine old plants from his mother's garden.

RareFind Nursery is the connoisseur's nursery Schannen founded in 1998 after his rhododendron collection burst from storage and had to start supporting itself. The nursery's 11-acre central-New Jersey site, purchased in 1995, is situated on a northern finger of the Jersey Pine Barrens. This botanically rich landscape provides perfect rhododendron habitat—shady, acidic, moist, and well-drained. It took a year to clear four acres, install irrigation and deer fencing, and plant 3000 rhododendrons. Schannen's collection, having matured and multiplied, had plenty of fine stock plants. All it took was a skilled staff to make it an instant collectors' nursery.

RareFind today has as many dazzling plants as can be imagined in a single venue. The rhododendrons, of course, are heart-stopping. Together with elegant azaleas, mountain laurels, hollies, and boxwoods, they form the region's most diverse selection of broad-leaved evergreens. Rare rhododendrons include coveted hardy yellows, deep reds, double-flowered forms, and varieties with unusual fragrance and leaf variegation—the list of hybrids and fine species is exceptional. RareFind's native rosebay rhododendron selections, for example, sport unusual curly leaves or peachy-yellow flower trusses. Like its azalea multitude, the nursery's lesser-known lepidote rhododendrons (early-bloomers with small leaves) offer greater floral variety than most gardeners think possible. Our favorite rock-garden azalea has no flowers at all, though—just tiny leaves resembling its name, 'Rice Kernel'.

An equally alluring tree and shrub inventory offers such things as golden dawn redwood, double-flowered mountain laurel, Zone 5-hardy abelia, and white-flowered redvein enkianthus. RareFind grows variegated forms of English oak, hedge maple, Japanese kerria, and pagoda dogwood. (Rumor says it's hoarding a variegated *Clethra barbinervis*.) From Asia come exotics such as Chinese pistachio, red-twig Korean maple *(Acer barbinerve)*, and Wilson's horse chestnut (now endangered in the wild). Did we mention the magnolia with dinner-plate size blooms (*Magnolia* 'Big Dude')?

Rare native plants get some respect. From the Jersey Pine Barrens come staggerbush *(Lyonia mariana)*, box-leaved sandmyrtle *(Leiophyllum buxifolium)*, and a blueberry relation called dangleberry *(Gaylussacia frondosa)*. American wisteria *(Wisteria frutescens)* could be paired with Mexican climbing hydrangea *(Hydrangea seemanii)*. Native dwarf conifers include prostrate bald cypress and a number of queerly shaped Eastern hemlocks.

This wonderful nursery casts itself as a "purveyor of fine plants." Like an upscale *chocolatier*, it offers so many delicious goods it's hard to choose. Plants are generously sized and well grown. Shipping practices are excellent. Every year, the nursery offers mail-order customers a representative assortment of its inventory, rotating and introducing many startling wonders. Visitors have an advantage, though, for the staff can sometimes be swayed to part with a spare seedling derived, say, from an exotic cross or a plant-collecting expedition to Tibet—the kind of plants gardeners feel excited and privileged to own. It's no wonder that RareFind's sales have doubled every year since inception.

RareFind occupies a magical woodland, part nursery and part rhododendron arboretum. Under an oaken canopy, nursery and plant collection merge, their division blurred by an unseen boundary. Shoppers are therefore cautioned against hungering after some enchanting gem that is actually a reserved arboretum plant or experimental seedling. It's more common to discover in the nursery a rarity you had assumed was *verboten,* though. The only real boundary to watch carefully is the deer fence, which packs enough electrical current to flatten a moose.

Visitors should understand, before arrival, that hard-core "rhodie people" are in the grip of an eccentric mania that tends to discount the legitimacy of other plant groups—viewing oaks, for example, as having come into being in order to provide shade for rhododendrons. The entire RareFind staff jokes about this fixation. Over lunch one day, a staff member surmised that rhododendrons could be converted into grain crops, obviating the world's need for wheat. Another suggested that a rhododendron silk worm be developed, allowing mulberry trees to be eliminated in favor of enlarged rhododendron habitat.

Schannen himself is such a devoted extremist that he only recently admitted to liking azaleas (a subclass of rhododendrons). He is a generous supporter of rhododendron causes and has traveled the globe in pursuit of rare rhododendrons. His 40-year quest has earned him many honors, including a gold medal from the American Rhododendron Society and leadership roles in the Rhododendron Research Foundation and Rhododendron Species Foundation. Although Schannen now limits his collection to 3000 specimens, he continues to acquire new gems, donating or composting plants that fail to meet his exacting standards.

In addition to world-class collector, Schannen is an accomplished hybridizer whose most successful rhododendron hybrids count among the nursery's offerings. His signature introduction, *Rhododendron yakusimanum* 'Solidarity', is a beautiful shrub with luminous pink flower trusses fading to angelic pink, and matte leaves bronzed underneath with a decorous felt (indumentum). The American Rhododendron Society recommends it as a "proven performer" for the Mid-Atlantic region; some consider it the world's best "yak" hybrid. In a feature article in the *New York Times*, Patricia Taylor wrote a droll account of Schannen's name selection: "He wanted to name it after his mother, but she refused, saying, 'No one will buy a rhododendron called 'Wanda Pipchinski'.' Instead, she selected 'Solidarity', to honor the Polish labor movement."

Directions: From Route 195 in central New Jersey, take exit 21 onto Route 527 south. At the first light, turn right onto Route 526, and in 2.5 miles, turn right onto Patterson Road. The nursery is on the right at #957. From the New Jersey Turnpike, take exit 7A onto Route 195 east and follow directions above.

Nearby attractions: At the junction of Routes 526 and 527, Glory's Deli/Butcher Shop/Grocery/ATM/Coffee-Beer-Wine-Liquors/Family Market (732-928-0677) is a busy little market with good sandwiches.

Related sources: The American Rhododendron Society's database (www.rhododendron.org) posts searchable descriptions of 1200 rhododendron species and hybrids. Hillhouse Nursery, 90 Kresson-Gibbsboro Road, Voorhees, NJ 08043 (856-784-6203; Theodore Stecki; open by appointment, 15 miles east of Philadelphia), is a small private nursery propagating the Linwood azaleas bred by the late G. Albert Reid, a personal friend of the owner.

ROHSLER'S ALLENDALE NURSERY

100 Franklin Turnpike (Route 507), Allendale, NJ 07401
(201) 327-3156; fax (201) 327-0663
www.rohslers.com
Mark and Bruce Rohsler

Trees and shrubs, perennials, bonsai, houseplants. Family-run garden center. Retail and wholesale. Open year-round, Monday through Saturday, 9 to 6, Sunday, 9 to 5. No catalog. No mail order. Landscape design. Florist. Gift items. Visitors welcome.

Rohsler's Allendale Nursery and Flower Shoppe is a large, well-stocked independent garden center in lush suburban Allendale. Housed in a vintage Dutch Colonial building backed by 14 acres of land, Rohsler's carries a full range of horticultural material—annuals, perennials, grasses, shrubs, trees, herbs, bulbs, houseplants, grave blankets, and Christmas trees. There's no catalog or plant list, so most customers just show up, take a red cart, and load what they need.

What makes Rohsler's notable is the quality of its stock and the knowledge and helpfulness of its staff. It buys in stock from high-quality growers and takes the trouble to maintain it well. Even gardeners who prefer to buy plants from nurseries find Rohsler's on their must-visit itinerary in buying season. The woody plants and evergreens are particularly good, prompting the region's botanical gardens to make periodic visits to pick out specimens.

Our own visit to the tree yard confirms rumors of its superiority. The yard supervisor, who refers to plants as "my babies," patrols the area to assure that everything is mulched, watered, and sniffle-free. Selection is first-rate, even at times of year when many garden centers run thin. Trees are chosen for graceful form, multiseasonal interest, and appropriate size for garden use—the very criteria used by landscape professionals. The stock is varied, and when there are only a few of a variety, extras can be—and often are—ordered in.

Lovely trees spied on our visit were 'China Rose' yellowwood; variegated tulip tree; 'Twisty Baby' contorted honey locust; 'Maypole' columnar crab; 'Mme. Butterfly' kousa dogwood (with hovering, butterfly-like flowers); and Japanese hornbeam (with incised foliage seemingly stamped by machine). Good azaleas, hydrangeas, and woody ground covers inhabit the shrub yard alongside yellow buddleia, dwarf pink crape myrtle, and 'Flamingo' box elder. Pink littleleaf lilac and white Chinese wisteria come as tree-form patio plants.

Rohsler's stocks enough weeping conifers to pack a funeral. Dwarf conifers include marvelous oddballs and top-grafted evergreen globes resembling topiary. Even the life-size conifers come gold, blue, or variegated. No formal display garden is kept, but a handsome planting along the back driveway illustrates what exotic conifers look like at maturity.

Rohsler's accommodates serious horticultural shoppers and harried parents ("Daddy! Hurry!") sprinting in for a few garden mums. The perennial yard has plants for sun and shade, alpines, and aquatics—good performers from good suppliers. There are some respectable houseplants in the greenhouse, especially the cactus. First-rate seasonal bulbs and supplies vie for retail space with geegaws and holiday items, all of which function a bit like a horticulture tax, making possible the smart staff and fine plants.

Directions: From Route 17, exit onto Sheridan Avenue and turn toward Waldwick. Bear right onto East Prospect Street and turn right onto Route 507/Franklin Turnpike. Rohsler's is at #100. From New York City, take the George Washington Bridge/Route 95 south to Route 4 west, merge onto Route 17 north, and follow directions above.

STEVEN KRISTOPH NURSERY
P.O. Box 746, 9 Roberts Road, Englishtown, NJ 07726
(732) 446-1440; (732) 446-8633
E-mail *stevenkristoph@man.com*
Steven Kristoph

Rhododendrons. Flowering trees and shrubs. Small specialty nursery. Open by appointment. No catalog. No mail order. Nursery-propagated plants. Private garden. Visitors welcome.

Steven Kristoph Nursery is a small, incubator nursery in central New Jersey specializing in rhododendrons and collector's plants—especially elite flowering trees and shrubs for Zone 6 gardens. Owner Steve Kristoph has a Master's degree in horticulture from Rutgers University and is an accomplished educator, plant collector, nurseryman, native-plant enthusiast, and bird watcher. He started the nursery in 1984, having been mesmerized in childhood by the goings-on at an uncle's nursery. He has been an American Rhododendron Society member since 1975, and, somewhat incongruously, he loves golf.

Kristoph is an expert propagator with a keen understanding of what makes a good ornamental plant. Amid the noise of the plant trade, he knows how to discriminate—rejecting plants that don't perform well or are just repeats of earlier, better hybrids. Through rare-plant circles he secures cutting-edge plants that have the promise to be superstars. Kristoph was an early grower of a red-flowered form of enkianthus ('Princeton Redbells'), for example, as well as a white redbud (*Cercis canadensis* 'Alba'). He grows uncommon magnolias and a knock-out Chinese dogwood (*Cornus kousa* 'Heartthrob') with deep red flowers.

Kristoph has terrific contacts among the region's most influential horticulturists. Before Hank Schannen opened RareFind Nursery (see profile), he housed a private rhododendron collection in Kristoph's greenhouses. Today, Kristoph supplies RareFind with plants. He also does some growing for friends Heidi and Rick Hesselein at Pleasant Run Nursery (see profile), specializing in fine magnolias and flowering trees. He sells plants to Marty Brooks, a cigar-chomping, gravel-voice nurseryman whose rare-plant nursery in Pennsylvania is the region's foremost provider of large-caliper Hinoki false cypress.

Kristoph also sells rare plants at arboretum and plant society sales. For years, he grew Franklin tree seedlings *(Franklinia alatamaha)* for Philadelphia's historic Bartram's Garden. (John Bartram discovered the Franklin tree in Georgia in 1765 and is credited with saving it from extinction.) Through Rutgers, Kristoph knows Dr. Elwin Orton, New Jersey's foremost plant breeder, who created the Rutgers' hybrid dogwoods and 'Jersey Princess' holly. Kristoph propagates Dr. Orton's shiniest American holly (*Ilex opaca* 'Dan Fenton') and is often first to grow upcoming selections.

As a rhododendron connoisseur, Kristoph has a special love of Charles Dexter's hybrids, especially 'Helen Everett'. "It has everything," he says. "It's white, sweet as a gardenia, and hardy." He also grows 'Phipps' Yellow', a reliably hardy primrose-yellow rhododendron from Long Island's Old Westbury Gardens (see profile). He has *Rhododendron metternichii bretifolia*, a wild Japanese rhododendron with pale pink flowers, rarely found in cultivation. He grows *Rhododendron yakusimanum* variants, including Hank Schannen's own 'Solidarity', which he considers the best "yak."

While Kristoph's love of golf and rhododendrons may seem mismatched, he manages to unite them by teaching horticulture at Rutgers' Professional Golf Turf Management School. That way, he gets to influence an important landscape development and play the best golf courses in the country. In 2004, Kristoph was chosen to supply plants for New Jersey's new waterfront golf course, Bayonne Golf Club, located on a former waste site in Bayonne.

Kristoph's nursery is surrounded by land once devoted to cranberry farming. Rising property values drove out the cranberry farmers and, like much of New Jersey, it's now mostly housing development. On 21 acres and in 40 greenhouses, Kristoph propagates and grows most of the nursery's plants—generally in pots, though some are field-grown. The stock is healthy and, at grower's prices, often a bargain.

As with most nurseries kept by the botanically curious, Kristoph's tends to be a bit eclectic. The shrub inventory includes roses, top-grafted littleleaf lilacs, and native shrubs such as dwarf witch alder *(Fothergilla gardenii)*. At some point tropical plants seem to have taken Kristoph's fancy, for he grows named passionflowers and mandevilla vines, as well as tibouchina standards. A few perennials are here to appease landscapers, mainly performance hostas and the odd monkshood *(Aconitum napellus)*.

Visitors to the nursery should not leave without viewing "the pond," a greenish, murky, life-filled sump in the back of the property. In good weather, Kristoph uses a 4-by-8-foot raft, "the Titanic," to explore the pond's dimly visible and no doubt underappreciated life forms. Those less curious about algae might spend a quiet moment in Kristoph's private "spiritual garden," a serene and elegant space filled with plants resonating harmony and peace.

Directions: From Route 195, take exit 21 onto Route 527 north, cross Route 537, and at a 4-way stop sign, continue straight on Alternate Route 527 (Route 527 goes right). In 0.8 mile, turn left onto Roberts Road. The nursery is 1000 feet on the left.

Nearby attractions: Hidden Hills Farm and Nursery, 12 Pine Hill Road, English-town, NJ 07726 (732-446-3853; e-mail syringa12@aol.com; Anne and John Haines), is a start-up mail-order nursery growing exceptional own-root roses, including some found along local highways ('Hwy. 290 Pink Buttons'); it bears watching for its devel-oping list of vintage lilacs and deer-resistant "plants of history and romance." A Garden State Garden Shop, 57 State Highway 34, Colts Neck, NJ 07722 (732-462-2284), is an attractive garden center known for its garden ornaments and architectural artifacts—from classical urns to flying cement pigs.

SUMMERVILLE GLADIOLUS WORLDWIDE

801 Bridgeton Pike, Mullica Hill, NJ 08062

(856) 223-1687

E-mail *summervillegladiolus@yahoo.com*

Dana Summerville

Gladiolus bulbs. Family-run gladiolus farm. Wholesale and retail. Catalog $3. Mail order only. Wholesale cut flowers. Open by appointment.

Among the old truck farms south of Philadelphia, Summerville Gladiolus Worldwide operates the region's foremost gladiolus farm. The farm was founded by Alexander Summerville, a leading 20th-century gladiolus hybridizer, who first knew gladiolus in the 1930s in his grandfather's garden. He decided to grow them himself on return from World War II. A neighbor urged him to exhibit his flowers at local gladiolus shows, and championship awards followed. Spurred by show-bench victories, he began collecting and growing the best new gladiolus hybrids.

Summerville's hobby became a passion and, in 1955, a commercial mail-order bulb farm. Demand for his top-size gladiolus bulbs (technically corms) so exceeded expectation that, in 1965, he bought a 100-acre farm in South Jersey. The farm prospered by growing gladiolus bulbs and cut flowers for the florist trade. As a breeder, Summerville won countless awards, including the North American Gladiola Council's Gold Medal Award. He was inducted into the International Gladiolus Hall of Fame in 1996.

Summerville's son Dana, an expert gladiolus grower and hybridizer in his own right, took over the farm with a promise to maintain "business as usual." Such skilled work is rarely done any more outside Holland—hand-digging, dividing, weeding, irrigating, sorting, inspecting, heat-treating, and cataloging named flower bulbs. Dana Summerville does this labor himself, with capable help, to ensure a high level of quality and selection.

Gladioli are charismatic members of the iris family, derived from the wild "sword lilies" of South Africa. Though their popularity has varied over the years, they've always attracted passionate admirers. Florists prize the showy spikes, hobbyists enjoy exhibiting "show glads," and home gardeners love them as cut flowers. Contemporary hybridizers around the world continue to breed new varieties, offering such improvements as brighter colors, stronger stems, waxen substance, and all manner of ruffled embellishments.

Known internationally for its prize-winning glads, Summerville Worldwide each year offers 15 to 20 new introductions, 230 recent hybrids, and 20 previous releases. All are named varieties from leading breeders. Each is described by flower size, color, bloom date, and bulb size. Top-quality bulbs come in units of one or ten, or in collections—exhibition bulbs, miniatures, jumbos, novelties, and All-America selections. Wholesale bulbs are sold in lots of 250 and 1000, mainly to cut-flower growers. A brand-new hybrid may sell at a premium, but many named varieties go for just 75 cents a bulb—the "odds and ends" for even less. Bulbs are sent by mail order to customers around the world.

Even gardeners who dismiss gladiolus as funeral flowers have to admire the new hybrids. Substantial blooms, seemingly cut from velvet and silk, are adorned with blotches, knuckles, edges, and fancy ruffling. Colors are voluptuous—soft lilac, glowing peach, and a gray-blue pastel called "smoke." One of Alex Summerville's last hybrids is 'Black-heart', an outstanding vampire-red. 'A. Summerville', a hybrid from the late Robert Sprinkle honoring his old patron, is a luscious shade of heavy cream.

Summerville Worldwide's gladiolus hybrids excel in championship awards and often achieve the Top Ten show-hybrid list of the North American Gladiolus Society. 'Darlin' Clementine', a pale-orange Pletcher hybrid, made the Top Ten in 2001 and was the highest-rated NAGS Recent Introduction. 'Lady Lucille', a pink-and-white Martin hybrid, has made the Top Ten every year since 1996; many consider it the best gladiolus ever introduced.

Gladioli are a spectacular, easy-care floral bargain with almost no downside for the busy gardener. Given simple winter storage, an initial investment in bulbs can last for years. In New Jersey, succession planting can keep a gladiolus bed in flower for months, producing exhibition-quality flowers that can be cut fresh for the house. With grandeur so easily achieved, why wait for a funeral?

Nearby attractions: Creamy Acres Farm, 448 Lincoln Mill Road, Mullica Hill, NJ 08062 (856-223-1669; www.creamyacres.com), is a 100-acre family dairy farm owned by the Ambrusters; its many side attractions include 20 greenhouses with annuals, perennials, herbs, hanging baskets, potted containers, and garden gifts.

TOADSHADE WILDFLOWER FARM

53 Everittstown Road (Route 513), Frenchtown, NJ 08825
(908) 996-7500 phone and fax
www.toadshade.com; e-mail *toadshad@toadshade.com*
Randi V. Wilfert Eckel

Native perennial wildflowers. *Small specialty nursery. Retail only. Open by appointment. Printed catalog on request. Catalog on Web site. Mail order. Shipments weekly, April 1 through June 30 and September 1 through October 30. Nursery pick up by prior arrangement. Gift certificates.*

Few nurseries have the knack of appreciating the flora of a native place— what naturalist Donald Culross Peattie called "the art of investigating the commonplace in the certainty that it will yield up treasure."

Toadshade Wildflower Farm is a small mail-order nursery in Frenchtown specializing in perennial wildflowers native to the northeastern United States. Owner Randi Wilfert Eckel is an entomologist and plant lover who started the nursery in 1996, frustrated with the scarcity of native meadow plants in the horticultural trade. The nursery logo depicts a wood toad sitting under toadshade trillium *(T. sessile)*—"And yes," she says, "we have both at our farm."

As any wildflower devotee knows, it's hard to find authentic native plants. "I discovered that almost all the seed mixes and many plants offered for sale as 'wildflowers' were not native," Eckel recalls. Most seed mixes contain alien or naturalized plants (predominantly European and Asian wildflowers), salted with quick-effect annuals that Eckel says "look terrible" in the second year of planting. Commercial sources often list seeds by common names that are hard to identify or just plain wrong. "So we started Toadshade Wildflower Farm to make some of our favorite native wildflowers more easily available," she says.

Toadshade's plants are authentic natives of New Jersey and the Northeast that grow well in naturalistic settings. Because it's hard to grow perennial meadow and woodland plants from seed, Toadshade sells nursery-propagated seedlings that establish well and look better every year. "We have found that plants are much more successful when they are grown in pots and then transplanted," Eckel says. "We take care of getting them past the most difficult stages."

Although native perennials are often ignored, Toadshade's selections suggest an uncommon loveliness. A rare winged monkey flower *(Mimulus alatus)* produces lavender flowers all summer (and will grow in a ditch). Golden Eastern columbine is a butter-yellow variant of the region's wild columbine. The calico aster *(A. lateriflorus)* blooms throughout autumn with masses of tiny color-shifting flowers—first white with yellow centers, then lavender with red. For bold effects, purple giant hyssop *(Agastache scrophulariifolia)* produces purple flowers and bracts, attracting butterflies all summer long.

The grass family produces native plants that are practically never seen in nurseries—bottlebrush grass, scouring rush, and cat-tail sedge, to name a few. "We clear a square meter and introduce plants we like, including native grasses," Eckel says. "Eastern meadows are not grassless, but it's hard to trust the accuracy of grasses in seed mixes." Stately meadow plants include tall coreopsis, Autumn sneezeweed, and tall meadow rue.

The farm also grows native wild strawberry *(Fragaria virginiana)*, wreath goldenrod, blue-eyed grass, and hardy cactus *(Opuntia humifusa)*. Lovers of lost causes will savor Confederate violet *(Viola sororia priceana)*, popular with the Great Spangled Fritillary butterfly. Who ever heard of the drought-tolerant wild hairy petunia *(Ruellia humilis)*, endangered in Pennsylvania? Rarities that cannot be shipped—such as threatened winged false aster *(Boltonia decurrens)* and a delicate native loosestrife *(Lythrum alatum)* critical to the endangered Karnac blue butterfly—are sometimes available at the nursery.

In all, Toadshade lists some 86 native wildflowers, all propagated on-site by seed or cuttings. Plant handling is conscientious. Eckel collects seed from local genotypes, but no seed is taken from the wild. (Ecologists consider "nursery-grown" a weasel-word on this issue, while "nursery-propagated"— as is done here—equates with ethical treatment.)

Toadshade is wise about plants native to the northeastern region. A delightful printed catalog (also posted on the Web site) lists wildflowers by species name, common name, preferred habitat, and resistance to deer browse. Each plant's natural range and wildlife allies are included. The listings are embellished with original line drawings, and the Web site posts photographs.

Randi Eckel prefers to operate by mail order, "simply because there won't always be someone available to answer the phone—we'll probably be outside somewhere!" Stock is healthy and reasonably priced. Customers report "great success" in establishing plants in naturalistic gardens. Most come in 3½-inch pots, shipped on Monday in sturdy boxes to assure freshness.

Toadshade is located on a former chicken farm in Frenchtown, an historic town on the Delaware River. The farm occupies a 2½-acre sunny meadow scattered with native foxgloves, penstemons, and deer tongue grass—all experimental plantings that further the nursery's work. The operation is small, clean, and practical. Visitors must call ahead for an appointment, and anyone truly interested in native plants is sure to be fascinated by what is offered.

This is the kind of nursery that inspires reverence for nature's complexity as it is revealed close at hand, in home ground. Toadshade's catalog quotes Albert Einstein: "Look deep into nature, and you will understand everything better."

Directions: From Newark, take Route I-78 west to exit 12 and turn left onto Route 173 toward Jutland/Norton. In 0.1 mile, turn left onto Route 625 south/Perryville Road; in 2 miles it becomes Mechlin Corner Road. In 3 miles, bear right onto Route 513/Everittstown Road. Call ahead for local directions and an appointment.

Nearby attractions: The Frenchtown Inn, 7 Bridge Street, Frenchtown (908-996-3300; http://frenchtowninn.com), is a restored 1805 tavern whose superb bistro uses local produce. Toadshade's Web site has other local links.

Related sources: Across the Delaware River, Bowman's Hill Wildflower Preserve, 1635 River Road/Route 32, New Hope, PA 18938 (215-862-2924; www.bhwp.org), is a 100-acre preserve where important native-plant sales are held in spring and fall; a seed list is posted on the Web site. Arrowwood Native Plant Nursery, 961 Clark Avenue, Franklinville, NJ 08322 (856-697-6065; Cathy Arsenault), is a small wholesale grower of native species (free plant list; mail order).

TRIPLE OAKS NURSERY & HERB GARDEN
P.O. Box 385, 2359 S. Delsea Drive, Franklinville, NJ 08322
(856) 694-4272; fax (856) 694-0603
www.tripleoaks.com; e-mail *greatplants@tripleoaks.com*
Tom and Lorraine Kiefer

Perennials, herbs, roses, native wildlife plants, grasses, flowering trees and shrubs, shade trees. *Family-run teaching nursery. Open year-round, September through December, weekdays, 9 to 7, Saturday, 9 to 5, and Sunday, 10 to 4. Hours may vary in season. No printed catalog. Catalog on Web site. Mail order. Online store. Shipping in February, March, and June. Planting service. Lectures, classes, and teas. Articles and recipes on Web site. Herb Festival in June. Gift shop. Florist. Recipes. Display gardens. Seasonal items. Visitors welcome.*

Triple Oaks Nursery & Herb Garden is a family-operated garden center in South Jersey, founded in 1976 by Tom and Lorraine Kiefer on their 10-acre property. Two Kiefer sons now help run Triple Oaks and its Web site, and a third son operates a wholesale nursery that supplies many of its plants. The Kiefers are an energetic family of free spirits who have thrown themselves headlong into horticulture. Today, they also grow and sell the largest selection of retail plant material in the Delaware Valley region.

Triple Oaks is an atmospheric "teaching nursery" with everything imaginable for gardeners. Despite an ambitious plant list and A-level horticulture, it presents itself as homey and personal. Bountiful in May, frazzled in August, and fragrant at Christmas, it functions as an outstanding gardeners' resource year-round.

The Kiefers pride themselves on offering unusual plants. A lengthy tree list contains—by way of example—exceptional magnolias, dogwoods, and hardy camellias; *Amur maakia*; hardy rubber tree; rare maples; and a large-flowered snowdrop-tree (*Halesia diptera* var. 'Magnaflora'). The fine conifers include cedar-of-Lebanon and Serbian spruce. Among shrubs, long-stalk holly *(Ilex pedunculosa)* is the kind of shrub—glossy, fruitful, self-grooming, and attractive to birds—signifying a nursery that's paying attention. Many handsome oaks are native to the South Jersey terrain. A beloved Delaware-valley tree, known as "granny greybeard" and "cole-slaw tree" *(Chionanthus virginicus),* is emblematic of Triple Oaks' ecological interests.

Among the many perennials, herbs are prominent. Diverse ornamental grasses and dry-land prairie flowers give gardeners beset with deer and drought something to work with. All the nursery's holdings are listed on the Web site along with helpful availability lists.

The Kiefers have a fascination with growing tropical and desert plants not normally attempted in the area. Their most popular plant is a 15-foot hardy fiber banana *(Muso basjoo).* Only the truly plant-crazed would try to get a banana plant to bloom, fruit, and winter over in New Jersey. Specimens the Kiefers planted on-site not only survive but produce bananas. Other hot-climate triumphs are needle palm, dwarf palmetto, cactus, and agave (the source of tequila).

Of all Triple Oak's amenities, its education program is perhaps the most valuable. Lorraine Kiefer is founder and chairman of the South Jersey Unit of Herb Society of America and a noted expert on culinary herbs. She's also a tireless teacher, lecturer, and garden writer who produces a regular garden column for local newspapers; contributes articles to garden magazines; and wrote a chapter in the Brooklyn Botanic Garden's *Gardening for Fragrance.* More than 100 of her gardening-related articles are posted on the nursery's Web site.

Keifer lectures regularly at Triple Oaks—as well as at the Philadelphia Flower Show—on such topics as kitchen gardening, flower arranging, herbal history, and fragrant plants. She's a talented cook who shares family recipes on the Web site, including beet soup and potato donuts. Like Martha Stewart, she learned how to make *pisanki* (traditional hand-painted Easter eggs) from her Polish grandmother. A $25 fee for the *pisanki* class includes eggs, dyes, beeswax, instruction, and a round of egg folklore.

Triple Oaks' cozy garden shop is located in a creaky Swiss-style chalet fronting the entry drive. Mood music, wind chimes, and candle scents suggest a gypsy tearoom (the nursery holds teas). The shop sells dried herbs, horticulture books, folk crafts, and Polish knickknacks such as lamb butter molds. There's also a florist and space for tropical houseplants. Frankincense and myrrh plants are sold here during the holidays.

Did we mention the Herb Weekend Festival, with herb talks and walks? Fall Harvest Weekend Festival? Christmas Open House? Landscape design and planting services? The online garden shop? Triple Oaks has such a rich density of activities, plants, and gardening gear, it's easy to feel a little overwhelmed.

For respite, be sure to penetrate the garden paths that ribbon behind the nursery near the Kiefers' home and chicken coop. Raffish plantings bordering a creek are worth viewing for their experimental beds of hardy bananas and noisy towering grasses. The creek is a tributary to the Maurice River, a "wild and scenic" river of brown cedar water that broadens, southward, into the state's largest delta of wild rice plants and bird sanctuary.

Directions: From the Philadelphia area, take Route I-295 to exit 26 onto Route 42 south, or alternatively, take the Ben Franklin or Walt Whitman Bridge onto Route 676 south and turn onto Route 42 south. Turn onto Route 55 south, take exit 43, turn left off the ramp onto Little Mill Road, and turn right at the light onto Route 47/Delsea Drive; the nursery is 2.5 miles on the right. From Trenton, take Route I-295 south toward Philadelphia; where the road forks, bear right onto Route 42 south, and follow directions above. The Web site has further directions.

Nearby attractions: Country Rose Restaurant, Dutch Neck Village, 97 Trench Road, Bridgeton, NJ (856-455-9294), makes great pie.

Related source: Rivendell Nursery, 320 Strathem's Neck Road, P.O. Box 82, Greenwich, NJ 08323 (856-453-0708; www.rivendellnursery.com), is Ted Kiefer's 260-acre wholesale production nursery for premium woody plants; they're so good that one botanical garden director suggested, "Send your landscaper."

WALDOR ORCHIDS

10 East Poplar Avenue, Linwood, NJ 08221-2526
(609) 927-4126; fax (609) 926-0615
www.waldor.com; e-mail *waldor@waldor.com*
Walter and Bill Off

Orchids. Wholesale and retail. Open to retail customers year-round, Friday and Saturday, 9 to 5:30. Wholesale by appointment. No catalog or mail order. Mailing list for notices. Annual sales. Frequent stock changes. Discount to Pennsylvania Horticultural Society members. Visitors welcome.

Orchids—the most glamorous dynasty in the kingdom of vegetables. Its 25,000 species, numerous kinship "alliances," and countless named hybrids attest to the orchid's charisma, not only with obsessed collectors but with insect pollinators that guarantee the success of any plant group. Lured by beguilements, bees, wasps, butterflies, moths, birds, and ants relish orchid nectar, and none gets away without tracking pollen. With its queenly throated blossoms and inventive perfumes, the orchid's flamboyance assures its immortality.

Waldor Orchids is a family-owned orchid specialist in Linwood, not far from Atlantic City. Owners Walter and Bill Off inherited the business from their father, George Off, who founded it with backing from his father, owner of the old Brighton Hotel (now the Sands Casino/Hotel Atlantic City). George Off prospered by selling orchids during the Great Depression. "Orchids sell better in hard times," says Walter Off. "People want something nice, and those with money want to flaunt it." The nursery's name comes from the English firm that designed the greenhouses in the 1950s—among the first aluminum greenhouses in the country.

As the Delaware Valley's largest orchid supplier, Waldor Orchid's main business today is weekly deliveries to florists and garden centers. Between 2000 and 4000 plants come and go every week. Open two days a week to retail customers, Waldor's warren of linked greenhouses has long been a destination for orchid hobbyists far and wide. With no catalog or mail order, customers come in person to discover what's in stock and seize the best plants.

Waldor's inventory of orchid seedlings, divisions, and "mericlones" (tissue-culture clones) is rich and varied. According to Elizabeth Off, who helps her sons in the office, "When people ask the number, I just invite them to go out and count." In the old days, Waldor propagated its own orchids. A few orchids are still sent out for propagation—mostly from George Off's original cattleya collection. Today, though, most orchids are bought in from growers in Hawaii, California, and Florida, then repotted, staked, and cleaned up for sale. Because it's so well established, Waldor gets the cream of the crop from its suppliers.

The general focus is on top-quality mainstream orchids. A random sampling still reveals extraordinary specimens, such as the tiny clamshell orchid *(Encyclia cochleata);* a Panamanian orchid *(Schomburgkia tibicinis)* with magenta bloom-spikes to ceiling height; and orchids smelling of raspberries, carrion, mothballs, suntan lotion, and chocolate. Butterfly orchids *(Psychopsis papilio)* seem to hop with fluttering insects. Some orchids are collected for their variegated or tumescent leaves. Others look downright menacing—mule-ear oncidiums resembling a swarm of yellow attack bees and spider orchids *(Brassia Rex.)* with mean-looking sulphur flowers.

Visitors strolling the premises are first directed to a Greenhouse 4, a humid show house with a ferny grotto and orchids growing on trees, as they often do in nature. (Tree bark is a main component of orchid potting mix.) Each greenhouse has a special function—one is a stock house or a potting house, another contains cut-flower orchids, yet another is devoted solely to moth orchids. Rare and one-of-a-kind varieties that Waldor wants to show and propagate are squirreled away in Greenhouse 6. Valuable collector's specimens include an exquisite fluted Brazilian orchid *(Laelia purpurata* var. *flamea* 'Nancy') and a spectacular almost-blue corsage orchid *(Laelia* × *cattleya* var. C. G. Roebling 'Blue Magic').

Waldor Orchids prides itself on good value and "old-fashioned service," which includes complementary greenhouse tours, as staff time allows. Orchids are handled impeccably, and only those in perfect bud are put up for sale. Plant tags show the full botanical name and any awards the plant has won. Considering quality, prices are reasonable. A perfect white moth orchid runs $25, for example, with large plants (what the staff call "real lunkers") going for $60. A special bargain table offers "open" (blooming) orchids. Annual sales are held in July and early December, and half-price discounts are given on plants used in flower shows.

Waldor Orchids' credentials are well established. For 70 years, the Offs have been loyal supporters of the Philadelphia Flower Show. Their dazzling 2004 exhibit smothered the show's entryway arch with 100,000 blooming orchids. Waldor is also a key vendor at the New York International Orchid

Show, held annually in March at Rockefeller Plaza, and many area shows. Walter Off is a respected American Orchid Society judge who casts a canny eye on his own inventory. The best plants passing through the greenhouse are often pulled aside for competition. Waldor has won countless AOS trophies for its show plants.

Like a drug counselor, Waldor Orchids cautions about the orchid's addictive power. "Once you purchase your first plant, you will be 'hooked' for the rest of your life," writes Walter Off. "We offer counseling and advice to those with this serious disease known as 'orchiditis.'" As might be expected, kicking the orchid habit can be a challenge. A woman from Georgia was once caught in a greenhouse, licking orchid sap. "We have found that the best cure," says Off, "is just to buy some more orchids."

Directions: The nursery is 10 miles from Atlantic City. From the Garden State Parkway, take exit 36, bearing right off the ramp onto Tilton Road. Turn right at the first light onto Fire Road. In 3.1 miles, turn left onto Poplar Avenue. The greenhouses are at the end on the left. From Philadelphia, take Route I-76 east to Route 42 east. Take the Atlantic City Expressway to exit 7S, turn onto the Garden State Parkway south, and follow directions above.

Related sources: The New York International Orchid Show at Rockefeller Plaza in April (www.gnyos.org) is a tropical delight, perfect for awakening the spring horticulture gene. The American Orchid Society (www.orchidweb.org) lists 14 local orchid societies in the Tri-State area with member show tables, auctions, and workshops.

WATERFORD GARDENS
74 East Allendale Road, Saddle River, NJ 07458
(201) 327-0721; fax (201) 327-0684
www.waterford-gardens.com; e-mail *splash@waterford-gardens.com*
John W. Meeks

Water lilies and aquatic plants. *Specialty nursery. Open year-round, Monday through Saturday, 9 to 5. Extended hours, mid-April through July, Wednesday, 9 to 7, Sunday, 9 to 4. Open Memorial Day, 9 to 4; closed other major holidays. Catalog $2.50. Catalog on Web site. Mail order. Pond supplies and fish. Design and installation. Books. Flower shop (201-327-0337; www.floralsofwaterford.com). Display gardens. Visitors welcome.*

Waterford Gardens is one of the country's premier aquatic nurseries—on a scale with Lilypons Water Gardens in Maryland, but nicer to look at. Owner John Meeks is a landscape architect who's been building water gardens since childhood. He established the enterprise in 1985 on the site of another water garden nursery. Legacy gardens, enhanced with contemporary ponds and waterfalls, attract visitors from afar—even earning a place in New Jersey guidebooks.

Waterford is an outstanding source of ornamental aquatics. It grows 100 percent of its stock (propagating about half) and runs a substantial mail-order business. Its plants are found in the region's most prestigious sites, including the New York Botanical Garden, Brooklyn Botanic Garden, Wave Hill, Longwood Gardens, and the Metropolitan Museum of Art in Washington, DC.

Water lilies have been fashionable ever since the Duke of Devonshire decided to raise *Victoria amazonica*, a gigantic water lily with huge platter-like leaves that a child can stand on. While few gardeners have room for this plant (the Duke had to get Joseph Paxton, who designed London's Crystal Palace in 1851, to build a large glasshouse), water lilies are still the reason most gardeners are seduced into building water gardens.

The Latin name for water lily, *Nymphaea* (water nymph), captures the beauty of these radiant floaters. Waterford grows 60 hardy and 80 tropical water lilies, offering about half through its handsome catalog. Blooms come in opulent shades of pink, red, peach, cream, yellow, chartreuse, and (in tropicals) azure and violet. Their virtues are enhanced by fragrance, spotting, shade tolerance, night bloom, and variegated foliage.

They're all gorgeous. Tricolor 'Pink Grapefruit', pure white 'Virginalis', and century-old 'Blue Beauty' are popular, but choice depends greatly on plant size and conditions. Waterford patronizes prominent hybridizers by introducing new cultivars each year. Recent examples are 'Charlie's Pride', a double magenta from Charlie Winch, and 'Foxfire', a blue tropical with orange petal boss from Craig Presnell.

Pygmy water lilies and "teacup" lotus allow city gardeners to indulge in water gardening on a diminutive scale. All it takes is a sunny deck, a durable black plastic tub from Waterford's catalog, and some oxygenator plants to keep the water fresh. The little 'Snow Princess' water lily and 'Spring Bird' lotus will even winter over in their pots.

Besides lilies and lotus, Waterford Gardens grows tropical marginal and bog plants—Egyptian papyrus, black taro, tropical water canna, and lily-like water snowflakes (*Nymphoides* spp.), to name a few. Marginals include red rice plant, variegated cattail, corkscrew rush, and such eastern United States natives as marsh marigold, sweet flag, and pitcher plant.

Waterford sells everything for water gardens "except the hole"—all the obligatory tubs, liners, pads, valves, test kits, additives, and sludgebusters. A fish emporium stocks elegant koi (ornamental Japanese carp) and other pond fish. There's even a flower shop and patio furniture.

Waterford is owned by a gifted landscape architect whose design-build department is esteemed and busy. Plant pick up can be arranged in advance, but if you drop by for service, be prepared to get in line. "Take a number for customer service and we will page you," announces a posted notice. It's just as well, for Waterford's idea-rich grounds provide first-rate stimulus—six acres of water gardens, ponds, fountains, bridges, walkways, and patios. You can buy a handful of fish food to feed koi in the Japanese-style stroll garden.

Such elegant water features require professional installation to work well. If you want anything like them, better hire the architects. Even choosing the right plants can be tricky. "Gardening requires lots of water," said writer Lou Erickson, "—most of it in the form of perspiration."

Directions: The nursery is 3 miles north of Paramus. From Route 17, take the Saddle River/Woodcliff Lake exit, turn east on East Allendale Road, and in 0.5 mile, after the first light, the nursery is on the right. From the Garden State Parkway, take exit 163 onto Route 17 north for 8 miles, and follow directions above. From New York City, take the George Washington Bridge to Route 4 west, exit onto Route 17 north, and follow directions above. From Route 287, take exit 15 onto Route 17 south and follow directions above.

WELL-SWEEP HERB FARM

205 Mount Bethel Road, Port Murray, NJ 07865

(908) 852-5390; (908) 852-1649

www.wellsweep.com; e-mail *herbs@goes.com*

The Hyde family

Herbs and perennials. *Family-run horticultural farm. Open year-round, Monday through Saturday, 9 to 5. Closed Sundays and holidays. Call ahead from January through March. Free catalog. Catalog on Web site. Mail order. Best selection mid-May. Newsletter. Workshops and lectures. Garden tours. Gift shop. Books, dried herbs, Christmas items. Exotic poultry. Knot and herb gardens. Visitors and picnics welcome.*

As deer eat, voles gnaw, and insects chew traditional gardens to the bone, many gardeners turn to traditional herbs—to discover a squadron of garden plants already in uniform, ready for combat. Herbs entered gardens more for utility than aesthetics, equipped to do one dirty job or another for most of history. That's why they're herbs. Since antiquity, herbs have been nature's pharmacy, providing medicines, drugs, poisons, insecticides, cosmetics, flavorings, and dyes—functions many retain to this day. The powerful traits that give herbs their distinction (toxic compounds, aromatic oils, bitter flavors, wooly leaves) also render them offensive to wildlife. As it turns out, they look nice in gardens, too. Indeed, they're probably the world's first garden plants.

Well-Sweep Herb Farm is a picturesque herb farm in northwestern New Jersey with one of the largest collections of herbs in the country. The nursery was founded in 1971 by Cyrus and Louise Hyde on a run-down farm they acquired as a homestead. A background in farming and a passion for gardening got them going in the herb business. Or was it their genes? Cyrus Hyde's ancestress was an herbalist who succored troops during the Revolutionary War, receiving, in thanks, a pair of silver shoe buckles from General George Washington. Hyde himself is a noted herbalist, hybridizer, and recipient of the loftiest medals of the Herb Society of America and International Herb Association. Louise Hyde is a licensed physical therapist, nursery commandant, and author of *Favorite Recipes from Well-Sweep.* Today, the farm absorbs the Hydes, their son David, and a crew of expert propagators in a year-round enterprise that has become a national attraction.

What Well-Sweep has that other nurseries don't is an exhaustive collection of herbs—1800 varieties of familiar and exotic herbs (and their many cultivars) for cooking, dosing, scenting, drying, dyeing, and—well, plain old gardening. Ornamental herbs make attractive flower borders that repel deer, tolerate drought, remain evergreen in winter, and attract butter-flies and hummingbirds.

Well-Sweep's plant catalog literally spans the alphabet from A to Z (acanthus to zatar). Most herbs are pleasant-looking rather than showy, but who can do without them? Take Well-Sweep's extraordinary thyme collection—76 creeping and 34 upright varieties, including 'Well-Sweep Wedgewood', a bluish-leaved English thyme developed at the nursery. Consider the incredible sweeps of thyme—red, pink, white, lemon, varie-gated, gray, silver, and wooly—that could carpet a gravel driveway or swimming pool garden. Similar schemes can be imagined for the farm's 62 hardy lavenders, 39 basils, 72 flavored mints, 37 oreganos, and 20 cranesbill geraniums. The farm's traditional cottage-garden plants (many with herbal properties) are also deep in cultivars—foxgloves, pinks, bleeding-hearts, and bellflowers. Prickly ornamentals such as teasels, sea hollies, and globe thistles are present (we're thinking of deer again), as are bay laurel and citrus trees. One lovely addition, hardly ever found in nurseries these days, is night-blooming and winter-flowering jasmine (19 jasmines in all).

Well-Sweep sells herbs and perennials by mail order and at the farm. Although not every plant is always available, the supply is exceptional. Herbs are properly held to low fertilizer levels and, though small, have good root systems and transplant easily. Most herbs are grown fresh from seed or cuttings in 3½-inch pots (perennials in quarts). Values are good, especially considering the number of cultivars nigh unobtainable elsewhere.

Unlike the carnival tricks employed by commercial garden centers to attract traffic, Well-Sweep has beautiful display gardens and much to teach the herb gardener. Workshops and lectures are held on handy topics—herbal wreaths, herbal teas, fairy gardens, topiary, edible wild plants, and medicinal herbs. Cyrus Hyde is a collector of rare poultry with a stunning flock of Japanese fantail chickens. An aromatic gift shop offers dried herbs, books, and potpourri supplies. Brick-path gardens feature formal knot gardens and displays of culinary and medicinal herbs. Visitors are warmly welcomed. The Hydes say, "We invite you to bring a picnic lunch, play with your children on the swings, visit our farm animals, enjoy a leisurely stroll along our garden paths, or just relax and enjoy the beauty of the day."

The nursery's name, well-sweep, refers to a Y-shaped wooden contraption used by farming families to help draw well water in former times. Cyrus

Hyde used a well-sweep to water horses and chickens as a child and built a replica here in 1966, on an old stone well on the property. The Hydes adopted the well-sweep as their nursery logo, finding in it the defining symbol of their handsome old-fashioned herb farm and its "simple, back-to-basics way of life."

Directions: The farm is in northwestern New Jersey, between Hackettstown and Washington. From Route I-78, take exit 6 and turn left onto Route 632 east (no signs). In 4.5 miles, at a stop sign, turn left and immediately right onto Route 632 east. In 7 miles, in Washington, turn right onto Route 57 east. In 0.2 mile, turn left at the first light onto Route 629 north/Main Street. In 1.5 miles, turn right onto Route 629 north/Rockport Road. In 0.5 mile, bear left onto Mount Bethel Road; the farm is 1 mile on the left.

Nearby attractions: Italian Fig Trees, 9 Sliker Road, Califon, NJ 07830 (908-832-7770; al@italianfigtrees.com; Al Lerner), sells 10 kinds of Italian fig tree (open weekends; no mail order).

Related source: Norfolk Lavender, Ltd., 777 Durham Road, Pickering, NJ 08817 (800-886-0050; www.norfolklavender.com), sells lavender-scented products and lavender plants.

WOODSIDE NURSERY
327 Beebe Run Road, Bridgeton, NJ 08302
(856) 451-2162; fax (856) 451-2280
www.woodsidenursery.com; e-mail *darrel_apps@hotmail.com*
Marilyn and Darrel Apps

Daylily hybrids. *Nursery open from mid-June through late-July, daily, 10 to 5. Call for exact dates. Catalog $3. Catalog posted on Web site. Mail-order shipping season from mid-April through October. Minimum order $25. Call to check on availability. Daylily Dazzle Days in July. Closeout sales of unnamed plants. Gift certificates. Visitors welcome; buses call ahead.*

The only thing new about the daylily is its status as a garden plant. Cultivated for thousands of years in Asia for food and medicine, it became popular as an ornamental following Professor A. B. Stout's revolutionary breeding work at the New York Botanical Garden in the 1920s. Since World War II, intense hybridizing has produced some 50,000 named daylily cultivars.

Woodside Nursery is a small mail-order nursery specializing in new and cutting-edge daylily hybrids. Its proprietor, Dr. Darrel Apps, is a distinguished daylily breeder and gifted horticulturist who has created exceptional daylilies for the Mid-Atlantic states. His wife, Marilyn Apps, is a professional nurse who helps in the nursery as time allows. Before founding Woodside, Darrel Apps was head of Education at Longwood Gardens, following academic appointments at several universities. He began hybridizing daylilies in 1968 and describes his nursery, with unwarranted modesty, as "a hobby that got out of control."

Apps' best-known releases are the celebrated TrophyTaker and Happy Ever Appster series, trademarked daylilies first developed in 1993 in collaboration with Dennis Blew of Centerton Nursery in Bridgeton. Apps selects TrophyTaker hybrids for beauty, hardiness, rapid growth, long bloom, and clean foliage. Happy Ever Appster hybrids are everblooming descendants of Apps' award-winning 'Happy Returns'. Centerton grows and supplies these plants wholesale to fine independent garden centers. Both series have become something of a sales phenomenon, owing to their high provenance, reasonable price tags, and hefty 2-gallon pots.

Woodside Nursery itself grows and sells some 2000 named daylily selections directly to retail customers, mostly from Apps' own breeding efforts. "Our objectives are to produce beautiful new daylily flowers that are hardy in northern areas," says Apps. "We do most of our hybridizing in our greenhouse, but we do all of our selections in open, unmulched fields. All of our selections have come through at least three winters, sometimes more." The resulting plants are admired for their terrific looks and hardiness in Zones 5 to 8. Many are also salt tolerant.

The Apps daylilies are diverse, but track some important themes. Groundbreaking 'Happy Returns' (1986) cemented Apps' reputation for cold-hardy repeat-bloomers—inspiring later breakthroughs such as 'Rosy Returns' (the first pink everbloomer) and 'Red Hot Returns' (bright red). The 'Woodside' series honors floriferous plants such as 'Woodside Royalty' (electric purple with a violet eye) and 'Woodside Romance' (an award-winning rose). Named for his wife, 'Marilyn Apps' seems to have everything—hardiness, high bud count, branching, ruffles, warm rosy color, and rebloom from March to frost.

Apps also concentrates on hybridizing early- and late-season tetraploids (larger, more substantial daylilies with artificially doubled chromosomes) under the 'Bridgeton' name. Two good examples are 'Bridgeton Icon' (purple with a cream edge and green throat) and 'Bridgeton Icing' (beige with red eyes and edges—very catchy). Excellent vermillion-red daylilies— such as 'Bridgeton Hat Dancer' and 'Bridgeton Fireworks'—glow with special brightness.

Apps hand-pollinates 15,000 to 30,000 seedlings per year and evaluates them over 3 years—a tireless selection process that can easily involve 50,000 seedlings at a time. "I'm a hunter-gatherer," he says. "Gradually, we reduce the numbers to get a few good introductions." The odds of breeding a great new hybrid being something near 1 in 2000, Apps' ability to launch 20 to 25 fine daylilies a year is proof of his hybridizing brilliance.

Woodside's mail-order plants are dug fresh from the field, where they quickly grow a husky root system. Prices are excellent—about half to three-quarters of what most professional hybridizers charge for comparable high-voltage newcomers. Prices for last-year's introductions are for single fans lined out the prior year, but "if they have increased by spring, you'll get what's there," the catalog promises. A mere $8 buys many older breeders' classics.

Although 2000 kinds of daylily may sound like a multitude, it takes only 20 "saleable units" (single or double fans) to list a plant in the catalog, and these disappear quickly. If you want specific varieties—especially new introductions—it's best to call the nursery. Woodside also sells many container-grown varieties, obtainable only on-site.

Located in the remote, flat farming area of South Jersey, Woodside Nursery is open to retail traffic only in late June and July. Daylily Dazzle Days attract scores of visitors, not only for daylily door prizes and raffles but also because two other exceptional nurseries—Fairweather Gardens and Blue Sterling Nursery (see profiles)—open their doors on the same day. Woodside's closeout sales in July offer unnamed daylily discards (perfect for mass plantings; bring tags and boxes) that Apps wants cleared from the fields.

Gardeners who have never seen a top-notch hybridizer's farm should not miss visiting at peak bloom in early July. Woodside's flower fields—a rich sea of golds, lemons, melons, reds, pinks, and plums—stretch to the edge of vision. This spectacular show of edible colors is a visual reminder that in China's Ming Dynasty, daylilies were cultivated in the emperor's vegetable garden. Close examination reveals blossoms ornate with scallops, pleats, rutched edges, tinted throats, watermarks, and diamond dusting.

In his introduction to the republication of Dr. Stout's seminal work, *Daylilies*, Darrel Apps wrote, "For the most part, they are carefree plants filling temperate zone landscapes with bright colors during the hottest, most difficult parts of the year. But the real excitement in growing them is the daily landscape change, for individual blossoms last only a day, even though the flower stalks may have blooms for up to six weeks. Each dawn offers the gardener the thrill of a fresh palate and a new painting. With judicious cultivar selection, the crescendos can go on all summer."

Directions: From the New Jersey Turnpike, take exit 2 onto Route 322 east. In Mullica Hill, turn onto Route 77 south. In Deerfield, pass the blinking light and bear right onto Route 630 south. At the next Y, bear right onto Deerfield Pike/Route 606 south. Pass Overdevest Nursery and turn right on Silver Lake Road. At the end, turn right onto Beebe Run Road/Route 607. The nursery is second on the right. From Philadelphia, take the Commodore Barry Bridge, turn onto Route 322 east, and follow directions above. From the Garden State Parkway, take exit 20 onto Route 50 north, and in 7 miles bear left onto Route 49 west. In Bridgeton, turn right at the Middle School onto West Avenue; in 3.2 miles (the road becomes Beebe Run Road), the nursery is on the right.

Nearby attractions: Toadfish Bar and Grille, 222 Bridgeton-Fairton Road, Fairton, NJ 08302 (865-455-1300; evening music), is a fun, hip bistro with river views and terrific crab cakes. Marlboro Farm Market & Garden Center, 601 Route 49, Bridgeton (856-451-3138; open daily, 9 to 7), has lovely fresh produce and nursery stock. Bridgeton's historic district has intriguing small museums (856-451-9208).

RESOURCES
AND INDEX

RESOURCES FOR GARDENERS IN NEW YORK AND NEW JERSEY

PLANT DATABASES AND LIBRARIES

Brooklyn Botanic Garden Library and Information Resources
1000 Washington Avenue, Brooklyn, NY 11225
(718) 623-7298; www.bbg.org
A vast, user-friendly gardening information network, featuring an Online Library of Gardening Information, gardening articles, growing tips, and a searchable database of BBG books and living collections. Library walk-in hours, April through October, Tuesday through Saturday, 1:30 to 4:30; November to March, Tuesday through Friday 1:30 to 4:30. Gardener's Resource Center (Administration Building, 2nd floor), with reference services, nursery catalog database, and plant search services. Gardener's Help Line (718-623-7270; Tuesday to Thursday, 10:30 to 12:30 and 2 to 4).

Cornell Cooperative Extension and Cornell Plantations
Cornell University, Ithaca, NY 14853
(607) 255-2237; www.cce.cornell.edu
Cornell Cooperative Extension lists CCE offices in every county statewide; also gardening fact sheets and publications (www.gardening.cornell.edu/factsheets.html). The university's botanical garden, Cornell Plantations (www.plantations.cornell.edu), posts information on its educational programs, magazine, and plant collections (including a heritage vegetable garden).

Missouri Botanical Garden Plant Science: *www.mobot.org/plantscience*
The world's largest plant-information database, with searchable records for 900,000 plant names, 50,000 images, and 2 million specimens.

New York Botanical Garden Library and Information Resources
Bronx River Parkway at Fordham Road, Bronx, NY 10458
(718) 817-8700; www.nybg.org
A world-renowned library for scholarly plant-science research, with cutting-edge electronic resources and digitized rare texts. Online access to NYBG Online Catalog

of Library holdings and Index to American Botanical Literature (http://librisc .nybg.org). E-mail links to Reference Librarians and Plant Information Specialists. Library open Tuesday through Thursday, 12 to 6, Friday and Saturday, 12 to 5 (718-817-8604; recorded message). Searchable databases at Library terminals; copying and reproduction services. Periodic museum-style exhibits of botanical images and rare books.

Ohio State University Web Garden: *www.webgarden.osu.edu*
A powerful online search engine for plant data and images (260,000 pages), rated as "friendlier and more cutting edge than most academic sites" by Forbes Magazine.

Rutgers Cooperative Research & Extension
Cook College, Rutgers University
88 Lipman Drive, New Brunswick, NJ 08901
(732) 932-9306; www.rcre.rutgers.edu (click "Extension")
Rutgers Cooperative Research & Extension has up-to-date research information, Master Gardener help lines, and soil testing; Cooperative Extension offices are listed for each county. Downloadable publications on garden and landscaping topics (www.rcre.rutgers.edu/pubs/), including the Jersey Gardener *newsletter.*

USDA Plant Database: *http://plants.usda.gov*
A national plant database maintained by the U.S. Department of Agriculture for vascular plants and mosses of the United States; includes plant names, distributional data, species abstracts, images, links, and crop information.

GARDENING LINKS

Garden Guides: *www.gardenguides.com*
Garden Web: *www.gardenweb.com*
LinkLane: *www.linklane.com/p/plants.htm*
New Jersey State Parks: *www.state.nj.us/dep/forestry/parks/parkindx.html*
New York State Parks: *http://nysparks.state.ny.us/parks*
U.S. National Arboretum: *www.usna.usda.gov*

NATIVE AND INVASIVE PLANT LINKS

Center for Plant Conservation: *www.centerforplantconservation.org*
Invasive Plant Atlas of New England: *http://invasives.eeb.uconn.edu/ipane*
Invasive Plant Council of New York State: *www.ipcnys.org*
Invasive Species Information: *http://invasivespecies.nbii.gov*
Landscaping with Native Plants: *www.epa.gov/glnpo/greenacres*
Native Plant Network: *www.nativeplantnetwork.org*
The Native Plant Society of New Jersey: *www.npsnj.org*
New England Wild Flower Society: *www.newfs.org*
Plant Conservation Alliance: *www.nps.gov/plants*

PLANT SHOWS AND SALES

Shows and sales of special merit are marked ★

The Garden Conservancy's Garden Tours★
P.O. Box 219, Cold Spring, NY 10516
(845) 265-2029; www.gardenconservancy.org
May, June, July, and September; thousands of extraordinary private gardens open for tours throughout the country, including locations in New York's Hudson River Valley, Long Island, and Eastern New Jersey; benefiting the nation's foremost garden preservation organization. Admission to each garden $5, no reservations required.

New York City

Brooklyn Botanic Garden Plant Sale and Events★★
Brooklyn Botanic Garden, 1000 Washington Avenue, Brooklyn, NY 11225
(718) 623-7298; www.bbg.org
Early May, the BBG Spring Plant Sale, a huge sale, under tents, with everything from vegetable seedlings to rare trees and perennials. Late January, Plant-O-Rama, a garden-catalog extravaganza for plant professionals. Late April cherry blossom festival. September harvest fair. October chile pepper fiesta. Year-round lectures, seminars, and events in a premier 50-acre botanic garden with restored Japanese garden and old-rose collection.

Gramercy Garden & Antiques Show★
69th Regiment Armory, Lexington Avenue at East 26th Street, New York, NY
(212) 255-0020; www.stellashows.com
Early March; a stunning sale of antique garden ornaments, furniture, and architectural
elements from 80 exhibitors.

New York Botanical Garden Events and Sales★★
Bronx River Parkway at Fordham Road, Bronx, NY 10458
(718) 817-8700; www.nybg.org
March, Orchid Show with orchid displays, lectures, and sale of conservatory orchids.
April, antique garden furniture show and sale. September Fiesta de Jardines,
celebrating Latin cultures. Christmas garden and train show. Year-round, the new Shop
in the Garden (at the main gate) sells elegant garden gifts, first-rate outdoor plants,
and an exceptional inventory of garden books. An unparalleled educational program,
in a 250-acre landscape with 48 gardens (including two rare-conifer arboreta, spring
daffodil walk, lady's border, rose collection, and kids' adventure gardens).

New York International Orchid Show★★
Greater New York Orchid Society
30 Rockefeller Center, 50th Street at 6th Avenue, New York City
www.gnyos.org
Mid-April, distinguished international orchid show and sale, with numerous lectures,
workshops, and specialty vendors of rare and fine orchids.

Queens Botanical Garden Arbor Day Celebration
Queens Botanical Garden, 43–50 Main Street, Flushing, NY 11355
(718) 886-3800; www.queensbotanical.org
April, a family-oriented Arbor Day celebration with exhibits, tree planting activities,
and music at New York City's most multicultural botanical garden.

Staten Island Botanical Garden
Snug Harbor Cultural Center, 1000 Richmond Terrace, Staten Island, NY 10301
(718) 273-8200; www.sibg.org
May, annual plant sale. Year-round, gift shop (718-362-1019) with plants, Chinese
items, garden accessories, books, and children's items. The garden has the country's first
authentic Chinese Scholar's Garden, with traditional courtyards, ponds, poetry wall,
moon portal, and "tea house of hearing pines"; also a Garden of Healing honoring
victims of the 9/11 World Trade Center disaster.

Wave Hill Sales and Events★
West 249th Street and Independence Avenue, Bronx, NY 10471
(718) 549-3200; www.wavehill.org
Year-round, a hip new shop with distinctive garden, educational, and gift items, including an exclusive handcrafted lawn chair (a modified version of the Reitveld chair, designed in 1918); in a 28-acre garden landscape of exceptional beauty, with greenhouses and urban woodland; arts activities, concerts, exhibits, and lectures focusing on art and nature; March kite festival.

Eastern New York

Capital District Garden and Flower Show★
Hudson Valley Community College, 80 Vandenburg Avenue (Route 4), Troy, NY 12180
(518) 629-4829; www.gardenandflowershow.com
Third week of March, a large Albany-area flower show with gardens, floral arrangements, lectures, demonstrations, advice, and a large marketplace.

IES Spring Plant Sale★
Institute of Ecosystem Studies, 181 Sharon Turnpike, Millbrook NY 12545-0178
(845) 677-5359; www.ecostudies.org
Third week of May, a plant sale with a broad selection of choice perennials and woody plants, benefiting the IES horticulture program.

Landis Arboretum Spring and Fall Plant Sales★
174 Lape Road, Esperance, NY 12066
(518) 875-6935; www.landisarboretum.org
May and September, annual spring and fall plant sales with unusual and extra-hardy plants and used books, in a 200-acre arboretum.

Montgomery Place Spring Garden Festival
Montgomery Place, River Road (Route 103), Annandale-on-Hudson, NY 12504
(914) 758-5461; www.hudsonvalley.org
Mid-May, horticultural show with lectures, workshops, and a plant-and-garden sale. In season, a museum shop and farm stand, on a 434-acre Hudson River estate with magnificent views and gardens.

Central and Western New York

Buffalo & Erie County Botanical Gardens Events
2655 South Park Avenue, Buffalo, NY 14218
(716) 827-1584; www.buffalogardens.com
Three annual flower shows—spring bulbs, fall chrysanthemums, and winter poinsettias. Seasonal shows and sales for coleus, iris, bonsai, and orchids, in a Victorian conservatory and Frederick Law Olmsted park.

Farmers' Museum Spring Festival
The Farmers' Museum, Lake Road (Route 80), Cooperstown, NY 13326
(888) 547-1450; www.fenimoreartmuseum.org
Memorial Day weekend, annual sheep shearing festival with sale of hard-to-find heirloom plants and seeds in the museum's heritage gardens.

GardenScape★★
Gardenscape Professionals Landscape Association
Dome Center, 2695 East Henrietta Road (Route 15), Henrietta, NY
(585) 265-9018; www.rochesterflowershow.com
Mid-March, renowned Rochester-area event with landscaped garden displays, seminars and demonstrations, and a large well-stocked Gardener's Marketplace.

Highland Park Lilac Festival★
Monroe County Parks Department
Highland Park, Highland Avenue, Rochester, NY
www.lilacfestival.com
Mid-May, celebrated lilac festival with many entertaining events; coincides with peak bloom of the park's lilac collection (500 varieties), the largest in North America, in a 155-acre municipal arboretum designed by Frederick Law Olmsted. During the festival, lilac plants are sold at Lamberton Conservatory, 180 Reservoir Drive, Rochester, to benefit the park (mcparks@co.monroe.ny.us).

Plantasia Flower and Garden Show
Western New York State Nursery and Landscape Association
Late march/early April, Hamburg Fairgrounds, Hamburg, NY (near Buffalo)
www.plantasiany.com

Long Island

Hofstra University Arboretum Flower and Garden Show
Hofstra University Arena, North Campus, Hempstead, NY 11549
(516) 463-6504; www.hofstra.edu/COM/Arbor
Mid-April, Garden Marketplace with local and regional vendors, horticultural displays, floral competition, and educational exhibits; in a 240-acre campus arboretum.

Old Westbury Plant Sale & Arbor Day Celebration
Old Westbury Gardens, 71 Old Westbury Road, Old Westbury, NY 11568
(516) 333-0048; www.oldwestburygardens.org
Opening day plant sale at historic Gold coast estate (see profile).

Spring Flower and Garden Show
Hicks Nurseries, 100 Jericho Turnpike, Westbury, NY 11590
(516) 334-0066; www.hicksnurseries.com
Early March, horticultural fair with garden displays, seminars, cooking demonstrations, children's events, in a commercial garden center (see profile).

New Jersey

Colonial Park Arboretum's Garden Events
156 Mettlers Road, East Millstone, NJ
(732) 873-2459; www.somersetcountyparks.org
Early June, Rose Day, and mid-July, Garden Party, with lectures, demonstrations, live music, and sale of garden items. Rose Day coincides with thousands of blooming roses.

Earth Day Celebration and Plant Sale
Leonard J. Buck Garden Visitor's Center, 11 Layton Road, Far Hills, NJ 07931
(908) 234-2677; www.somersetcountyparks.org
Third week in April, garden tours, lectures, and plant sale at a significant rock and woodland garden.

Frelinghuysen Arboretum's Plant Sales★★
53 East Hanover Avenue, Morristown, NJ 07962
(973) 326-7600; www.parks.morris.nj.us
First Saturday in May, large and sophisticated Spring Plant Sale focusing on an

annual garden theme; mid-September, Harvest Show and Plant Sale with judged exhibits, lectures, plant sales, and family entertainment.
Mid-October, National Chrysanthemum Society Show

Garden State Home Show
Garden State Convention Center, 50 Atrium Drive, Somerset, NJ
(800) 811-7469; www.macevents.com
Early February, show gardens by area landscapers with large home-and-garden marketplace.

Reeves-Reed Arboretum Events
Reeves Reed Arboretum, 165 Hobart Avenue, Summit, NJ 07901
(908) 273-8787; www.reeves-reedarboretum.org
Annual plant auction and garden tours.

Rutgers Gardens' Plant Sales★
Rutgers Gardens, Cook College, 112 Ryders Lane, New Brunswick, NJ 08901
(732) 932-8451; http://aesop.rutgers.edu/~rugardens/
Mid-May, Rutgers Gardens' Spring Flower Fair and Agricultural Field Day, a huge sale of landscape plants grown on campus, concurrent with the New Jersey folk festival; late July, Open House, and mid-October, Fall Foliage Festival; with garden tours, lectures, and plant sales in a 50-acre botanical collection dating to 1932.

Sayen Botanical Garden's Open House Events
155 Hughes Drive, Hamilton Square, NJ 08690
(609) 890-3543; www.sayengardens.org
April, Daffodil Days, and mid-May, Mother's Day Azalea Festival; peak bloom periods at a 30-acre garden with 250,000 bulbs and 1500 azaleas and rhododendrons.

Skylands Spring Festival & Plant Sale★
New Jersey Botanical Garden at Skylands, Morris Road, Ringwood, NJ 07456
(973) 962-9534; www.njbg.org
Mid-May; excellent plant sale with unusual material, plus house and garden tours; a botanical treasure with crabapple allée, lilacs, and unusual flowering trees.

Southern New Jersey Home & Garden Show
Atlantic City Convention Center, Atlantic City, NJ
(830) 980-4078; www.showtechnology.com

Late March/early April; a large indoor display, celebrity speakers, and a home-and-garden vendor marketplace.

Spring Water Garden Festival
Deep Cut Gardens, Monmouth County Park System, 352 Red Hill Road, Middletown, NJ
(732) 671-6050; www.monmouthcountyparks.com
Mid-June water-garden festival with displays, lectures, and a vendor marketplace.

Pennsylvania

Bowman's Hill Wildflower Preserve Plant Sales★
1635 River Road (Route 32), New Hope, PA 18938
(215) 862-2924; www.bhwp.org
Spring and Fall Native Plant Sales, with 200 species of high-quality native wildflowers, trees, shrubs, vines, and ferns native to the region. Native plant sale catalog, mail-order seed catalog, and plant information sheets posted on Web site. In season, native plants sold at the Visitor Center; in a 200-acre Bucks County wildflower preserve with woodland trails, classes.

Historic Bartram's Garden Plant Sale★
54th Street and Lindbergh Boulevard, Philadelphia, PA 19143
(215) 729-5281; www.bartramsgarden.org
First week of May, Native Plant Sale with Franklin trees and other treasures in the Bartram barnyard, outside the oldest barn in Pennsylvania.

Philadelphia Flower Show★★
Pennsylvania Convention Center, 12th and Arch Streets, Philadelphia, PA 19107
(215) 988-8833; www.theflowershow.com
The region's preeminent plant show and sale, with gorgeous displays and exceptional vendors, sponsored by the Pennsylvania Horticultural Society (www.pennsylvania horticulturalsociety.org). PHS also sells plants at Meadowbrook Farm, a 25-acre nonprofit affiliate (www.meadowbrook-farm.com) in the Philadelphia suburbs.

SELECTED GARDENING BOOKS

The American Horticultural Society A-Z Encyclopedia of Garden Plants
Edited by Christopher Brickell and Judy Zuk. A monumental reference
profiling 15,000 garden plants, with color photos, cultivation advice for each
genus, and a useful glossary of horticultural terms—an instant classic, widely
used. Zuk is president of the Brooklyn Botanic Garden.

The Brooklyn Botanic Garden Handbooks
An excellent series of garden handbooks published by the Brooklyn Botanic
Garden on practical topics; favorites are *The Potted Garden* and *Indoor Bonsai;*
sold by mail order (*www.bbg.org*).

The City Gardener's Handbook:The Definitive Guide to Small-Space Gardening
By Linda Yang
A terrific general reference for urban and small-space gardening, by a well-
known garden writer with personal experience gardening on a penthouse
roof and dark urban backyard.

Gardener's Desk Reference
Edited by Janet Marinelli (Brooklyn Botanic Garden)
Comprehensive general reference for North American gardeners, with
contributions from 20 experts. Marinelli is the Brooklyn Botanic Garden's
director of publishing and author of *Stalking the Wild Amaranth: Gardening in
the Age of Extinction.*

Garden Guide: New York City
By Nancy Berner and Susan Lowry
An indispensable pocket-size guide to gardens in New York City's five
boroughs: public parks, museums, community gardens, and other peaceful
enclosures.

A Garden Lover's Guide to the Northeast
By Paul Bennett
Enjoyable descriptions of 140 of the most beautiful public gardens in the
Northeast (including New York and New Jersey), by a senior editor of
Landscape Architecture magazine.

Gardenscapes
Text by Verlyn Klinkenborg, photographs by Lynn Geesaman
Reflections on garden landscapes by *New York Times* editor Verlyn Klinkenborg, with eerie, unexpectedly beautiful photography. Klinkenborg's other well-loved titles are *The Rural Life*, essays on the American landscape, and *Making Hay*, a memoir of haying on an uncle's farm.

Horticulture Magazine: *www.hortmag.com*
"The Horticulture 100" lists the magazine editors' top-100 classic garden books.

The Natural History of New York
By Stan Freeman and Mike Nasuti
Short natural history listing New York's common wildflowers, trees, birds, butterflies, and pond life, with good summaries of major ecosystems, climate, and geology.

New Jersey Gardener's Guide
By Pegi Ballister-Howells
A compendium of plants for New Jersey gardens—trees, shrubs, vines, roses, grasses, perennials, lawns, ground covers, bulbs, annuals, and seashore plants—with planting and maintenance instructions.

The New York Times 1000 Gardening Questions and Answers
By Leslie Land, Bobbi Angell, Elayne Sears
A gardener's reference based on the *New York Times* Column, "Gardeners Q & A."

The New York/Mid-Atlantic Gardener's Book of Lists
By Bonnie Lee Appleton and Lois Trigg Chaplin
Plant lists for every possible use in New York and New Jersey.

New York State Farm Fresh Guides
Free paperback guides to roadside farm markets, wineries, cheese makers, and community farmers' markets. Separate editions for New York's Metro, Eastern, Central and Western regions. Also published online (*www.agmkt.state.ny.us*).

Orchid Growing for Wimps
By Ellen Zachos
Insightful orchid-growing guide, with orchid profiles and step-by-step instructions for easy and tricky varieties; perfect for city gardeners. Zachos is a greenhouse landscaper, garden writer, and contributor to the Brooklyn Botanical Garden's *Landscaping Indoors.*

The Passion for Gardening: Inspiration for a Lifetime
By Ken Druse *(www.kendruse.com)*
An account of ten extraordinary gardens by New York's most prominent garden writer and photographer, winner of "Best Book of the Year" from the American Horticultural Society. Druse's other titles include *The Natural Garden, The Natural Shade Garden, The Natural Habitat Garden, The Collector's Garden,* and *Making More Plants: The Science, Art, and Joy of Propagation.*

Jane Pepper's Garden: Getting the Most Pleasure and Growing Results from Your Garden Every Month of the Year
By Jane G. Pepper
A useful guide for growing flowers, vegetables, herbs, and houseplants throughout the year. Pepper is the president of the Pennsylvania Horticultural Society and a well-known garden columnist.

Roses of America: The Brooklyn Botanic Garden's Guide to Our National Flower
By Stephen Scanniello
An introduction to the 200 best roses for North American gardens. Scanniello is an expert horticulturist and former rosarian of the Brooklyn Botanic Garden; other titles include *Climbing Roses* and the BBG's *Easy Care Roses: Low Maintenance Charmers.*

The Tri-State Gardener's Guide: New York, New Jersey, Connecticut
By Ralph Snodsmith
Plants recommended for Tri-State gardens, with special advice on city, small-space, and seaside gardens. Snodsmith is a noted garden expert and radio host.

INDEX TO PLANT SOURCES

Sources of special merit are marked ★

African Violets
Lyndon Lyon Greenhouses, Dolgeville, NY★
The Violet Barn, Naples, NY★

Alpines and Rock Garden Plants
Ambleside Gardens, Belle Mead, NJ★
Fort Pond Native Plants, Montauk, NY
Hicks Nurseries, Westbury, NY
Jane's Herb Farm, Webster, NY
The Magic Garden, Newfield, NY
Marders Garden Shop, Bridgehampton, NY
Mountain Pine Nursery, Warwick, NY
Palmiter's Garden Nursery, Avon, NY
The Plantsmen Nursery, Groton, NY★
Rohsler's Allendale Nursery, Allendale, NJ
Rosedale Nurseries, Hawthorne, NY
Schroon Falls Farm, Schroon Lake, NY
Stonecrop Gardens, Cold Spring, NY★★
Stony Hill Farm, Binghamton, NY
Talmage Farm Agway, Riverhead, NY
Trimble's of Corchaug Nursery, Cutchogue, NY
Zena Green Nursery, Kingston, NY★

Annuals and Tender Perennials
Ambleside Gardens, Belle Mead, NJ
Anything Grows Flower Farm, Barnegat, NJ★
Atlock Farm, Somerset, NJ
Barlow Flower Farm, Sea Girt, NJ★
Beds & Borders, Laurel, NY★★
Claire's Garden Center, Patterson, NY
Faddegon's Nursery, Latham, NY
Godlewsky Farms, Great Meadows, NJ★
Graceful Gardens, Mecklenburg, NY
Hicks Nurseries, Westbury, NY★
Landcraft Environments, Mattituck, NY★★
Loomis Creek Nursery, Hudson, NY★
The Magic Garden, Newfield, NY
Marders Garden Shop, Bridgehampton, NY
Martin Viette Nurseries, East Norwich, NY
Mountain Pine Nursery, Warwick, NY
Nabel's Nurseries, White Plains, NY★
Old Westbury Gardens, Old Westbury, NY★
Palmiter's Garden Nursery, Avon, NY
Peconic River Herb Farm, Calverton, NY
The Plantsmen Nursery, Groton, NY★
Popes' Gardens, Waterford, NJ
Rochester Public Market, Rochester, NY
Rosedale Nurseries, Hawthorne, NY
Schroon Falls Farm, Schroon Lake, NY
Sprainbrook Nursery, Scarsdale, NY★
Talmage Farm Agway, Riverhead, NY
Trimble's of Corchaug Nursery, Cutchogue, NY★
Zena Green Nursery, Kingston, NY★

Aquatic and Water Garden Plants

Ambleside Gardens, Belle Mead, NJ
Cape May Bird Observatory, Goshen, NJ
Catskill Native Nursery, Kerhonkson, NY
Fort Pond Native Plants, Montauk, NY
Helderledge Farm, Altamont, NY
Hicks Nurseries, Westbury, NY
Masterson's Aquatic Nursery, East Aurora, NY★
Matterhorn Nursery, Spring Valley, NY★
Mountain Pine Nursery, Warwick, NY
Peconic River Herb Farm, Calverton, NY
Popes' Gardens, Waterford, NJ
Rohsler's Allendale Nursery, Allendale, NJ
Rosedale Nurseries, Hawthorne, NY
S. Scherer & Sons, Northport, NY★★
Sprainbrook Nursery, Scarsdale, NY
Trimble's of Corchaug Nursery, Cutchogue, NY
Waterford Gardens, Saddle River, NJ★★

Bamboo

Little Acre Farm, Howell, NJ★★
Rohsler's Allendale Nursery, Allendale, NJ

Bonsai

International Bonsai, Rochester, NY★★
Japan Nursery, Monroe Township, NJ★
Oriental Garden Supply, Pittsford, NY

Books—Horticulture

Cape May Bird Observatory, Goshen, NJ★
Fort Pond Native Plants, Montauk, NY
Hicks Nurseries, Westbury, NY
Marders Garden Shop, Bridgehampton, NY★
Martin Viette Nurseries, East Norwich, NY
Old Westbury Gardens, Old Westbury, NY
Rosedale Nurseries, Hawthorne, NY
St. Lawrence Nurseries, Potsdam, NY
Sylvan Botanicals New York Ginseng, Cooperstown, NY
Talmage Farm Agway, Riverhead, NY
Triple Oaks Nursery & Herb Garden, Franklinville, NJ★
Turtle Tree Seeds, Copake, NY
Waterford Gardens, Saddle River, NJ★
Well-Sweep Herb Farm, Port Murray, NJ★

Bulbs

Al Dolinski & Son Dahlias, Franklinville, NJ★
Harris Seeds, Rochester, NY
Hicks Nurseries, Westbury, NY
International Bulb Company, Montvale, NJ★★
Jane's Herb Farm, Webster, NY
Marders Garden Shop, Bridgehampton, NY
Martin Viette Nurseries, East Norwich, NY
Rohsler's Allendale Nursery, Allendale, NJ
Rosedale Nurseries, Hawthorne, NY
Sprainbrook Nursery, Scarsdale, NY

Summerville Gladiolus Worldwide,
   Mullica Hill, NJ★
Talmage Farm Agway, Riverhead, NY
The Temple Nursery,
   Trumansburg, NY★
Van Bourgondien Bros., Babylon,
   NY★★
Van Dyck's Flower Bulbs,
   Brightwaters, NY★★

Camellia
Fairweather Gardens, Greenwich, NJ★
Pleasant Run Nursery, Allentown, NJ
Roslyn Nursery, Dix Hills, NY★
Triple Oaks Nursery & Herb Garden,
   Franklinville, NJ

Christmas Trees and Holiday Plants
Ambleside Gardens, Belle Mead, NJ
Anything Grows Flower Farm,
   Barnegat, NJ
Barlow Flower Farm, Sea Girt, NJ
Godlewsky Farms, Great Meadows, NJ
Hicks Nurseries, Westbury, NY
Holmes Hollow Farm, Victor, NY
Marders Garden Shop,
   Bridgehampton, NY★
Martin Viette Nurseries, East
   Norwich, NY
Nabel's Nurseries, White Plains, NY★
Rohsler's Allendale Nursery,
   Allendale, NJ
Rosedale Nurseries, Hawthorne, NY
Sprainbrook Nursery, Scarsdale, NY★
Trimble's of Corchaug Nursery,
   Cutchogue, NY★
Triple Oaks Nursery & Herb Garden,
   Franklinville, NJ
Well-Sweep Herb Farm, Port
   Murray, NJ

Chrysanthemum
Anything Grows Flower Farm,
   Barnegat, NJ★
Bakers' Acres, Groton, NY
Barlow Flower Farm, Sea Girt, NJ
Hicks Nurseries, Westbury, NY
Martin Viette Nurseries, East
   Norwich, NY
Mountain Pine Nursery, Warwick, NY
Nabel's Nurseries, White Plains, NY
Palmiter's Garden Nursery, Avon, NY
Peconic River Herb Farm,
   Calverton, NY
Rohsler's Allendale Nursery,
   Allendale, NJ
Rosedale Nurseries, Hawthorne, NY
Sprainbrook Nursery, Scarsdale, NY
Talmage Farm Agway, Riverhead, NY

Clematis (*See also* Vines and Climbing Plants)
Spring Valley Greenhouse,
   Walworth, NY★★
Van Bourgondien Bros., Babylon, NY

Cold Hardy (Zone 4) Plants
Claire's Garden Center, Patterson, NY
Schroon Falls Farm, Schroon Lake,
   NY★★
St. Lawrence Nurseries, Potsdam, NY★
Turtle Tree Seeds, Copake, NY
Well-Sweep Herb Farm, Port
   Murray, NJ

Coleus
Anything Grows Flower Farm,
   Barnegat, NJ
Barlow Flower Farm, Sea Girt, NJ
Beds & Borders, Laurel, NY★
Hicks Nurseries, Westbury, NY

Coleus *continued*

Landcraft Environments,
Mattituck, NY★★

Loomis Creek Nursery, Hudson, NY★

Collector's Plants

Ambleside Gardens, Belle Mead, NJ

Atlock Farm, Somerset, NJ

Azalea House, Voorheesville, NY

The Bayberry Nursery,
Amagansett, NY★

Bedlam Gardens, King Ferry, NY

Blue Sterling Nursery, Bridgeton, NJ★

Cross Country Nurseries,
Rosemont, NJ

Dave's Nursery, Hillsborough, NJ★

Der Rosenmeister, Ithaca, NY

Fairweather Gardens,
Greenwich, NJ★★

Henry Leuthardt Nurseries, East
Moriches, NY★

Hildebrant Nurseries, Oldwick, NJ★

International Bonsai, Rochester, NY★

Kale's Nursery and Landscape Service,
Princeton, NJ★

Landcraft Environments,
Mattituck, NY★

Little Acre Farm, Howell, NJ

Loomis Creek Nursery, Hudson, NY★

Mapleton Nurseries, Kingston, NJ

Marders Garden Shop,
Bridgehampton, NY★

Phoenix Flower Farm, Phoenix, NY★

The Plantsmen Nursery, Groton, NY★

Pleasant Run Nursery,
Allentown, NJ★★

RareFind Nursery, Jackson, NJ★★

Rosedale Nurseries, Hawthorne, NY

Roslyn Nursery, Dix Hills, NY★★

Seneca Hill Perennials,
Oswego, NY★★

Smirnow's Son's Peonies,
Huntington, NY★

Steven Kristoph Nursery,
Englishtown, NJ★★

Stonecrop Gardens, Cold Spring, NY★

The Temple Nursery,
Trumansburg, NY

The-Run-De-Quot Gardens,
Irondequoit, NY

Triple Oaks Nursery & Herb Garden,
Franklinville, NJ

Waterford Gardens, Saddle River, NJ

Zena Green Nursery, Kingston, NY

Container Plants

Anything Grows Flower Farm,
Barnegat, NJ★

Atlock Farm, Somerset, NJ★

Bakers' Acres, Groton, NY

Barlow Flower Farm, Sea Girt, NJ★

Beds & Borders, Laurel, NY★★

Bumps & Co., West Nyack, NY

Claire's Garden Center, Patterson, NY

Godlewsky Farms, Great
Meadows, NJ★

Hicks Nurseries, Westbury, NY

Landcraft Environments,
Mattituck, NY★★

Loomis Creek Nursery, Hudson, NY★

The Magic Garden, Newfield, NY

Marders Garden Shop,
Bridgehampton, NY

Martin Viette Nurseries, East
Norwich, NY

Nabel's Nurseries, White Plains, NY

Old Westbury Gardens, Old
Westbury, NY★

Palmiter's Garden Nursery, Avon, NY

Peconic River Herb Farm,
Calverton, NY

The Plantsmen Nursery, Groton, NY★

Cottage-Garden Plants (*See also* Annuals and Perennials)

Cut Flowers and Florist

Daffodil Bulbs (*See* Bulbs)

Dahlias (*See also* Bulbs)

Dahlias *continued*

Bakers' Acres, Groton, NY

International Bulb Company,
Montvale, NJ

Marders Garden Shop,
Bridgehampton, NY

Van Bourgondien Bros., Babylon, NY

Van Dyck's Flower Bulbs,
Brightwaters, NY★

Daylilies

Anything Grows Flower Farm,
Barnegat, NJ

Bakers' Acres, Groton, NY

Cottage Gardens, Medina, NY★

Grace Gardens, Penn Yan, NY★

Hicks Nurseries, Westbury, NY

LorJon Nursery, Pine Bush, NY

Marders Garden Shop,
Bridgehampton, NY

Martin Viette Nurseries, East
Norwich, NY

Mountain Pine Nursery, Warwick, NY

Nabel's Nurseries, White Plains, NY

North Country Daylilies, Saratoga
Springs, NY★★

Palmiter's Garden Nursery, Avon, NY

Peconic River Herb Farm, Calverton,
NY

Popes' Gardens, Waterford, NJ

Rosedale Nurseries, Hawthorne, NY

Roslyn Nursery, Dix Hills, NY

Sprainbrook Nursery, Scarsdale, NY

Talmage Farm Agway, Riverhead, NY

Trimble's of Corchaug Nursery,
Cutchogue, NY

Van Bourgondien Bros., Babylon, NY

VerDerBer's Garden Center,
Aquebogue, NY

Woodside Nursery, Bridgeton, NJ★★

Display Gardens

Amanda's Garden, Springwater, NY★

Ambleside Gardens, Belle Mead, NJ

Atlock Farm, Somerset, NJ★

Bakers' Acres, Groton, NY

The Bayberry Nursery, Amagansett,
NY★

Beds & Borders, Laurel, NY★

Blue Sterling Nursery, Bridgeton, NJ★

Cape May Bird Observatory, Goshen,
NJ★

Catskill Native Nursery, Kerhonkson,
NY★

Fort Pond Native Plants, Montauk,
NY

Harris Seeds, Rochester, NY

Helderledge Farm, Altamont, NY★

Hicks Nurseries, Westbury, NY

Hildebrant Nurseries, Oldwick, NJ★

International Bonsai, Rochester,
NY★★

Jane's Herb Farm, Webster, NY★★

Kale's Nursery and Landscape Service,
Princeton, NJ

Landcraft Environments, Mattituck,
NY★★

Loomis Creek Nursery, Hudson,
NY★★

LorJon Nursery, Pine Bush, NY★

Marders Garden Shop,
Bridgehampton, NY★

Martin Viette Nurseries, East
Norwich, NY★

Masterson's Aquatic Nursery, East
Aurora, NY

Miller Nurseries, Canandaigua, NY

Mountain Pine Nursery, Warwick,
NY★

North Country Daylilies, Saratoga
Springs, NY★

Old Westbury Gardens, Old Westbury, NY★★
Ornamental Plantings, Southold, NY
Palmiter's Garden Nursery, Avon, NY★★
Peconic River Herb Farm, Calverton, NY★★
The Plantsmen Nursery, Groton, NY★
RareFind Nursery, Jackson, NJ★
Schroon Falls Farm, Schroon Lake, NY★
Sprainbrook Nursery, Scarsdale, NY
Stonecrop Gardens, Cold Spring, NY★★
Stony Hill Farm, Binghamton, NY★
Trimble's of Corchaug Nursery, Cutchogue, NY★
Triple Oaks Nursery & Herb Garden, Franklinville, NJ★
Waterford Gardens, Saddle River, NJ★★
Well-Sweep Herb Farm, Port Murray, NJ★

Dwarf and Unusual Conifers
(*See also* Trees—Evergreens)
Ambleside Gardens, Belle Mead, NJ
The Bayberry Nursery, Amagansett, NY
Blue Sterling Nursery, Bridgeton, NJ★★
Dave's Nursery, Hillsborough, NJ★★
Hicks Nurseries, Westbury, NY
Hildebrant Nurseries, Oldwick, NJ★
Kale's Nursery and Landscape Service, Princeton, NJ
Marders Garden Shop, Bridgehampton, NY★
Martin Viette Nurseries, East Norwich, NY★

Nabel's Nurseries, White Plains, NY
Palmiter's Garden Nursery, Avon, NY
The Plantsmen Nursery, Groton, NY
Rohsler's Allendale Nursery, Allendale, NJ★
Rosedale Nurseries, Hawthorne, NY★
Roslyn Nursery, Dix Hills, NY★★
Schroon Falls Farm, Schroon Lake, NY
Sprainbrook Nursery, Scarsdale, NY
Stony Hill Farm, Binghamton, NY
Talmage Farm Agway, Riverhead, NY
VerDerBer's Garden Center, Aquebogue, NY★

Everlastings (*See also* Herb Plants)
Jane's Herb Farm, Webster, NY
Peconic River Herb Farm, Calverton, NY
Triple Oaks Nursery & Herb Garden, Franklinville, NJ
Well-Sweep Herb Farm, Port Murray, NJ

Ferns
Amanda's Garden, Springwater, NY
Ambleside Gardens, Belle Mead, NJ
The Bayberry Nursery, Amagansett, NY
Catskill Native Nursery, Kerhonkson, NY
Helderledge Farm, Altamont, NY
Hicks Nurseries, Westbury, NY
Landcraft Environments, Mattituck, NY
Loomis Creek Nursery, Hudson, NY
LorJon Nursery, Pine Bush, NY
Mapleton Nurseries, Kingston, NJ
Marders Garden Shop, Bridgehampton, NY
Palmiter's Garden Nursery, Avon, NY

Ferns *continued*

Peconic River Herb Farm, Calverton, NY

The Plantsmen Nursery, Groton, NY

Pleasant Run Nursery, Allentown, NJ

Rohsler's Allendale Nursery, Allendale, NJ

Rosedale Nurseries, Hawthorne, NY

Roslyn Nursery, Dix Hills, NY

Schroon Falls Farm, Schroon Lake, NY

Talmage Farm Agway, Riverhead, NY

Well-Sweep Herb Farm, Port Murray, NJ

Fruit Plants

Bakers' Acres, Groton, NY

Cape May Bird Observatory, Goshen, NJ★

Catskill Native Nursery, Kerhonkson, NY★

Cummins Nursery, Geneva, NY★

Henry Leuthardt Nurseries, East Moriches, NY★

Jersey Asparagus Farms, Pittsgrove, NJ

Martin Viette Nurseries, East Norwich, NY

Miller Nurseries, Canandaigua, NY★

St. Lawrence Nurseries, Potsdam, NY★★

Well-Sweep Herb Farm, Port Murray, NJ

Fruit Trees

The Catholic Homesteading Movement, Norwich, NY★★

Catskill Native Nursery, Kerhonkson, NY★

Cummins Nursery, Geneva, NY★★

Henry Leuthardt Nurseries, East Moriches, NY★

Hicks Nurseries, Westbury, NY

John Gordon Nursery, Amherst, NY★★

Marders Garden Shop, Bridgehampton, NY

Miller Nurseries, Canandaigua, NY★

Rohsler's Allendale Nursery, Allendale, NJ

Rosedale Nurseries, Hawthorne, NY

Schroon Falls Farm, Schroon Lake, NY

St. Lawrence Nurseries, Potsdam, NY★★

Gladiolus

International Bulb Company, Montvale, NJ

Summerville Gladiolus Worldwide, Mullica Hill, NJ★★

Van Bourgondien Bros., Babylon, NY

Van Dyck's Flower Bulbs, Brightwaters, NY★

Grasses

Amberg Perennial Farm, Scotch Plains, NJ

Ambleside Gardens, Belle Mead, NJ

Anything Grows Flower Farm, Barnegat, NJ

Atlock Farm, Somerset, NJ

Bakers' Acres, Groton, NY

The Bayberry Nursery, Amagansett, NY

Cape May Bird Observatory, Goshen, NJ★

Catskill Native Nursery, Kerhonkson, NY

Church's Beachgrass and Nursery, Cape May, NJ★

Claire's Garden Center, Patterson, NY

Fort Pond Native Plants, Montauk, NY★

Helderledge Farm, Altamont, NY★

Herb Plants *continued*

Marders Garden Shop,
Bridgehampton, NY

Martin Viette Nurseries, East
Norwich, NY

Mountain Pine Nursery, Warwick, NY

Nabel's Nurseries, White Plains, NY

Old Westbury Gardens, Old Westbury,
NY

Ornamental Plantings, Southold, NY

Palmiter's Garden Nursery, Avon, NY

Peconic River Herb Farm, Calverton,
NY★★

The Plantsmen Nursery, Groton, NY

Rochester Public Market, Rochester,
NY★

Rohsler's Allendale Nursery,
Allendale, NJ

Rosedale Nurseries, Hawthorne, NY

Schroon Falls Farm, Schroon Lake, NY

Sprainbrook Nursery, Scarsdale, NY

Stony Hill Farm, Binghamton, NY

Talmage Farm Agway, Riverhead, NY

Trimble's of Corchaug Nursery,
Cutchogue, NY

Triple Oaks Nursery & Herb Garden,
Franklinville, NJ★★

Union Square Greenmarket, New
York, NY★

Well-Sweep Herb Farm, Port Murray,
NJ★★

Hosta (*See* Perennials—Shade)

Houseplants (*See* Tropical and
Conservatory Plants)

Hybridizers

Atlock Farm, Somerset, NJ (dwarf
amaryllis)

The Catholic Homesteading
Movement, Norwich, NY (fruits)

Cummins Nursery, Geneva, NY (apple
rootstock)

John Gordon Nursery, Amherst, NY
(nut trees)★

Hildebrant Nurseries, Oldwick, NJ
(boxwood)

North Country Daylilies, Saratoga
Springs, NY (daylilies)

Ornamental Plantings, Southold, NY
(grasses)

P & P Seed Company, Hamburg, NY
(big vegetables)★

RareFind Nursery, Jackson, NJ
(rhododendrons)

Roslyn Nursery, Dix Hills, NY
(rhododendrons)

Summerville Gladiolus Worldwide,
Mullica Hill, NJ (gladiolus)

Woodside Nursery, Bridgeton, NJ
(daylilies)★

Iris (*See also* Perennials—Sun)

Borglum's Iris Gardens, Geneva, NY★

International Bulb Company,
Montvale, NJ

Phoenix Flower Farm, Phoenix,
NY★★

Seneca Hill Perennials, Oswego, NY

Waterford Gardens, Saddle River, NJ

Jack-in-the-pulpit (*See also*
Native Plants and Wildflowers)

Seneca Hill Perennials, Oswego, NY★

Japanese Maples (*See also* Trees—
Ornamental and Shade)

Ambleside Gardens, Belle Mead, NJ

Blue Sterling Nursery, Bridgeton, NJ

Native Plants and Wildflowers

Amanda's Garden, Springwater, NY★★
Ambleside Gardens, Belle Mead, NJ
Bakers' Acres, Groton, NY
The Bayberry Nursery, Amagansett, NY★
Bumps & Co., West Nyack, NY★
Cape May Bird Observatory, Goshen, NJ★★
Catskill Native Nursery, Kerhonkson, NY★★
Church's Beachgrass and Nursery, Cape May, NJ★
Fort Pond Native Plants, Montauk, NY★★
Helderledge Farm, Altamont, NY
Hicks Nurseries, Westbury, NY
Holmes Hollow Farm, Victor, NY★
Jane's Herb Farm, Webster, NY
John Gordon Nursery, Amherst, NY★
LorJon Nursery, Pine Bush, NY
Mapleton Nurseries, Kingston, NJ★
Mountain Pine Nursery, Warwick, NY
Nabel's Nurseries, White Plains, NY
Ornamental Plantings, Southold, NY
Palmiter's Garden Nursery, Avon, NY
Pinelands Nursery, Columbus, NJ★★
The Plantsmen Nursery, Groton, NY
Pleasant Run Nursery, Allentown, NJ
Rohsler's Allendale Nursery, Allendale, NJ
Rosedale Nurseries, Hawthorne, NY
Roslyn Nursery, Dix Hills, NY★
Schroon Falls Farm, Schroon Lake, NY
Seneca Hill Perennials, Oswego, NY★
Sheffield's Seed Company, Locke, NY★★
Shepherd Hill Farm, Putnam Valley, NY
St. Lawrence Nurseries, Potsdam, NY★
Stonecrop Gardens, Cold Spring, NY

Stony Hill Farm, Binghamton, NY
Sylvan Botanicals New York Ginseng, Cooperstown, NY★★
Talmage Farm Agway, Riverhead, NY★
Toadshade Wildflower Farm, Frenchtown, NJ★★
Trimble's of Corchaug Nursery, Cutchogue, NY
Triple Oaks Nursery & Herb Garden, Franklinville, NJ★
Well-Sweep Herb Farm, Port Murray, NJ
White Oak Nursery, Canandaigua, NY★★

Nut Trees

John Gordon Nursery, Amherst, NY★★
Miller Nurseries, Canandaigua, NY★
Saratoga Tree Nursery, Saratoga Springs, NY
Sheffield's Seed Company, Locke, NY★
St. Lawrence Nurseries, Potsdam, NY★★
Triple Oaks Nursery & Herb Garden, Franklinville, NJ
White Oak Nursery, Canandaigua, NY

Orchids

Lyndon Lyon Greenhouses, Dolgeville, NY
Marders Garden Shop, Bridgehampton, NY
Marlow Orchids, Scottsville, NY★
Waldor Orchids, Linwood, NJ★★

Organic Garden Supplies

Catskill Native Nursery, Kerhonkson, NY★

Gunning River Herbs, Barnegat, NJ
Harris Seeds, Rochester, NY
Hicks Nurseries, Westbury, NY
LorJon Nursery, Pine Bush, NY
Marders Garden Shop,
  Bridgehampton, NY★★
Peconic River Herb Farm, Calverton,
  NY
Rochester Public Market, Rochester,
  NY
Talmage Farm Agway, Riverhead, NY
Trimble's of Corchaug Nursery,
  Cutchogue, NY★
Well-Sweep Herb Farm, Port Murray,
  NJ

Organic Growers

Amanda's Garden, Springwater, NY★
Bumps & Co., West Nyack, NY★
Cape May Bird Observatory, Goshen,
  NJ★
The Catholic Homesteading
  Movement, Norwich, NY
Catskill Native Nursery, Kerhonkson,
  NY★
Cross Country Nurseries, Rosemont,
  NJ★
Graceful Gardens, Mecklenburg, NY
Gunning River Herbs, Barnegat, NJ★
Harris Seeds, Rochester, NY
Hicks Nurseries, Westbury, NY
Marders Garden Shop,
  Bridgehampton, NY★★
Rochester Public Market, Rochester,
  NY
St. Lawrence Nurseries, Potsdam, NY
Trimble's of Corchaug Nursery,
  Cutchogue, NY★
Turtle Tree Seeds, Copake, NY★★
White Oak Nursery, Canandaigua,
  NY★

Ornaments—Garden

Ambleside Gardens, Belle Mead, NJ
Anything Grows Flower Farm,
  Barnegat, NJ
Atlock Farm, Somerset, NJ★
Barlow Flower Farm, Sea Girt, NJ
The Bayberry Nursery, Amagansett,
  NY★★
Catskill Native Nursery, Kerhonkson,
  NY
Claire's Garden Center, Patterson, NY
Fort Pond Native Plants, Montauk,
  NY
Hicks Nurseries, Westbury, NY
Japan Nursery, Monroe Township, NJ★
Kale's Nursery and Landscape Service,
  Princeton, NJ
Loomis Creek Nursery, Hudson, NY★
Marders Garden Shop,
  Bridgehampton, NY★★
Martin Viette Nurseries, East
  Norwich, NY★
Mountain Pine Nursery, Warwick, NY
Peconic River Herb Farm, Calverton,
  NY★
The Plantsmen Nursery, Groton,
  NY★★
Rochester Public Market, Rochester,
  NY
Rosedale Nurseries, Hawthorne, NY
Schroon Falls Farm, Schroon Lake, NY
Sprainbrook Nursery, Scarsdale, NY
Stony Hill Farm, Binghamton, NY
Talmage Farm Agway, Riverhead, NY
Trimble's of Corchaug Nursery,
  Cutchogue, NY★
Triple Oaks Nursery & Herb Garden,
  Franklinville, NJ★
Well-Sweep Herb Farm, Port
  Murray, NJ

Peonies

Bakers' Acres, Groton, NY
Fort Pond Native Plants, Montauk, NY
Loomis Creek Nursery, Hudson, NY
LorJon Nursery, Pine Bush, NY
Marders Garden Shop,
    Bridgehampton, NY
Martin Viette Nurseries, East
    Norwich, NY
Miller Nurseries, Canandaigua, NY
Mountain Pine Nursery, Warwick, NY
Nabel's Nurseries, White Plains, NY
Old Westbury Gardens, Old Westbury,
    NY
Palmiter's Garden Nursery, Avon, NY★
Peconic River Herb Farm, Calverton,
    NY
The Plantsmen Nursery, Groton, NY
Pleasant Run Nursery, Allentown, NJ
Rohsler's Allendale Nursery,
    Allendale, NJ
Rosedale Nurseries, Hawthorne, NY
Schroon Falls Farm, Schroon Lake, NY
Seneca Hill Perennials, Oswego, NY★
Smirnow's Son's Peonies, Huntington,
    NY★
Sprainbrook Nursery, Scarsdale, NY
Stony Hill Farm, Binghamton, NY
Talmage Farm Agway, Riverhead, NY
Trimble's of Corchaug Nursery,
    Cutchogue, NY
Van Bourgondien Bros., Babylon, NY

Perennials—Seedlings (*See* Transplants)

Perennials—Shade

Amanda's Garden, Springwater, NY★
Amberg Perennial Farm, Scotch
    Plains, NJ

Ambleside Gardens, Belle Mead, NJ
Anything Grows Flower Farm,
    Barnegat, NJ
Bakers' Acres, Groton, NY
The Bayberry Nursery, Amagansett,
    NY★
Beaver Meadowlands, Java Center, NY
Cape May Bird Observatory, Goshen,
    NJ
Catskill Native Nursery, Kerhonkson,
    NY★
Claire's Garden Center, Patterson, NY
Faddegon's Nursery, Latham, NY
Fort Pond Native Plants, Montauk,
    NY
Godlewsky Farms, Great Meadows, NJ
Graceful Gardens, Mecklenburg, NY
Helderledge Farm, Altamont, NY
Hicks Nurseries, Westbury, NY
Jane's Herb Farm, Webster, NY
Kale's Nursery and Landscape Service,
    Princeton, NJ
Loomis Creek Nursery, Hudson, NY
LorJon Nursery, Pine Bush, NY★
Marders Garden Shop,
    Bridgehampton, NY
Martin Viette Nurseries, East
    Norwich, NY
Masterson's Aquatic Nursery, East
    Aurora, NY
Matterhorn Nursery, Spring Valley,
    NY★
Mountain Pine Nursery, Warwick, NY
Nabel's Nurseries, White Plains, NY★
Old Westbury Gardens, Old Westbury,
    NY
Ornamental Plantings, Southold, NY
Palmiter's Garden Nursery, Avon, NY★
Peconic River Herb Farm, Calverton,
    NY

The Plantsmen Nursery, Groton, NY
Pleasant Run Nursery, Allentown, NJ
Popes' Gardens, Waterford, NJ
Rochester Public Market, Rochester,
NY
Rohsler's Allendale Nursery,
Allendale, NJ
Rosedale Nurseries, Hawthorne, NY
Roslyn Nursery, Dix Hills, NY
Schroon Falls Farm, Schroon Lake, NY
Seneca Hill Perennials, Oswego, NY★
Sprainbrook Nursery, Scarsdale, NY
Stony Hill Farm, Binghamton, NY
Talmage Farm Agway, Riverhead, NY
Toadshade Wildflower Farm,
Frenchtown, NJ★
Trimble's of Corchaug Nursery,
Cutchogue, NY
Triple Oaks Nursery & Herb Garden,
Franklinville, NJ

Perennials—Sun
Amberg Perennial Farm, Scotch
Plains, NJ
Ambleside Gardens, Belle Mead, NJ
Anything Grows Flower Farm,
Barnegat, NJ★
Atlock Farm, Somerset, NJ
Bakers' Acres, Groton, NY★
Barlow Flower Farm, Sea Girt, NJ
The Bayberry Nursery, Amagansett,
NY
Beaver Meadowlands, Java Center, NY
Bumps & Co., West Nyack, NY★
Cape May Bird Observatory, Goshen,
NJ
Catskill Native Nursery, Kerhonkson,
NY
Claire's Garden Center, Patterson, NY
Faddegon's Nursery, Latham, NY

Fort Pond Native Plants, Montauk,
NY★
Godlewsky Farms, Great Meadows, NJ
Graceful Gardens, Mecklenburg, NY
Helderledge Farm, Altamont, NY★
Hicks Nurseries, Westbury, NY
Jane's Herb Farm, Webster, NY★
Kale's Nursery and Landscape Service,
Princeton, NJ
Loomis Creek Nursery, Hudson, NY
LorJon Nursery, Pine Bush, NY★
The Magic Garden, Newfield, NY★
Marders Garden Shop,
Bridgehampton, NY
Martin Viette Nurseries, East
Norwich, NY
Masterson's Aquatic Nursery, East
Aurora, NY
Matterhorn Nursery, Spring Valley,
NY★
Mountain Pine Nursery, Warwick,
NY★
Nabel's Nurseries, White Plains, NY★
Old Westbury Gardens, Old Westbury,
NY★
Ornamental Plantings, Southold, NY★
Palmiter's Garden Nursery, Avon, NY★
Peconic River Herb Farm, Calverton,
NY★
Phoenix Flower Farm, Phoenix, NY★
The Plantsmen Nursery, Groton, NY★
Pleasant Run Nursery, Allentown, NJ
Popes' Gardens, Waterford, NJ★
Rochester Public Market, Rochester,
NY
Rohsler's Allendale Nursery,
Allendale, NJ
Rosedale Nurseries, Hawthorne, NY★
Roslyn Nursery, Dix Hills, NY
Schroon Falls Farm, Schroon Lake,
NY★

Perennials—Sun *continued*
Seneca Hill Perennials, Oswego, NY★★
Smirnow's Son's Peonies,
    Huntington, NY
Sprainbrook Nursery, Scarsdale, NY★
Stony Hill Farm, Binghamton, NY★
Talmage Farm Agway, Riverhead,
    NY★★
Toadshade Wildflower Farm,
    Frenchtown, NJ★
Trimble's of Corchaug Nursery,
    Cutchogue, NY★
Triple Oaks Nursery & Herb Garden,
    Franklinville, NJ
Van Bourgondien Bros., Babylon, NY
VerDerBer's Garden Center,
    Aquebogue, NY
Well-Sweep Herb Farm, Port
    Murray, NJ

Rhododendrons and Azaleas
(*See also* Shrubs—Broad-leaf
Evergreen)
Carlson's Gardens, South Salem, NY★★
Hildebrant Nurseries, Oldwick, NJ
RareFind Nursery, Jackson, NJ★★
Roslyn Nursery, Dix Hills, NY★★
Shepherd Hill Farm, Putnam, Valley,
    NY★★
Steven Kristoph Nursery,
    Englishtown, NJ★

Roses
Anything Grows Flower Farm,
    Barnegat, NJ
Atlock Farm, Somerset, NJ
Azalea House, Voorheesville, NY★★
Bakers' Acres, Groton, NY
The Bayberry Nursery, Amagansett,
    NY

Claire's Garden Center, Patterson, NY
Der Rosenmeister, Ithaca, NY★★
Godlewsky Farms, Great Meadows,
    NJ★
Hicks Nurseries, Westbury, NY
LorJon Nursery, Pine Bush, NY
Marders Garden Shop,
    Bridgehampton, NY
Martin Viette Nurseries, East
    Norwich, NY
Matterhorn Nursery, Spring Valley,
    NY★★
Miller Nurseries, Canandaigua, NY
Mountain Pine Nursery, Warwick, NY
Old Westbury Gardens, Old Westbury,
    NY★
Ornamental Plantings, Southold, NY
Palmiter's Garden Nursery, Avon, NY★
Peconic River Herb Farm, Calverton,
    NY
Pleasant Run Nursery, Allentown,
    NJ★★
Rohsler's Allendale Nursery,
    Allendale, NJ
Rosedale Nurseries, Hawthorne, NY
Roslyn Nursery, Dix Hills, NY
Schroon Falls Farm, Schroon Lake, NY
Sprainbrook Nursery, Scarsdale, NY
Stony Hill Farm, Binghamton, NY★
Talmage Farm Agway, Riverhead, NY
Trimble's of Corchaug Nursery,
    Cutchogue, NY
Triple Oaks Nursery & Herb Garden,
    Franklinville, NJ

Seacoast Plants
Anything Grows Flower Farm,
    Barnegat, NJ★
Barlow Flower Farm, Sea Girt, NJ★★
The Bayberry Nursery, Amagansett,
    NY★

Cape May Bird Observatory, Goshen, NJ★★

Fort Pond Native Plants, Montauk, NY★★

Gunning River Herbs, Barnegat, NJ★

Hicks Nurseries, Westbury, NY★

Marders Garden Shop, Bridgehampton, NY★

Martin Viette Nurseries, East Norwich, NY★

Old Westbury Gardens, Old Westbury, NY

Ornamental Plantings, Southold, NY★

Peconic River Herb Farm, Calverton, NY

Roslyn Nursery, Dix Hills, NY

Talmage Farm Agway, Riverhead, NY★

Trimble's of Corchaug Nursery, Cutchogue, NY★

VerDerBer's Garden Center, Aquebogue, NY

Seeds

Alchemy Works Seeds & Herbs, Horseheads, NY★

Cape May Bird Observatory, Goshen, NJ

The Catholic Homesteading Movement, Norwich, NY★

Crosman's Seeds, East Rochester, NY★★

Harris Seeds, Rochester, NY★★

Hicks Nurseries, Westbury, NY

John Gordon Nursery, Amherst, NY★

P & P Seed Company, Hamburg, NY★

Peconic River Herb Farm, Calverton, NY

Sheffield's Seed Company, Locke, NY★★

Stonecrop Gardens, Cold Spring, NY★

Sylvan Botanicals New York Ginseng, Cooperstown, NY★

Turtle Tree Seeds, Copake, NY★★

Shrubs—Broad-leaf Evergreen

Ambleside Gardens, Belle Mead, NJ

Blue Sterling Nursery, Bridgeton, NJ

Carlson's Gardens, South Salem, NY★★

Fort Pond Native Plants, Montauk, NY

Hicks Nurseries, Westbury, NY

Hildebrant Nurseries, Oldwick, NJ★★

LorJon Nursery, Pine Bush, NY

Mapleton Nurseries, Kingston, NJ

Marders Garden Shop, Bridgehampton, NY

Martin Viette Nurseries, East Norwich, NY★

Nabel's Nurseries, White Plains, NY

Peconic River Herb Farm, Calverton, NY

RareFind Nursery, Jackson, NJ★★

Rohsler's Allendale Nursery, Allendale, NJ

Rosedale Nurseries, Hawthorne, NY★

Roslyn Nursery, Dix Hills, NY★

Schroon Falls Farm Schroon Lake, NY

Shepherd Hill Farm, Putnam Valley, NY★★

Sprainbrook Nursery, Scarsdale, NY

Steven Kristoph Nursery, Englishtown, NJ

Talmage Farm Agway, Riverhead, NY

Trimble's of Corchaug Nursery, Cutchogue, NY

VerDerBer's Garden Center, Aquebogue, NY

Shrubs—Conifers (*See* Dwarf and Unusual Conifers)

Shrubs—Deciduous Woody

Ambleside Gardens, Belle Mead, NJ
Anything Grows Flower Farm,
    Barnegat, NJ
Azalea House, Voorheesville, NY
The Bayberry Nursery, Amagansett,
    NY
Beaver Meadowlands, Java Center, NY
Bumps & Co., West Nyack, NY
Cape May Bird Observatory, Goshen,
    NJ
Catskill Native Nursery, Kerhonkson,
    NY
English Basketry Willows, Norwich,
    NY
Fort Pond Native Plants, Montauk,
    NY
Helderledge Farm, Altamont, NY
Hicks Nurseries, Westbury, NY
Hildebrant Nurseries, Oldwick, NJ★
Holmes Hollow Farm, Victor, NY
Kale's Nursery and Landscape Service,
    Princeton, NJ★
LorJon Nursery, Pine Bush, NY
Mapleton Nurseries, Kingston, NJ
Marders Garden Shop,
    Bridgehampton, NY
Martin Viette Nurseries, East
    Norwich, NY
Matterhorn Nursery, Spring Valley,
    NY★
Miller Nurseries, Canandaigua, NY
Mountain Pine Nursery, Warwick, NY
Nabel's Nurseries, White Plains, NY
Palmiter's Garden Nursery, Avon, NY
Peconic River Herb Farm, Calverton,
    NY
The Plantsmen Nursery, Groton, NY

Pleasant Run Nursery, Allentown, NJ
Popes' Gardens, Waterford, NJ
Rosedale Nurseries, Hawthorne, NY
Roslyn Nursery, Dix Hills, NY
Schroon Falls Farm, Schroon Lake, NY
Sprainbrook Nursery, Scarsdale, NY
St. Lawrence Nurseries, Potsdam, NY★
Steven Kristoph Nursery,
    Englishtown, NJ★
Stony Hill Farm, Binghamton, NY
Talmage Farm Agway, Riverhead, NY
Trimble's of Corchaug Nursery,
    Cutchogue, NY
Triple Oaks Nursery & Herb Garden,
    Franklinville, NJ
VerDerBer's Garden Center,
    Aquebogue, NY★
White Oak Nursery, Canandaigua,
    NY★

Topiary

Ambleside Gardens, Belle Mead, NJ
Atlock Farm, Somerset, NJ★★
The Bayberry Nursery, Amagansett,
    NY
Henry Leuthardt Nurseries, East
    Moriches, NY★
Landcraft Environments, Mattituck,
    NY★
Marders Garden Shop,
    Bridgehampton, NY
Martin Viette Nurseries, East
    Norwich, NY
Matterhorn Nursery, Spring Valley, NY
The Plantsmen Nursery, Groton, NY★

Transplants—Flats and Tubelings

Barlow Flower Farm, Sea Girt, NJ
Beds & Borders, Laurel, NY

Trees—Ornamental and Shade *continued*

Catskill Native Nursery, Kerhonkson, NY

Fort Pond Native Plants, Montauk, NY

Hicks Nurseries, Westbury, NY★

Hildebrant Nurseries, Oldwick, NJ★

Holmes Hollow Farm, Victor, NY★

John Gordon Nursery, Amherst, NY★

Kale's Nursery and Landscape Service, Princeton, NJ★

Mapleton Nurseries, Kingston, NJ★

Marders Garden Shop, Bridgehampton, NY★★

Martin Viette Nurseries, East Norwich, NY★★

Miller Nurseries, Canandaigua, NY

Nabel's Nurseries, White Plains, NY

Palmiter's Garden Nursery, Avon, NY

Peconic River Herb Farm, Calverton, NY

Pleasant Run Nursery, Allentown, NJ★★

Rohsler's Allendale Nursery, Allendale, NJ★★

Rosedale Nurseries, Hawthorne, NY★★

Roslyn Nursery, Dix Hills, NY★

Schroon Falls Farm, Schroon Lake, NY

Sprainbrook Nursery, Scarsdale, NY

St. Lawrence Nurseries, Potsdam, NY

Stony Hill Farm, Binghamton, NY

Talmage Farm Agway, Riverhead, NY

Trimble's of Corchaug Nursery, Cutchogue, NY

Triple Oaks Nursery & Herb Garden, Franklinville, NJ★★

VerDerBer's Garden Center, Aquebogue, NY★

White Oak Nursery, Canandaigua, NY★

Tropical and Conservatory Plants

Anything Grows Flower Farm, Barnegat, NJ

Atlock Farm, Somerset, NJ★★

Barlow Flower Farm, Sea Girt, NJ

Beds & Borders, Laurel, NY★

Faddegon's Nursery, Latham, NY

Hicks Nurseries, Westbury, NY

Landcraft Environments, Mattituck, NY★★

Loomis Creek Nursery, Hudson, NY★★

Marders Garden Shop, Bridgehampton, NY

Martin Viette Nurseries, East Norwich, NY

Nabel's Nurseries, White Plains, NY

Old Westbury Gardens, Old Westbury, NY

Peconic River Herb Farm, Calverton, NY

The Plantsmen Nursery, Groton, NY★

Rochester Public Market, Rochester, NY

Rohsler's Allendale Nursery, Allendale, NJ

Rosedale Nurseries, Hawthorne, NY

Steven Kristoph Nursery, Englishtown, NJ★

Stony Hill Farm, Binghamton, NY

Talmage Farm Agway, Riverhead, NY

Trimble's of Corchaug Nursery, Cutchogue, NY

Triple Oaks Nursery & Herb Garden, Franklinville, NJ★

The Violet Barn, Naples, NY★

Zena Green Nursery, Kingston, NY★

The Bayberry Nursery, Amagansett, NY

Bumps & Co., West Nyack, NY★

Cape May Bird Observatory, Goshen, NJ★★

Catskill Native Nursery, Kerhonkson, NY★

Fort Pond Native Plants, Montauk, NY★

John Gordon Nursery, Amherst, NY★★

Pinelands Nursery, Columbus, NJ★★

Saratoga Tree Nursery, Saratoga Springs, NY★★

Schroon Falls Farm, Schroon Lake, NY

Sheffield's Seed Company, Locke, NY★

St. Lawrence Nurseries, Potsdam, NY★★

Sylvan Botanicals New York Ginseng, Cooperstown, NY

Talmage Farm Agway, Riverhead, NY★

Toadshade Wildflower Farm, Frenchtown, NJ★★

Triple Oaks Nursery & Herb Garden, Franklinville, NJ★

White Oak Nursery, Canandaigua, NY★★

Winter-Interest Plants

Ambleside Gardens, Belle Mead, NJ

The Bayberry Nursery, Amagansett, NY

Catskill Native Nursery, Kerhonkson, NY★

Fort Pond Native Plants, Montauk, NY

Helderledge Farm, Altamont, NY

Hildebrant Nurseries, Oldwick, NJ

Kale's Nursery and Landscape Service, Princeton, NJ

Marders Garden Shop, Bridgehampton, NY★

Martin Viette Nurseries, East Norwich, NY

Mountain Pine Nursery, Warwick, NY

Nabel's Nurseries, White Plains, NY

Peconic River Herb Farm, Calverton, NY

Pleasant Run Nursery, Allentown, NJ

Rosedale Nurseries, Hawthorne, NY

Roslyn Nursery, Dix Hills, NY

Schroon Falls Farm, Schroon Lake, NY★

St. Lawrence Nurseries, Potsdam, NY

Talmage Farm Agway, Riverhead, NY

Trimble's of Corchaug Nursery, Cutchogue, NY

Triple Oaks Nursery & Herb Garden, Franklinville, NJ

VerDerBer's Garden Center, Aquebogue, NY

Well-Sweep Herb Farm, Port Murray, NJ

ALPHABETICAL INDEX
TO NURSERIES

ORDER FORM

THE ADVENTUROUS GARDENER
Where to Buy the Best Plants
in New York and New Jersey
By Ruah Donnelly
ISBN 0-9677303-2-5

Please send me _____ copies at $25.95 each. Add $5 shipping for first book and $0.50 for each additional book. Massachusetts residents add 5% sales tax. For quantity discount information, please call (877) 427-3362.

Payable by check or credit card.

Name (please print)_____

Address_____

City/State/Zip Code_____

Phone_____ E-mail_____

Credit Card [VISA] [Master Card] [American Express]_____

Card #_____ Exp. date_____

Your Signature_____

Please make checks payable to:

THE HORTICULTURAL PRESS
c/o Publishers Storage & Shipping Corp.
46 Development Road, Fitchburg, MA 01420

For telephone credit card orders:
Call toll-free (877) 427-3362
Fax: (978) 348-1233   E-mail: *orders@pssc.com*
Web site: *www.adventurousgardener.com*